Management and Administrative Communication

Management and Administrative Communication

Workbook with Supporting Text

Dean S. Ellis
Associate Professor of Management, Marketing, and Industrial Relations
University of Hawaii

Macmillan Publishing Co., Inc.
New York
Collier Macmillan Publishers
London

To Jan

Printed in the United States of America

Macmillan Publishing Co., Inc.
866 Third Avenue, New York, New York 10022

Collier Macmillan Canada, Ltd.

ISBN 0-02-332510-0

Printing: 1 2 3 4 5 6 7 8 Year: 8 9 0 1 2 3 4

Preface

This book was written in an attempt to bridge the gap between the type of basic communication skills that managers and administrators need and the type of training being offered in most universities today. Even though communicating is the most important and time-consuming activity of all managers from top administrators to first-line supervisors, often too little emphasis is placed on developing management communication skills.[1,2]

This workbook with supporting text material was written as a result of five years of teaching an experimental course titled, "Basic Communication Training for Managers and Administrators." The material for this course started as a few dozen feedback and evaluation forms. Because of the positive response to the course and after much trial, error, and suggestions from students and faculty, those few forms have been expanded and refined to produce this book. Many of the approaches used here are rather innovative and do not fit into traditional molds, but all have been thoroughly tested and have proven their worth. Although this book is designed for students majoring in business, the basic skills being taught are universal. The course can be made just as effective for other majors simply by changing the topics used for the papers and workshops.

The focus of the exercises in this book is on encouraging students to integrate the four basic communication skills of reading, writing, speaking, and listening and to combine these skills with the research, reasoning, and logic skills that make communications meaningful.

The exercises are designed so that the instructor is relieved of much of the traditional lecturer-evaluator role and is placed in the more appropriate role for a management-level communication course—that of managing the learning system. This book is designed to be used with equal effectiveness by instructors whose backgrounds are in business, speech, English, or any of a number of other fields. This is possible because subject matter expertise necessary for evaluation and grading may be developed by the instructors as well as by the students as they progress through the course. The instructors are then left free to specialize in their own fields of expertise to enrich the courses and to focus the learning in the areas most appropriate to their students' needs.

Why a New Type of Course Is Needed

Many business schools offer no courses that deal specifically with developing the basic interpersonal communication skills most needed by managers and administrators. The majority of schools that do offer communication-training limit themselves to teaching only written communication or letter-writing skills, training that is crucial but by itself not adequate since 75% of all management-level communication is oral, face-to-face communication.

Communication activities of all types occupy nearly 90% of a manager's day.[3,4] The communication

---

[1] Carl Duerr, *Management Kinetics* (New York: McGraw-Hill Books, 1971).

[2] William H. Bickner, "The Manager of Today Looks at Those of Tomorrow," paper presented at the Academy of Management Convention, Seattle (1974).

[3] Dean S. Ellis, "The Central Role of Communication in Organization," *Communication in Complex Organizations*, edited by James L. Owen et al. (Minneapolis: West Publishing Company, 1976).

[4] J. H. Horne and T. Lupton, "The Work Activities of Middle Managers," *Journal of Management Studies*, Vol. 1 (1956).

that takes up the majority of a manager's time is dynamic, ongoing communication in which listening, reading, writing, and speaking are all intertwined with reasoning and logic. Problems and opportunities are constantly being presented to the manager. He must listen and read to gain knowledge, insight, and understanding. He must raise questions, probe deeper, propose solutions, and then seek still more feedback. If he decides to take action, he must deal with objections and try to win support. This requires more reading, listening, and talking. At the same time, he must keep abreast of additional problems and opportunities which might require more change, so the communication and reasoning processes go on and on. The exercises in this book are designed to introduce the students to the complexity of the communication process by breaking it down into simple, understandable components. This book is designed to assist the instructors in integrating the oral with the written communication skills as well as with the research and reasoning skills.

The exercises are intended to relieve the instructors of many of the routine and often monotonous grading tasks and to allow them to focus their attention and time on giving special help to individual students. It frees the instructors to focus their teaching preparation time on their special areas of interest.

The exercises also will involve the students more fully in the total communication process. Traditionally, courses are weighted heavily toward teaching the presentation skills of speaking and writing. The exercises in this book are devised to provide a practical and convenient means of also grading the listening, reading, researching, reasoning, and logic skills so that performance in these areas may also be rewarded. The author has found it is especially critical that these skills be given adequate attention because managers and administrators typically spend the majority of their working days listening, reading, and evaluating rather than just talking and writing.

The Introduction presents an overview of this text, its objectives, and the methodology used. It is the author's hope and belief, based on his experience, that this new approach offers a desirable alternative method for teaching basic communication skills.

There are many people to thank for their help in preparing this book. First I would like to thank the secretaries of the Department of Management, Marketing, and Industrial Relations at the University of Hawaii for their assistance in typing the early drafts. I would also like to express my appreciation to the directors of the Graduate Program in Administration at the Federal University of Paraíba in João Pessoa, Brazil. They have allowed me time away from my research duties here to complete the final editing of this book. The most important assistance has been that of my wife, Janice, who offered her expertise in management and communication. She has worked with this project from the beginning, contributing much to the content of this book and providing constant encouragement.

D. S. E.

Contents

INTRODUCTION

A New Approach to Teaching Management-Level Communication Skills:

A Course Overview

This text is comprised of two parts. Part I is a set of eight semiprogrammed exercises with accompanying text material integrated with each exercise. Part II presents three supplemental chapters of background material. A careful reading of this introduction will make it much easier to understand the purpose of each exercise and how all relate to the total objective of the course. Although the exercises have been carefully tested and developed, there is nothing sacred about any of them. Instructors should feel free to rearrange, modify, or even omit sections to fit their individual needs.

The focus of the eight semiprogrammed exercises is on learning to effectively research, develop, present, evaluate, and defend a proposal in both oral and written form. The exercises deal with communication activities which involve learning to use communication as a tool to influence others. Such activities were selected because the objective of most management communication is to influence some one or some group to take some action. (1,3) Rarely do managers merely write prose. The informative writing they do is usually to clarify or provide backup material to support some proposal or request. Such informative writing is necessary if one is to gain support for most proposals and thus will be an important element in the exercises in this text.

The main learning in this course comes from the experience of group interaction. The learning exercises are designed to de-emphasize the dependency relationship of students to instructors and to stress the adult learning model based on interaction with one's peers.

The eight semiprogrammed exercises are presented in pairs. The odd-numbered exercises are to be written, and the even-numbered ones are to be presented orally in small workshop groups. The progression of the exercises through the course is based on two criteria: The complexity of the assignment and the focus of the feedback.

The primary purpose of the first pair of exercises is to help students start associating writing with reading skills and speaking with listening skills. The objective is to encourage students to start thinking of communication as a two-way, interactive activity rather than something they do *to* someone.

Although the format of each exercise is preprogrammed, the text is designed to allow instructors much latitude and flexibility. By his or her own ingenuity and design, each instructor can shape the course to meet the needs of individual groups of students. Neither students nor instructors should be rigidly bound by any of the forms or feedback sheets that are included with the exercises. These materials have been carefully designed and tested, but individual instructors are likely to have some materials of their own which they wish to stress. The addition of such material is encouraged. There is adequate class lecture time and workshop group time allowed in the course design for the inclusion of such material.

The degree of difficulty of the course can be varied from freshman to graduate student level. The less sophisticated the students, the more time will have to be spent discussing basic skills. When desirable, this workbook may be used in conjunction with basic business communication, English, or public speaking tests. The workbook is designed to give students the motivation to learn those skills that beginning students frequently do not see as valuable. The workbook, when used in a basic course, should provide the students with a vehicle for learning why the often scorned basic skills are so crucial to success in the real world. When used in more advanced courses, the exercises provide the students with a chance to polish basic skills in competition with equally advanced peers.

The Exercises

The first six exercises are all practice learning experiences. Although they are graded, the grades are only a form of feedback. The grades are mock grades and do not affect the course grade. The final two exercises are the ones in which the students display what they have learned during the first six exercises. The grades on these final two exercises are the only ones which contribute toward the course grades.

Exercise 1 is a simple assignment. Students begin by reviewing various controversial, business-related topics. Then each student selects a topic which he finds interesting and prepares a short paper. The paper is to present a proposal that will be read and evaluated by fellow students. In this first paper, the students present what they consider to be acceptable work for a college-level course. By reading and evaluating the work of their peers, they begin to build a frame of references against which to judge their own work.

In Exercise 1A, the entire class evaluates the various proposals and selects a single topic. The entire class will research, document, attack, and defend this topic for the remainder of the course. Using a single topic allows students to research that topic in depth. Topics chosen in the past have dealt with such matters as the desirability of no-fault insurance, the need for international monetary reforms, how to protect the economy from shipping strikes without destroying unions' rights to bargain, and how to cope with the rising cost of medical malpractice insurance.

Another advantage of using a single topic for the entire course is that it forces students to pay closer attention to feedback, or what is commonly called listening skills. In many traditional courses, students write a paper and the instructor returns it with comments and a grade. Since the grade is final, there is often inadequate incentive for the student to study the instructor's comments; they are after-the-fact feedback. That topic is finished and the grades are in. By using the same topic in every exercise, the students have an incentive to incorporate the feedback they receive in one exercise so they can improve on five similar exercises before any final grades are given.

Exercise 2 is an activity conducted as a small workshop group. In the workshop, students each give a presentation containing one argument supporting and one argument opposing the class proposal. The students learn how to give constructive feedback to each other. They practice giving and then receiving feedback, both on their presentations and on the value and quality of their feedback to others. The primary focus of the feedback for the first two exercises is on presentation skills.

Exercise 3 introduces requirements that force all students to bring their work up to a minimum standard. This highly structured exercise is a practice drill in which students learn how to combine material to effectively support a proposal. The work focuses only on showing a need for a change. In the Exercise 4 workshop, students take the next step, which is learning how to present a plan by which the change can be brought about. In Exercise 3 and 4, all presentations must follow exactly the same organizational pattern and contain specified types and amounts of support material. This shows students how to bring their presentations up to a minimum standard before they start to develop their own free styles. The primary focus of the feedback for these two exercises is on organization and the use of supporting material.

Teamwork begins in Exercise 4. Each student selects a partner to work with in researching and preparing materials. Having partners helps students learn to do team research and gives them an opportunity to bounce their ideas off of someone else before they present them. In the Exercise 4 workshop sessions, a new element of feedback is added. Students not only practice evaluating their peers' presentations and reasoning, but they also begin offering reasoning of their own in the form of counterarguments.

Exercise 5 introduces an exciting step in proposal preparation that is new to many students. Each student is given an opportunity to completely refute, on a point-for-point basis, the arguments he presented in his own Exercise 3 and 4 proposals. Through this technique, students truly learn to understand a proposal's benefits by learning to understand its weaknesses.

In the Exercise 6 workshop session, students add the final step to their proposal: a section describing the benefits and advantages of their proposal. Each student as an evaluator has an opportunity to challenge the content and logic of the proposal as presented by the other members of his workshop group. Then, each may present counter-counterarguments to help the speakers re-establish their cases. Thus, by the time Exercise 6 is completed, students will have learned how to thoroughly prepare, document, and evaluate cases both supporting and opposing the class topic.

Exercise 7 and 8 are the graded assignments; all previous assignments were practice and learning exercises. These final exercises are designed to enable students to display what they have learned. The grades for Exercises 7 and 8 each account for 50% of the final grade in the course.

For Exercise 7 students write a paper similar to a proposal in an actual business situation. The papers propose adoption of the class proposal. The papers may also contain a one-half page supplement in which students justify the strengths and weaknesses of their own papers. The papers are then evaluated and graded by peers. Each author in turn grades his or her peer evaluators on the quality and value of their feedback. The paper grades and feedback grades combined comprise the final grades for Exercise 7.

Exercise 8 usually proves to be the most enjoyable exercise in the course. Students work in teams to present their proposals in panel discussions similar to those one might encounter in formal business presentations Each team is given an opportunity to present proposals both supporting and opposing the class topic. The practice sessions help students to gain confidence and experience before the final presentations are given for a grade. There are several formats which this final exercise might follow, depending on the level and wishes of the class.

During the eight exercises, the focus of the learning progresses from (1) delivery to (2) organization-documentation to (3) analysis of content and reasoning to (4) final grading. The logic of this progression is that a presentation, written or oral, must be adequately delivered before it can be understood; once delivery (grammar, spelling, and voice quality) is adequate, the material must be organized into a logical sequence before it can be meaningful; organization requires documentation to support assumptions, so students must develop those skills at the same time that they learn to organize; finally, an effectively delivered, well-organized, well-documented presentation will be understandable, but it may still need to be strengthened in the areas of reasoning and content. Thus, the sequence of feedback progresses from (1) delivery to (2) organization and documentation to (3) reasoning and content. The second half of the course usually is devoted almost exclusively to working on reasoning and content. Since students research and study only one topic, they gain in-depth knowledge, both pro and con, on that topic. As they progress through the course, they become capable of meaningfully evaluating, refuting, and, finally, grading their peers.

The instructions for each of the exercises contain explanatory text material. Careful attention should be given to reading and discussing this material before the students attempt to do the exercises. There are also three chapters of supplemental material in Part II which should be read concurrently with the exercises.

Chapter One discusses the importance of communication training for managers, administrators, and all persons who work in an organization. This chapter, which includes a guide for additional reading for advanced students, is usually assigned during the second or third week of the course as background material.

Chapter Two presents a condensed review of the basic principles of communication theory. This provides a good introduction for beginning students or a review for more advanced students. A study of the thought processes usually helps students to analyze the validity of both their own beliefs and of the counterarguments to those beliefs. A bibliography suggests additional reading material. This chapter usually is assigned some time before students begin work on Exercise 5.

Chapter Three, which may be assigned with Chapter Two or later, discusses how misconceptions of the communication process lead to breakdowns of communication and the implications of such breakdowns for managers and students. A bibliography provides a reference guide for further reading.

The Appendix at the back of the book offers a list of basic reference materials that may help students to locate sources of information on business-related topics.

Semiprogrammed Material

The exercises in this text can be considered semiprogrammed materials in that each exercise is a self-contained unit. Each unit contains a text section that describes how to develop a basic skill. The text section is followed by an exercise assignment, designed to help students practice and perfect that skill.

As an integral part of each exercise, students also learn to evaluate their own performance. They learn to do this by practice, using carefully worked out evaluation and grading criteria guides. Thus, the exercises provide students both the techniques to practice and perfect their own skills and the means to measure their own progress. At the same time, they are also learning the crucial management skills of how to constructively listen to and evaluate others.

This is not a true programmed text because it does not program the learning of each individual student separately; rather, it aids the instructor and the students by programming the behavior of the class as a whole. Delegation is the key to efficiency in this course, as it is in all management. Students are given the responsibility for active participation in conducting most of the learning activities of the class, but this participation is directed by carefully prescribed guidelines provided by the instructor and this text. It is these guidelines which prevent delegation of duties from becoming abdication of responsibility. The delegated activities include conducting workshop meetings, evaluating and grading peers, and keeping most of the class records. Such delegation frees the instructor for the more creative aspects of teaching and guiding the development of learning.

Outline of Content of Exercises

Following is a summary of the basic elements contained within each exercise:

1. An explanation of the purposes of the exercise and all necessary background and text materials needed for conducting the exercise.
2. A detailed explanation of how to prepare for the exercise.
3. A detailed explanation of how to constructively evaluate and grade the exercise activities.
4. A set of all forms and guides needed for the evaluation, grading, and record keeping of the exercise.
5. A complete set of instructions on how to conduct the class during each exercise, including how to form into workshop groups and how to determine who is responsible for coordinating the activities of each workshop.

As the list indicates, the exercise instructions take care of most of the routine-type instructional and grading activities. This frees the instructor and students to devote their in-class time to dealing with exceptional situations. It allows the instructor more time to plan and revise the course. The instructor's most important roles are providing examples and setting standards for the class. There are many workshops and review sessions in which the instructor has the opportunity to influence and tailor the course to fit the specific needs of the class.

Peer Evaluation

One of the most controversial teaching techniques used in the exercises is peer evaluation. The author is firmly convinced that this technique will become more prevalent in the future as students begin to be seen as adults who are capable of taking responsibility for their own behavior. There is currently a definite trend in textbooks toward the use of student interaction types of exercises which include some peer evaluation. (2, 5, 6) However, this practice is still not widely accepted in spite of the research evidence available to support its validity. There are many students, as well as faculty, who oppose peer grading. Many students cannot break from their roles as children. These students still seek the approval of an authority figure, a parent substitute, to tell them what is right and wrong. This, of course, is much easier for them than it is to take the responsibility of making decisions for themselves. (4) If they are to become managers or administrators, it is critical that they learn to take responsibility for evaluating and controlling their own behavior.

There are many faculty members who see students as children and believe it is the teacher's personal responsibility to help them and tell them what is right and wrong. But a student must at some point be allowed to break from the role of a child and become an adult who can judge for himself what is right and wrong. The exercises in this book are designed to help provide that transition.

Peer grading is actually a form of delegation of authority. Management often preaches delegation of authority and talks of how this builds responsible new management personnel. But classes in management frequently are still conducted as paternalistic autocracies in which instructors make all major decisions, especially those regarding grades. This book encourages the use of delegation as it is taught. Of course, as in any management system, the manager (in our case, the instructor) must be able to override the system if it is abused; but so far, in many years of developing and teaching this course, this has rarely been necessary.

The instructors need to retain only one major responsibility for grading in this course. They should determine the cutoff scores between "A's" and "B's" and "C's." In effect, they give each class as a whole a grade, but do not tamper with the grades of any individual student. The instructor's grading of a class as a whole is necessary to maintain consistency in grading from class to class and from year to year.

Peer grading is the key to the efficiency of the teaching method used in this text and therefore proportionate attention will be given to justifying its use. The technique will be reviewed by raising a number of questions one might ask.

Are students qualified to grade each other?

In most cases, they are not, at least not without help and guidance. But they can and should be taught to evaluate work as well as to do it. Only when they have learned to evaluate their own work are they ready to leave school and function without a teacher. Students who use this text are given detailed instructions explaining how to evaluate and grade each assignment. They also have available checklists and other grading aids as well as the advice and counsel of their instructors. The ability to grade communication is actually the ability to read and to listen. For peer grading, these skills must be actively taught. While students learn to grade the work of others, they are actually learning the crucial management skills of how to read, listen to, and evaluate the work of others. They also as a by-product learn to evaluate and grade their own work before submitting it.

What about grading friends?

All grades in this course except those on the final presentations and papers are feedback grades. They are not part of the course grade. Therefore, students usually feel it is their responsibility to give a "D" paper a "D." To give a friend a "C" is only to deceive the friend so he will not realize where he needs to improve. Ultimately, this only hurts the friend, so it is seldom done.

Are mock-graded assignments taken seriously?

Yes, by most students. To catch those who might not take them seriously, there is a rule that students may not proceed to a new assignment until they have completed all earlier assignments at a passing level. If a student does not pass an assignment, the management-by-exception rule comes into play. The student is temporarily removed from the system and is given necessary help by the instructor to bring him back up to par.

Does the instructor also grade all assignments?

No. Obviously, an instructor would take weeks to effectively grade the hundreds of papers and reports. The instructors can usually better use the time helping those with special needs. The instructor need only read and listen to a small sample, which is enough to keep him or her abreast of the progress of the class. The adequacy of sampling techniques is well documented in the management literature.

Would there be any value in the instructor grading assignments and giving the students his feedback if he did have the time?

No. On the contrary, it is recommended that the instructor never let the students know how he or she would grade a specific paper. Too many students tend to be overly dependent. They seek right and wrong answers from authority figures. One of the primary goals of this course is to teach the students to be responsible men and women capable of judging their own work. As managers, they will have to listen to contradictory and conflicting opinions and then make their own judgment. In this course, students must do the same. Their writing is judged by many peers. The grades vary, and the comments are often contradictory. The students must decide for themselves which comments to accept and which to reject. This does not mean that the instructor should not provide a wealth of examples. That is always helpful for it gives the students models to follow.

What is the value of having students grade each other aside from being a work saver for the instructor?

Grading teaches reading and listening skills whereas presenting teaches speaking and writing skills. All four of these communication skills are essential for dynamic communication. Grading also forces students to become familiar with alternative speaking and writing styles. This exposure is important. Students must have a frame of reference against which to judge their own work. In surveys which the author conducts at the beginning of each semester, students are asked how many times they have ever read another student's paper during high school or college. More than 70% of the students report "never." This means that the majority of students have never had the opportunity to develop a frame of reference against which to judge their own writing.

Do students accept the criticism and advice of their peers as much as they would that of a professor?

Yes and no. Usually students are skeptical and reluctant to accept the advice of one peer or, for that matter, the advice of one professor. If several peers independently and consistently offer the same suggestions, however, it is hard for the student to reject them. The same would be true if several professors independently made the same recommendations.

In this course, it is recommended that instructors and fellow students take care in their roles as evaluators to point out that certain writing and speaking habits are not generally acceptable. This can be done by surveying students to find out if they (as opposed to professors and other authority figures) find some traits offensive. One trait that is usually questioned is spelling. To see if poor spelling actually is offensive to other students, the author has frequently surveyed students. The results from class to class have been surprisingly constant. About 5% responded that they would totally reject a report that contains poor spelling (several words misspelled per page) as being the work of an ignorant and incompetent person. About 20% of the students are seriously bothered by poor spelling to the point that it lowers their opinion of the writer's intelligence but not to the point where they would totally reject his work. At the other extreme, about 30% of the students report that poor spelling does not bother them at all as long as they can figure out the words. With these percentages, students can determine for themselves the risk they take when they turn in a report with poor spelling. The high percentage of fellow students who object to poor spelling makes it difficult for writers to overlook their weakness with the excuse that negative response to poor spelling is an idiosyncrasy of school teachers. By providing students with insight as to how their own peers feel about certain behaviors, instructors can do much in this course to show the validity of peer grading and to make peer suggestions more helpful.

In conclusion, it seems safe to say that when properly controlled, grading by peers is not only an acceptable alternative to grading by an instructor, but it may produce more accurate grades and is also an effective teaching tool.

Forms of Support

An important feature of this book is the description in Exercise 3 of various forms of support. That section was developed in an attempt to help students find a way to systematically measure for themselves whether or not they are adequately supporting their ideas and arguments. A frequent comment on research papers is "Needs more support." The author has frequently heard the question from students, "How much support is enough?" Of course, there is no one answer to that question, for the amount and type of support needed to back any particular argument depends upon the answer to the question, "To whom is the argument being presented and why?" Once this question can be answered, it is simple to select the appropriate types and amounts of material to support the argument if—and these are the big if's—you know which different forms of support are available to choose from and if you know the basic effect each form of support will likely have on the intended receiver.

It has been the author's experience that few students are even vaguely aware of what forms of support are available. Even fewer seem to have an awareness of what effect each different form of support will have on the listeners or readers. To try to support arguments without such knowledge is like trying to play chess without knowing the chessmen's relative values or how each man can move.

This book groups the forms of support under three major headings: (1) forms of support designed primarily to inform, clarify, or arouse emotional response, (2) forms of support designed primarily to convince, and (3) forms of support that provide background data. In Exercise 3 there is a description of how to develop each form of support and how to organize the various forms of support to fit one's needs, according to the type of response sought from the receiver. With the knowledge of what forms of support are available to use and the knowledge of what impact each is likely to have on the audience, it becomes simple to list exactly how much and what types of support material are needed for a presentation, even before one begins to research a topic. With this ability, students never again need to fear seeing the comment on one of their papers, "Inadequate documentation." They can check their own work for adequacy of support material before it is turned in.

Summary

The semiprogrammed exercises, the grading by peers, and the categorizing of forms of support are all techniques designed to reduce the dependence of students on instructors. Remember, a manager on the job cannot run to an instructor for help. The goals of peer grading, of identifying forms of support, and of all other techniques used in this course are to encourage student independence and to discourage student dependence. College students are adult men and women who must accept responsibility for evaluating and controlling their own behavior. As they become tomorrow's administrators, they will be the decision-makers. Those who have not already done so must learn to accept that responsibility now. Ultimately, only they can determine the quality of work they will do in this world.

REFERENCES

1. Dale, Ernest. *Management Theory and Practice* (New York: McGraw-Hill Book Company, 1965).
2. Hall, Douglas T., et al. *Experiences in Management and Organizational Behavior* (Chicago: St. Clair Press, 1975).
3. Haney, William V. *Communication and Organizational Behavior: Text and Cases*, 3rd ed. (Homewood, Ill.: Richard D. Irwin, Inc., 1973).
4. James, Muriel and Dorothy Jongeward. *Born to Win* (Reading, Mass.: Addison Wesley Publishing Co., Inc., 1971).
5. Kolb, David A., Irwin M. Rubin, and James M. McIntyre. *Organizational Psychology: An Experiential Approach*, 2nd ed. (Englewood Cliffs, N.J.: Prentice-Hall, Inc., 1974).
6. Ruben, Brent D. and Richard W. Budd. *Human Communication Handbook* (Rochelle Park, N.J.: Hayden Publishing Co., Inc., 1975).

EXERCISE 1

Where We Start From

PURPOSE OF ASSIGNMENT

Before we can judge the quality of work, we must have some standard or frame of reference with which to compare it. The purpose of this exercise is to have you write what you now consider to be an acceptable college-level paper and then to compare your work with the papers of others so that you can develop a frame of reference against which to judge your own work.

A secondary goal of this exercise is to select a topic for the entire class to research and evaluate in depth. This topic will be used in all later assignments.

Introduction

A retired Army colonel friend often tells the story of when he first began teaching business writing in a small Southern university. One day, an attractive young coed came into his office to see about a low grade she had just received on a paper. She seemed to be a bright student, but her papers revealed that she just had no concept whatsoever of how to write a coherent, grammatically correct thought. Although the girl was very sincere and willing to work, it came out in the conversation that her writing in other courses as well was so poor that she was in danger of being flunked out of the university. The colonel, touched by the girl's sincerity, wanted to assist but realized that traditional teaching methods obviously were not helping her. Suddently he came upon an idea based on his World War II experience. The Army, at that time, was so short of personnel and had to train men so fast that often those who were only half trained themselves had to become instructors of the new recruits. It was amazing that as instructors these men seemed to learn twice as fast as they had as students. That was because they constantly had to observe the mistakes of the new recruits and try to tell them how to correct them. As instructors, they also learned by watching the good and comparing it to the bad. Such constant observation made them acutely aware of what alternative behaviors were possible, which were the best, and why.

The colonel thought for a moment. If it worked in the Army, why not in college? So he made a deal with the coed. He offered to drop the low grade on the paper if she would come to work for him as a student grader. With much apprehension, the coed agreed. The colonel gave her a stack of 30 papers and told her to read them and separate the good from the bad. Then she was to come back and explain what criteria she had used to separate them. The colonel had to redo some of the grading on those first few papers, but the coed quickly improved. Three years later, she was an excellent writer. She graduated from the university with honors and accepted a high-paying job with a national management consulting firm.

In this course, we will try to learn by actively observing and doing just as the coed did. It is surprising to find how many students have never read another student's term paper. If you have not read other students' papers, it is difficult for you to have a standard against which to judge your own. In this exercise and in all that follow, it is assumed that you as a college student are an adult, capable of learning to grade your own work. No longer should you rely upon a teacher or some other parent substitute to set your standards for you. We must all learn to set our own standards. This course is designed to help you develop a frame of reference against which to judge your ability to prepare, present, and evaluate professional quality proposals in both written and oral form. Only after you are able to evaluate your own performance are you in a position to be a <u>manager</u> of others.

How Administrators Spend Their Time

Whether an administrator is running a city, a hospital, or a business, his basic job is the same. He must work with people. The administrator cannot be in ten places at once, observing all of the company activities. To find out what is going on, he must depend upon reports from the managers and the workers. Since the administrator cannot possibly be an expert in all phases of his operation—the engineering, the finance, the sales—he must rely upon his subordinates to report on problems and also to propose ways to correct them. Frequently, the reports and proposals from one source will conflict with those from another. Those in sales may propose to increase profits by initiating a new multimillion-dollar sales campaign, while those in engineering are proposing that the same money could be better spent by installing a new multimillion-dollar machine, designed to cut operating costs.

The administrator must study such conflicting proposals and evaluate the evidence and logic supporting each. That requires much research, reading, questioning, and listening. Eventually, the administrator must make a decision on the proposals. Once the decision is made, the administrator frequently must put his decision into the form of a proposal and seek approval from his superiors. Even if the decision requires no higher approval, the administrator still must explain and justify his decision to subordinates because they are the ones who must actually carry out the action prescribed in the administrator's decision.

If those subordinates do not understand what the administrator desires, his plans cannot be put into effect. If the employees are not motivated to do as the administrator tells them, his plans are not likely to be put into effect. And, if the subordinates do not trust the administrator, they are likely to try to avoid putting his plans into effect. In short, for the administrator to be effective in administering people, he must be more than just a good reader, listener, and evaluator of information. He must also be a good writer, speaker, and persuader—an effective disseminator of information. He must be able to clearly inform others of what he expects, and then he must be able to motivate them to follow.

It is no surprise to find that administrators spend nearly 90% of their time communicating and that 75% of that time is spent in interpersonal, face-to-face communication. (3, 2) A text published by the American Management Association clearly defines the job of a management-level person:

> No matter how varied the activities or how special some of the skills involved; in the final analysis, the job of every executive or supervisor is *communication.* Essentially, he must get work done through other people, and to accomplish this, he must communicate effectively with them. (1, p.14)

Communication Is a Skill

Communication is a skill like statistics. Both are used as tools to give meaning to something else. Both are tools which managers use in their jobs. Neither are of value by themselves. Statistics are only as good as the data they are used to analyze. Likewise, communication is only as valuable as what the communicator has to communicate. Effective communication of inaccurate data is of no value. The important point is that the effective manager must not only develop knowledge of his field, but he must also develop the skills to communicate that knowledge to others.

For the administrator to communicate effectively, he must first know his field well enough to have something worthwhile to communicate. As students of communication, your first job will be to learn enough about a topic that you will have something worthwhile to communicate. Only after you gain a respectable knowledge of your topic are you in a position to benefit from effectively communicating your ideas. Of course, part of the skill of communication is the ability to listen to and evaluate the communication of others. It is virtually impossible for you to judge how effectively someone else communicated information regarding a topic on which you have no knowledge. Therefore, if all of you are to help yourself and to help each other develop skill in communicating, you must also develop competence in the topic area with which you wish to deal.

Find a Topic

This course is designed for students who eventually plan to go into some area of management or administration. That gives all of you one common area of knowledge or, at least, of interest. Therefore, it is suggested that you narrow your choice of topics to those related to business or to those that have a strong impact on the business community. Virtually any subject that is business-related will be equally as appropriate for students who plan careers in public administration. Such topics as inflation, labor relations, and business regulations certainly involve both public and private sectors of our economy.

The actual choice of a topic is up to the class. You must ultimately select your own topic because you are the ones who will benefit or waste your time by researching it. In Exercise 1, you will explore a number of possible topics. In Exercise 1A, you will select a topic to use for all later assignments. The topic should be valuable enough to merit the time you will devote to it.

The topic should also be controversial. If everyone agrees with what you are proposing, there is little skill required to make or to defend your proposal. Since you are trying to develop a skill, you will want to work with a challenging topic.

The topic should be one on which research material is available. Although this is not a course in research, research is an important part of this course. To research a topic in depth requires a great amount of time, even when information is readily available. To select a topic on which material is not readily available would ultimately lead to discouragement and frustration.

The reason for selecting only one topic for this class and using it for all later assignments is to cut down the amount of time devoted to superficial research and yet to allow you time to do in-depth research on that one topic. To prepare four or five presentations in a semester on as many different topics would ultimately force you to do shallow research on each topic. Many speaking and writing courses are taught with such a format, which may be why so few students are accustomed to doing in-depth research and why many students' reports are so poorly documented.

Another important criterion in selecting a topic is how interesting it is. If the topic is boring, it will make it harder for you to motivate yourself to do the research or to prepare your presentations.

In summary, there are four criteria to use in selecting a topic.

1. How valuable would the knowledge be that you would gain from in-depth research of this topic?
2. Is this topic one-sided or is it controversial?
3. How available is research material on this topic?
4. How interesting would this topic be to research in depth?

ASSIGNMENT INSTRUCTIONS

You are to select a controversial business-related topic that you believe would be appropriate for this class to use for all later exercises. This topic is to be in the form of a proposal, advocating some kind of a change. In this first presentation, you are to propose and support a change rather than to defend the present system.

You are to write a 1½- to 2-page paper supporting your proposal (between 900 and 1,200 words). All papers are to be typed, single-spaced. (The papers are single-spaced to save everyone money on making copies.) On the due date, bring to class the original and 16* copies of the paper. In scheduling preparation time, it is important to allow enough time for typing and having copies made.

You will each receive 16* other students' papers and are to grade them according to the instructions on the Exercise 1 Grading Instructions Sheet. The instructions for this first paper are very general since one of our goals is to find out what you now consider to be an acceptable college-level paper.

Because of the need to select a topic early, this first paper will be due during the second week of class. Consult the course syllabus for the exact date.

---

*Your instructor may vary this number.

Paper Heading

To ease the problem of distributing papers, you are all to use the same type of heading. In the top margin on the right-hand side, type your name and class number. Below that, type "Copy No.____" and then number the copies from 0 to 16. Below that, type "Grade____." Please number the papers before coming to class. In the center of the paper, one inch below the top, type "Exercise 1" and then the semester and year. Skip two spaces and then type the title of your paper.

FIGURE 1-1. Exercise 1 Paper Heading Sample

John Doe No. 63
Copy No. ______
Grade ______

Exercise 1 Spring 19

(TITLE)

Distribution of Papers

On the day the papers are due, bring to class the original for the instructor's file and 16 copies of your paper to hand out to fellow students. After you are told in class how the papers will be distributed, write on the Paper Number Record Form (see page 17) the class numbers of the students who are to receive copies of your paper and the class numbers of the students whose papers you are to receive.

EXERCISE 1 CHECKLIST

Steps in Grading the Papers

1. Grade the papers according to the Grading Instruction Sheet (page 18).
2. Record a grade on each paper and write constructive comments on papers with copy numbers 1-8.
3. Record each grade on the Exercise 1 Grading Form (page 19).
4. On the date assigned (date ______/______/______), bring to class your completed Grading Form and and the 16 graded papers.
5. Give the Grading Form to the instructor. Return the papers to their authors.
6. After receiving your graded papers, record the grades you received on your Grade Record Form (page 20), and compute your grade point.
7. No later than the end of the class period following the one in which your graded papers were returned, record your grade point on the Class Grade Summary Sheet across from your class number in the column labeled Exercise 1 Grade. (This record sheet will be provided by the instructor.)

SPECIAL NOTE: Late Papers.

This is a class in which we all learn by helping each other. If you bring a paper late, the other students will already have received 16 papers and will have given out all 16 copies of theirs. For the person who is late to be able to do the assignment, he must ask others to make extra copies of their papers for him to grade and must ask others to grade his as an extra paper. It is not fair to ask this of fellow students.

Being fair is not enough incentive for some students to be on time, so any exercise or part of an exercise including the grading which is turned in late *will lower the offending individual's final grade in the course by 15 points, or 5%**.

This penalty is severe because late work in this course causes problems for many people besides the one who is late.

REFERENCES

1. Dooher, M. Joseph and Vivienne Marquist, Eds. *Effective Communication on the Job* (New York: American Management Association, 1956).

2. Haney, William V. *Communication and Organizational Behavior*, 3rd ed. (Homewood, Ill.: Richard D. Irwin, Inc., 1973).

3. Horne, J. H. and T. Lupton. "The Work Activities of Middle Managers," *Journal of Management Studies*, Vol. 1 (1965).

---

*See explanation of final grade computation in Exercise 8. Your instructor may modify this penalty.

Your Name ______________________
No. ______ Group ______ Sec. ______

Exercise 1

PAPER NUMBER RECORD FORM

My papers are to be passed out to:

Paper No.	Student No.	Check When Returned Graded
1	______	______
2	______	______
3	______	______
4	______	______
5	______	______
6	______	______
7	______	______
8	______	______
9	______	______
10	______	______
11	______	______
12	______	______
13	______	______
14	______	______
15	______	______
16	______	______

I am to receive papers from:

Paper No.	Student No.
______	______
______	______
______	______
______	______
______	______
______	______
______	______
______	______
______	______
______	______
______	______
______	______
______	______
______	______
______	______
______	______

Papers from the following students were not returned graded:

Copy No.	Student No.
______	______
______	______
______	______

Check with these students. If you still do not find your paper, report the loss to the instructor.

I should have but did not receive papers from:

Copy No.	Student No.
______	______
______	______
______	______

Please report to your instructor if any papers are not received in time to be graded.

Your Name ____________________________
No. ________ Group ________ Sec. ________

Exercise 1

GRADING INSTRUCTIONS SHEET

Before grading these papers, take time to read three or four of them carefully. Compare among these so that you begin to develop a basis for deciding what makes one appeal to you more than another. Based on these preliminary readings, decide what criteria you will use for grading the papers. Write these criteria down on this sheet. Writing out the criteria will help clarify them. Do not grade any papers until you have written the criteria for grading. Write at least three criteria.

Write criteria here

1.

2.

3.

Now read several more papers and try to grade them, using the criteria you have written. You may find it would be better to use more specific criteria, or you may find that two of the criteria are really describing the same phenomenon. Take time now to rewrite and clarify the criteria.

Rewrite criteria here

1.

2.

3.

You now have the criteria to use in grading the 16 papers. Grade the papers in order, according to their copy numbers. On the back of each paper, write the criteria used to grade them. Indicate by a plus, check, or minus whether the paper is strong or weak on each criterion. Give each paper a letter grade, following the forced distribution printed at the bottom of the Exercise 1 Grading Form. The forced distribution system is used so that you will force yourselves to look for ways to discriminate between the effective and ineffective papers.

On papers with copy numbers *1-8 only*, add a 50-to 100-word evaluation of the paper. The purpose is to let the authors know specifically what you think of their papers. Mention specific strengths and specific ways in which they might improve.

The reason you are not required to write such comments on copies 9-16 is to avoid unnecessary work. We have tried to draw the fine line in this course between constructive exercises and busy work. We want you to grade enough papers to build a frame of reference but not so many that you lose interest. We want to provide each student with enough feedback on his paper but not with so much that it is repetitious. The amount of writing and grading for each exercise in this course has been carefully evaluated and set to maximize the work load-learning ratio. The work load is based on five years of experimenting with this course.

Your Name ____________
No. ______ Group ______ Sec. ______

Exercise 1

GRADING FORM

The criteria I used for grading were:

1. ____________
2. ____________
3. ____________

The grades I gave are:

Paper Copy No.	Student No.	Name	Grades
1	______	______	______
2	______	______	______
3	______	______	______
4	______	______	______
5	______	______	______
6	______	______	______
7	______	______	______
8	______	______	______
9	______	______	______
10	______	______	______
11	______	______	______
12	______	______	______
13	______	______	______
14	______	______	______
15	______	______	______
16	______	______	______

Distribution of grades I gave:

A = ______% B = ______% C = ______% D = ______% F = ______%

If this distribution does not fit within the following distribution, regrade the papers and make it fit.

Grade distribution: To aid you in grading and to force you to discriminate between papers, the following curve is imposed:

A = 5-10%, B = 10-20%, C = 35-65%, D = 10-20%, F = 5-0%

Remember that these are only feedback grades and do not go on the student's permanent record. Be as honest as you can; overly high grades deceive the authors into thinking their work is better than it really is. An honest grade lets them know where they really stand.

This form is to be given to the instructor on the day the graded papers are returned.

Your Name____________________
No.______ Group______ Sec.______

Exercise 1

GRADE RECORD FORM

Grades I received from:

	Grader's Number	Grade		Grader's Number	Grade
1.	______	______	9.	______	______
2.	______	______	10.	______	______
3.	______	______	11.	______	______
4.	______	______	12.	______	______
5.	______	______	13.	______	______
6.	______	______	14.	______	______
7.	______	______	15.	______	______
8.	______	______	16.	______	______

Total A's ______ X 4 = ______

Total B's ______ X 3 = ______

Total C's ______ X 2 = ______

Total D's ______ X 1 = ______

Total F's ______ X 0 = ______

Sum______ ÷ by number of graders______ = ☐ grade point

Record your grade point on the Class Grade Summary Sheet. Use the square across from your class number in the column labeled Exercise 1 Grade. This grade is to be recorded before the end of the class period following the one in which you received your graded papers.

EXERCISE 1A

Selecting a Topic*

PURPOSE OF ASSIGNMENT

The purpose of this exercise is to select a class topic to use for all of our remaining exercises.

Introduction

The class will meet in small workshop groups during the class period following the one in which Exercise 1 papers were turned in. Each group will make a list of all of the topics used by their group members in Exercise 1. Each topic will then be evaluated as a possible topic for the class to use.

ASSIGNMENT INSTRUCTIONS

The first job of the group is to select a group recorder to keep a record of your group's activities. As soon as the recorder is selected, make a list of the topics each member of the group used in the Exercise 1 paper. List these on the following pages in the space provided.

Discuss each of these topics, using the criteria in the following list plus other criteria your group feels are relevant. Be sure to start the discussion of each topic by looking at its positive aspects. Too much early criticism can often cause the defeat of a good idea by nipping it in the bud.

a. How interesting would it be to research in depth?
b. How available is research material on this topic?
c. How could the topic be reworded to improve it?
d. Is the topic too one-sided?
e. How valuable would the knowledge be that you would gain by in-depth research of this topic?

List additional criteria your group would like to use:

f. ______________________________

____

g. ______________________________

____

The group should now rate each of the topics on these various criteria using the following rating scale. Then give each topic an over-all rating. After rating all of the topics, rank them in order of desirability.

---

*This course may be made as effective for those in other majors simply by selecting a different type of topic; for example, one in education, social work or science.

SCALE
Ratings: 1 = exceptional, 2 = excellent, 3 = good, 4 = fair, 5 = poor
Rank the topic 1st, 2nd, 3rd, and all the remainder 4th.

NOTE: Word all topics in the form of a resolution:
Resolved: That (*someone or some group*) should (*do something*).
Resolved: That (*something*) should be done by (*someone or some group*).

Examples:
Resolved: That Hawaii should adopt a no-fault auto insurance program.
Resolved: That the United Nations should establish a policy outlawing the further testing of nuclear weapons.
Resolved: That mass-media advertising should be more stringently controlled by the United States government.

The term *Resolved*: *That* will not necessarily be used as part of the topic. It is just a vehicle to help word topics.

After your discussion is finished (about 20 minutes), select the two topics the group believes are best. Write these topics on a sheet of paper. Examine each resolution and reword it as best the group can. Check the two topics selected to make sure they meet all of the criteria. Make necessary changes until they do fit. Especially note the criteria, "How available is research material on this topic?" Be prepared to write these topics on the board for the class to vote on. It is often helpful to seek advice from the instructor before taking a final vote.

Topic of Speaker Number ______ Name ________________________________
Topic stated in resolution form. Resolved: That ________________________________

____

____

Rating of topic on criteria (rate from 1-5 on each criterion a-g)

a = ___ b = ___ c = ___ d = ___ e = ___ f = ___ g = ___ overall rating ___ rank ______________

Topic of Speaker Number ______ Name ________________________________
Topic stated in resolution form. Resolved: That ________________________________

____

____

Rating of topic on criteria (rate from 1-5 on each criterion a-g)

a = ___ b = ___ c = ___ d = ___ e = ___ f = ___ g = ___ overall rating ___ rank ______________

Topic of Speaker Number ______ Name ______________________________
Topic stated in resolution form. Resolved: That ______________________________

____

____

Rating of topic on criteria (rate from 1-5 on each criterion a-g)

a = ___ b = ___ c = ___ d = ___ e = ___ f = ___ g = ___ overall rating ___ rank ______________

Topic of Speaker Number ______ Name ______________________________
Topic stated in resolution form. Resolved: That ______________________________

____

____

Rating of topic on criteria (rate from 1-5 on each criterion a-g)

a = ___ b = ___ c = ___ d = ___ e = ___ f = ___ g = ___ overall rating ___ rank ______________

Topic of Speaker Number ______ Name ______________________________
Topic stated in resolution form. Resolved: That ______________________________

____

____

Rating of topic on criteria (rate from 1-5 on each criterion a-g)

a = ___ b = ___ c = ___ d = ___ e = ___ f = ___ g = ___ overall rating ___ rank ______________

Topic of Speaker Number ______ Name ______________________________
Topic stated in resolution form. Resolved: That ______________________________

____

____

Rating of topic on criteria (rate from 1-5 on each criterion a-g)

a = ___ b = ___ c = ___ d = ___ e = ___ f = ___ g = ___ overall rating ___ rank ______________

Topic of Speaker Number ______ Name ______________________________
Topic stated in resolution form. Resolved: That ______________________________

____

____

Rating of topic on criteria (rate from 1-5 on each criterion a-g)

a = ___ b = ___ c = ___ d = ___ e = ___ f = ___ g = ___ overall rating ___ rank ______________

Topic of Speaker Number ______ Name ______________________________
Topic stated in resolution form. Resolved: That ______________________________

____

____

Rating of topic on criteria (rate from 1-5 on each criterion a-g)

a =___ b =___ c =___ d =___ e =___ f =___ g =___ overall rating___ rank___

Topic of Speaker Number______ Name___
Topic stated in resolution form. Resolved: That___

Rating of topic on criteria (rate from 1-5 on each criterion a-g)

a =___ b =___ c =___ d =___ e =___ f =___ g =___ overall rating___ rank___

EXERCISE 2

The Importance of Delivery

PURPOSE OF ASSIGNMENT

The primary focus of this first oral exercise will be on delivery, for no presentation is of much value if the intended receivers cannot understand what is being said. A secondary focus of this exercise will be to learn to research a topic in enough depth that you can meaningfully listen to and evaluate your own presentations and those of your peers.

Introduction

Communication is not an end unto itself; it is, rather, a tool used to achieve other goals. We do not just effectively communicate; we effectively communicate something. This course is designed for those going into any type of business or administration and so will focus on communicating business-related material. However, the skills learned will apply equally well to almost any other type of material.*

To practice communicating, we need something to communicate. We used Exercise 1A to help you select a topic to use for the remainder of this course. Each student should now begin in-depth research as part of the preparation for giving an oral presentation on this topic. The research must be done thoroughly because you cannot communicate what you do not understand. Communication involves much more than glib speech or grammatically correct writing.

The primary focus of this first oral presentation centers on delivery. This does not mean that the organization of material or logical content should be ignored. It means that the main effort should center on making your delivery presentable and relatively less time should be devoted to style and content.

To clarify why delivery is so important, let us compare a stereo set to a businessman giving a presentation. A great artist playing a song of classical quality may make a recording. The record may be a perfect, flaw-free print. The needle, cartridge, and amplifier may be of the highest distortion-free quality. But, if all of that quality is played through a cheap, two-inch transistor radio speaker, the output will still sound garbled. The same is true for the businessman as a speaker. He may research his topic thoroughly. He may organize and support each point in detail, but if he bores his colleagues when he presents the material or if he has annoying mannerisms that distract his listeners, then all of his preparatory effort is a waste. His communication is still garbled. The other businessmen have no way of knowing how bright or how prepared he really is. They must judge him by what was communicated to them. That is why delivery—written or oral—is important. One must hasten to add that delivery by itself is of little value, just as a cheap recording played through a fantastic speaker system still sounds like a cheap recording.

---

*This course may be made as effective for those in other majors simply by selecting a different type of topic; for example, one in education, social work, or science.

THE BASICS OF DELIVERY

There are some basic behaviors of delivery that apply to all oral presentations from formal speeches to informal group discussions. They are behaviors that have a potential of distracting the listener from what is being said. These behaviors can be grouped under two major categories (1) *physical appearance* and (2) *vocal quality*.

It is often nervousness that causes people to behave in a distracting way when making an oral presentation. Usually, the more formal the presentation, the more nervous the person and, thus, the more distracting his behaviors. Many people are terrified at the thought of giving a formal presentation called a *speech*. But in a bull session with a group of friends (or even strangers) they are not afraid to state and defend their positions. The word *speech* seems to hold more terror than the activity of speaking with a group. For this course, the oral presentations should not be considered speeches. Speeches are usually one-way communication. All presentations in this course involve two-way communication in which all group members are actively involved as both speakers and listeners. These presentations are to be like formalized conversations on a topic about which you have great knowledge. But even in the most informal of presentations, delivery is still important, so it is necessary that you learn to control the possible negative impact of your physical appearance and vocal quality in all situations.

Physical Appearance

There is one basic rule to follow regarding physical appearance while speaking: if something draws attention to itself and away from what the speaker is saying, it is bad. This includes any type of distraction from wearing a skirt that is too short to playing with keys in the pocket. Pacing, constantly repeating one gesture, or looking at the ceiling are other distractions that should be avoided. The only absolute rule to use in deciding if the speaker has a physical appearance or habit that is bad is to decide if it is distracting to you. Whether or not something is distracting depends upon its appropriateness to the situation. For example, an attractive coed wearing an extremely short skirt while talking to her girls' gym class is not likely to cause distraction. The same attractive coed in the same skirt speaking to a group of healthy middle-aged businessmen away at a convention might prove extremely distracting. The appropriate physical appearance depends upon the situation and the effect desired.

Stance. Stance is an important aspect of physical appearance because it often conveys a message the speaker does not wish to convey. If the speaker slumps with his weight on the back foot, this generally conveys that he is not too interested in communicating. Observe that when a person is presenting material about which he is really enthusiastic, his weight shifts forward toward the audience, and he stands or sits in an erect position. He is too excited to slump, and this excitement is contagious.

Many novice speakers, because of self-consciousness, stand in awkward positions that cause their bodies to rock or sway. Men tend to stand in the military parade rest position. This is one of the worst stances for causing swaying. Women frequently tend to stand with their weight on one leg and with the knee of the other leg aimed at the audience. This is distracting to most males. The ideal stance for men or women is one that is natural and draws no attention to itself. A good stance places the feet slightly apart with one foot slightly ahead of the other. The weight should be on the balls of the feet. That is a natural position that leaves a speaker free to walk around without first shifting his weight. Often business presentations are given from a sitting position, but it is best to practice speaking from a standing position. If you learn to give a presentation while standing, as is often necessary in a large room, you can always sit down if standing is not necessary. But experience has shown that those who have always practiced giving their presentations while sitting find it very unnerving to suddenly discover they must stand up for their presentation.

The Hands. The hands may also be a problem for those not used to speaking at meetings. Do not worry too much about the hands or gestures. Few people have problems with gestures when they talk conversationally with friends. It is only when they become nervous that the hands become a problem. As speakers gain confidence, such problems generally vanish. If you do not know what to do with your hands, just drop them down to your side and forget them. Avoid letting the hands play with keys, coins, or clothing. This is very distracting.

The Eyes. The eyes are the most revealing part of a speaker's body. A general rule regarding eyes is that the speaker should look directly into the eyes of his listeners at all times except when reading quotes. There are many exceptions to this rule, but, for now, accept it as a rule without exceptions. When eyes glance out the window or to the back wall, the listeners wonder what the speaker is looking at, and they also turn their attention outside or to the back wall. When a speaker looks right at a person and talks directly to him, it is hard for the listener to turn his own eyes or attention away. *In evaluating the presentations for Exercise 2, eye contact is the most important single thing to look for.*

Vocal Quality

We are each born with a voice that is quite difficult to change. If our pitch is higher or lower than we desire, it can be changed only with long practice and probably with the help of a speech therapist. Do *not* criticize a speaker about such voice qualities, for there are no facilities in this course to correct such defects. Making persons aware of voice problems is likely to make them overly self-conscious and therefore will hurt them more than it will help.

There are certain vocal patterns that can be corrected in a course such as this. These are patterns such as vocalizing "a" and "an" during all pauses or patterns involving pauses every so many words regardless of where the thought ends. Monotone delivery is another matter that is easily corrected. Such vocal patterns should be mentioned to the speaker during the feedback sessions. Again, the main rule must be that if you notice the way a person is behaving more than what he is saying, then the way he is behaving is not appropriate.

ASSIGNMENT INSTRUCTIONS

For Exercise 2 each student is to give to a group of peers a five- to six-minute oral presentation on the topic selected by the class. In this presentation, each student is to do the following:

1. State the topic and define any ambiguous terms used in that statement.
2. State and support a major argument favoring the proposal.
3. State and support a major argument opposing the proposal (by defending or supporting the present system).

Preparing to Give Evaluation and Feedback

When your presentation part of Exercise 2 is prepared, the assignment is still only half completed. Each presentation takes only five to six minutes, but each presentation will be followed by 12 minutes of feedback and evaluation for which you must also prepare. Skill in listening and giving feedback is probably more important to an administrator than is the ability to present a proposal. The most common activity of most administrators is listening to and evaluating proposals of others. The measure of a manager is how much help he can offer to those who are bringing proposals to him. In this assignment, you will be evaluated on the quality of your feedback to others as well as on the quality of your presentation.

The best way you can prepare to give feedback on this assignment is to be completely prepared and familiar with the assignment. The focus of the exercise is on delivery, so the focus of the feedback should be on the speakers' styles of delivery.

Purpose of Feedback and How to Give It

You must remember that the purpose of feedback is to help the other person improve. There is little value in telling a person what he did wrong if you cannot tell him how to overcome the problem. Specific comments are usually more helpful than general ones. To say that a person's stance is distracting is a general comment. The speaker will know that something about his stance was distracting, but what? A more specific and helpful comment might be: "When you stood so rigid with your feet together right at the first of your presentation, it caused you to sway. I wonder if you could stand with your feet a little apart and maybe walk a little? Would that help relax you?" From this specific comment and suggestion, the student is not left wondering what to do. He is given a specific suggestion on how to overcome his distracting mannerism.

It will be even more helpful if the group has the student stand up and practice giving part of his presentation again while trying the new stance. In the feedback sessions, it is important to always have the speakers *practice using the suggestions* made whether they involve stance, eye contact, or speaking louder. When we receive suggestions but do not try to adopt them, we usually forget them. To be of value, we need to practice the new suggested behavior. The Exercise 2 group meetings are designed as workshop sessions to permit such practice—make them worthwhile!

Why Have Peer Evaluators?

There will be four or five peer evaluators in each group, so the speaker will receive the opinions of several people. The author's guide (or bias) of what the feedback should cover is contained in the checklist on the Speaker Feedback Form. Your instructor's guidance will come from the class review session. The author and your instructor are only single individuals with their own biases. One of the first things an administrator must learn is that people (even instructors) differ in what they like and dislike. By having multiple evaluators, you receive a variety of opinions regarding how others respond to your style of delivery. During the feedback sessions, the group should seek multiple opinions and should avoid letting one person dominate the feedback or letting someone avoid offering any feedback. Both deprive you of receiving the full help of all group members. (See introduction, page 4, for more discussion of peer evaluation).

How to Do Research

To find support material for your selected topic, library research is vital. The library card catalogue is an excellent source for book material, and most students are familiar with it. In researching controversial business-related topics, it is likely that book material will be helpful but inadequate because it is usually outdated. Typically, textbook material is three to five years old by the time it is published. More current information can be found in magazines, trade journals, and professional journals. These are referred to as *periodical literature.*

A reference book, which lists most national and international journals, is *Ulrich's International Periodical Directory* (16th edition, published in 1975-76—later editions may be published). The most helpful part of this book is the list of abstracting and indexing services on pages 1-50.

When you begin researching a topic, these periodical indexes are most valuable for they save you from spending untold hours skimming over magazine after magazine trying to find an article on your specific area of interest. The indexes identify and group articles under proper headings. Many publications even provide abstracts of the articles. Reading abstracts enables a researcher to quickly skim over many articles and to eliminate those that are not directly relevant.

The single most valuable indexing tool for finding *magazine articles* on current business or financial topics is the *Readers' Guide to Periodical Literature.* This guide, published monthly, indexes more than 100 United States periodicals, covering all fields. Included are business-related magazines such as *Fortune, Business Week, Time, New York Times Magazine, Iron Age,* and many others. Another index that includes foreign periodicals is the *International Index to Periodicals*. It is similar to the *Readers' Guide*.

There also are many specialized indexes that index and abstract professional journal articles. A valuable source for business majors that is sometimes overlooked is *Psychological Abstracts*. It includes all of the studies in industrial and applied psychology. The *Accounting Digest*, *Air Pollution Abstracts*, *Applied Science and Technology Index*, *Business Periodicals Index*, and *Management Abstracts* are a few of the other major indexes that should be examined. In Appendix I there is a list of references adapted from a list prepared by the University of Hawaii Library which should be of great help to Business Administration majors.

Research Notes

While reading materials related to your topic, write research notes. On each note card be sure to identify the author, the name of the article or chapter, the page number, the book, magazine, or journal it is in, and its date. How to make a bibliographical notation is explained further in Exercise 3.

When you have read a helpful article, outline its key points. Write particularly important facts or statements verbatim so that they can be quoted directly from the research cards. Writing a record of the research material when it is *first* read saves much searching later for a statement that you can remember reading but cannot quite remember where you read it.

Speaking Notes

From these original cards, prepare a set of speaking note cards to use during the Exercise 2 presentation. Remember that this presentation is not a formal speech, and it is not to be written or memorized. It is to be delivered extemporaneously from notes in the same fashion that a businessman would present his proposal in a staff meeting. Being informal does not mean being less prepared. It means the meeting will be less structured and more open to interaction between speaker and listener. You must be prepared for the interaction as well as for the presentation.

The speaking note cards should contain a *brief* outline of the material to be presented. The first card should contain an exact statement of the topic and exact statements of the pro and con arguments to be used. The second and third cards should contain *key word* outlines of how you plan to support the pro arguments and con arguments in your presentation. Additional cards should contain any references and quotations that are to be used to support the argument. These note cards should be the only material held or used while giving the Exercise 2 presentation.

PROCEDURE FOR PRESENTATIONS

Practice

Before coming to class, practice giving the presentation out loud several times. Check to make sure that the material can be covered in the five to six minutes allotted for it. Look at the Speaker Feedback Form (page 33) that the listeners will be using as a checklist to help them evaluate the presentations. Use this list to check yourself. Next, go back and reread the section on the "Basics of Delivery." Try looking in a mirror to check your own physical behavior such as stance and eye contact. Some students may even wish to use a tape recorder and listen for vocal quality.

As you practice and review your own behavior, you are at the same time preparing to help others in your group. Remember that the function of group sessions is not only to learn to give a presentation, but also to learn to actively listen to and evaluate the presentations of others.

Class Review

This assignment is due for an in-class review the period before it is to be presented to the workshop group. All students are to bring to class a duplicate set of the speaking note cards that they plan to use for their presentations. These cards should be a Xeroxed copy on 8½ × 11 sheets of paper (two or three cards can be copied on each sheet of paper). Be sure to put your name and class number on the duplicates because they are to be given to the instructor at the end of the period.

There are two major reasons for having an in-class review. The first is so you can review each other's note cards. By this means, we can see if each student fully understands the assignment and is prepared to participate meaningfully in the workshop sessions. The main items that will be checked on the cards are as follows:

1. Is the topic stated correctly?
2. Is there an argument stated and supported that favors the proposal (advocates a change)?
3. Is there an argument stated and supported that opposes the proposal (advocates not changing)?
4. Are the arguments supported and documented by research?

Students will be allowed to participate in their peer groups as speakers or evaluators only when their cards show that they are prepared and that they understand the assignment. Those who are not prepared at that time must make special arrangements with their instructor before they will be permitted to participate in Exercise 2.

The second function of the in-class review is to demonstrate how to conduct the feedback and evaluation part of the workshop group meetings. In the workshop meetings, no one is ever a passive listener. All students are active participants at all times, as they would be in a business meeting. While one person is giving his proposal, the rest are to be *actively listening*, *observing*, and *evaluating*. When one participant finishes, the rest of the group members have a responsibility to give feedback. The feedback for Exercise 2 is to focus on the "Basics of Delivery," discussed earlier in this assignment. During the in-class review session, you will discuss the do's and don'ts of how to give feedback.

Demonstrations Before the Class

During the review session, several students will be asked to give their presentations before the entire class. The instructor will then demonstrate how to give feedback that will help others to improve their delivery. While these volunteer students are speaking, the rest of the class are to be actively listening and practicing using the Speaker Feedback Form (page 33). The checklist on this form provides a guide to listening by reminding you of the key things you should watch for during a presentation. The checklist also makes it possible for you to spend more time listening and less time taking notes. Following the presentations, several students may be asked to join the instructor in giving helpful feedback to the participants.

Operation of Workshop Groups

For Exercise 2 workshop groups, students will be divided into groups of six persons each, according to their class number. That is, numbers 1-6 will be group A, 7-12 will be group B, and so on. The person in each group with the lowest number will be the *group coordinator*. Coordinators will act as chairmen for their groups and will keep records of attendance and tardiness of group members. They will also be responsible for filling out the Group Coordinator's Grade Summary Sheet (page 69) and the Group Coordinator's Feedback Grade Summary Sheet (page 71). They are to record the grades for their group members on the Class Grade Summary Sheet. Then they are to give the instructor the Group Coordinator's Grade Summary Sheet and the Group Coordinator's Feedback Grade Summary Sheets.

The person with the highest number in each group will be the first speaker, and the others will follow in reverse numerical order. The first speaker will be timed by the group coordinator. The first speaker will then become the timer for all remaining speakers.

Time Limits. The presentations are to be from five to six minutes in length. The timer should make time cards numbered from 0 to 5 to show speakers how much time they have remaining to speak. Each presentation should be followed immediately by a two-minute period during which the evaluators can fill out the Student Grading Form (page 65).

The feedback to each student should last from 10 to·12 minutes. This should be timed by the timer, who should stop the group feedback at the end of 12 minutes. The timer should also make sure that all feedback lasts at least 10 minutes. Following the feedback session, the timer should allow two minutes for the previous speaker to fill out the checklist on the Feedback to Evaluators form, (page 49.)

Feedback Rating Sheets. All group members, when they are not speaking, are evaluators. The evaluators must carefully listen to each presentation so that they can give helpful feedback to the speakers. The Speaker Feedback Form should be used to guide your listening as you jot down notes on what to say in the feedback session.

All feedback for Exercise 2 is to be given orally. But, before you give any feedback, you should fill out the Student Grading Form (page 65). The timer should allow no more than two minutes for filling out this grading form. The grading forms are to be filled out *independently* with absolutely no consultation with other students. If two students talk before rating a speaker, they tend to influence each other. This reduces the number of independent ratings a speaker receives.

Feedback to Evaluators

Following the feedback session and while the next speaker is getting ready to begin, the speaker who has just received the feedback should rate the other five group members, using the Feedback to Evaluators form (page 49). Rate each group member, as to how valuable their comments (feedback) were. The timer should allow no more than two minutes for the student to do this. During class, fill out only the checklist, rating, and ranking sections of this form. Later, after class, when there is more time, comments are to be added to this form, explaining why certain types of feedback were or were not helpful.

Importance of Feedback. The ratings you receive for feedback are considered as equal in weight to the ratings you receive for speaking. The feedback phase of communication is as vital in a business meeting and often more important than the initial presentation. Speaking can be one-way communication. To give helpful feedback requires that you have carefully listened to and evaluated other communication before you begin to speak. Feedback is always two-way communication–the type of communication most important to administrators.

EXERCISE 2 CHECKLIST

Checklist of Things to Do (before coming to class)

1. Research topic and prepare a 5-6 minute oral presentation.
2. Prepare research notes.
3. The presentation must contain one argument *pro* and one *con*.
4. Read all evaluation and grading forms carefully. These are designed to help guide you in preparing as well as evaluating presentations.
5. Prepare a set of speaking notes and bring a Xerox copy of these to the in-class review session.
6. Prepare to evaluate the presentations of others by becoming familiar with the goals and procedures for this exercise.

Checklist for Conducting Workshops

1. The lowest-numbered student in each group is the group coordinator. He or she is to do the following:
   a. Call the group to order and take attendance.
   b. Time the first speaker.
   c. Coordinate activities during the sessions.
   d. At the end of the sessions, fill out the Group Coordinator's Grade Summary Sheet and the Group Coordinator's Feedback Grade Summary Sheet.
   e. Record grades from summary sheets onto the Class Grade Summary Sheet (to be provided by the instructor).
2. The highest-numbered student in each group is the first speaker and becomes the timer for all remaining speakers.
3. Time limits are as follows:
   5-6 minutes for presentations.
   2 minutes for filling out Speaker Feedback Form.
   10-12 minutes for feedback session.
   2 minutes for filling out checklist on Feedback to Evaluator form.
4. All feedback is to be specific and constructive.

Your Name ______________________
No. ________ Group ________ Sec. ________

Exercise 2

SPEAKER FEEDBACK FORM

Feedback to Speaker ________________ No. ______

Instructions: This form is for your own use. It is *not* to be turned in. As you listen to each speaker, use this form to take notes. A checklist is provided to help guide your listening and to allow you to devote time to listening rather than writing out comments. This checklist may also aid you in filling out the "Student Grading Form."

Checklist: (Circle One)

+ √ – Was the presentation interesting?
+ √ – Did the speaker avoid distracting physical behaviors or dress? (If "√" or "–," explain what was distracting to you in the notes below.)
+ √ – Was the speaker easy to hear and understand?
+ √ – *Did the speaker maintain good eye contact?*
+ √ – Was the speaker's material easy to follow?
+ √ – Did the speaker's arguments seem logically sound?
+ √ – Did the speaker have a clear presentation of a pro argument?
+ √ – Did the speaker have a clear presentation of a con argument?

Notes: Jot down briefly strong and weak points of the speaker's delivery so you will remember what to say during the feedback session.

Feedback: Jot down briefly things the speaker might do to improve.

Note: All feedback for Exercise 2 is to be given to the speaker orally in the twelve-minute feedback session. All feedback should be designed to *help* the speakers rather than to judge them. The feedback session is for learning and improving, not for criticizing.

Have the speakers practice the suggested new behavior so they can actually try to improve their eye contact, volume, and stance. Just to tell them about it is of little value for they can be passive. Make them actively work on suggested new behavior. This is a workshop session; make it worthwhile.

Two of these forms are for the class review session and six are for the group workshop session.

Your Name ______________________
No. ______ Group ______ Sec. ______

Exercise 2

SPEAKER FEEDBACK FORM

Feedback to Speaker ______________ No. ______

Instructions: This form is for your own use. It is *not* to be turned in. As you listen to each speaker, use this form to take notes. A checklist is provided to help guide your listening and to allow you to devote time to listening rather than writing out comments. This checklist may also aid you in filling out the "Student Grading Form."

Checklist: (Circle One)

+ √ – Was the presentation interesting?
+ √ – Did the speaker avoid distracting physical behaviors or dress?
(If "√" or "–," explain what was distracting to you in the notes below.)
+ √ – Was the speaker easy to hear and understand?
+ √ – *Did the speaker maintain good eye contact?*
+ √ – Was the speaker's material easy to follow?
+ √ – Did the speaker's arguments seem logically sound?
+ √ – Did the speaker have a clear presentation of a pro argument?
+ √ – Did the speaker have a clear presentation of a con argument?

Notes: Jot down briefly strong and weak points of the speaker's delivery so you will remember what to say during the feedback session.

Feedback: Jot down briefly things the speaker might do to improve.

Note: All feedback for Exercise 2 is to be given to the speaker orally in the twelve-minute feedback session. All feedback should be designed to *help* the speakers rather than to judge them. The feedback session is for learning and improving, not for criticizing.

Have the speakers practice the suggested new behavior so they can actually try to improve their eye contact, volume, and stance. Just to tell them about it is of little value for they can be passive. Make them actively work on suggested new behavior. This is a workshop session; make it worthwhile.

Two of these forms are for the class review session and six are for the group workshop session.

Your Name ________________

No. ______ Group ______ Sec. ______

Exercise 2

SPEAKER FEEDBACK FORM

Feedback to Speaker ______________ No. ______

Instructions: This form is for your own use. It is *not* to be turned in. As you listen to each speaker, use this form to take notes. A checklist is provided to help guide your listening and to allow you to devote time to listening rather than writing out comments. This checklist may also aid you in filling out the "Student Grading Form."

Checklist: (Circle One)

+ √ − Was the presentation interesting?

+ √ − Did the speaker avoid distracting physical behaviors or dress?
(If "√" or "−," explain what was distracting to you in the notes below.)

+ √ − Was the speaker easy to hear and understand?

+ √ − *Did the speaker maintain good eye contact?*

+ √ − Was the speaker's material easy to follow?

+ √ − Did the speaker's arguments seem logically sound?

+ √ − Did the speaker have a clear presentation of a pro argument?

+ √ − Did the speaker have a clear presentation of a con argument?

Notes: Jot down briefly strong and weak points of the speaker's delivery so you will remember what to say during the feedback session.

Feedback: Jot down briefly things the speaker might do to improve.

Note: All feedback for Exercise 2 is to be given to the speaker orally in the twelve-minute feedback session. All feedback should be designed to *help* the speakers rather than to judge them. The feedback session is for learning and improving, not for criticizing.

Have the speakers practice the suggested new behavior so they can actually try to improve their eye contact, volume, and stance. Just to tell them about it is of little value for they can be passive. Make them actively work on suggested new behavior. This is a workshop session; make it worthwhile.

Two of these forms are for the class review session and six are for the group workshop session.

Your Name ____________________
No. ______ Group ______ Sec. ______

Exercise 2

SPEAKER FEEDBACK FORM

Feedback to Speaker ______________ No. ______

Instructions: This form is for your own use. It is *not* to be turned in. As you listen to each speaker, use this form to take notes. A checklist is provided to help guide your listening and to allow you to devote time to listening rather than writing out comments. This checklist may also aid you in filling out the "Student Grading Form."

Checklist: (Circle One)

+ √ – Was the presentation interesting?
+ √ – Did the speaker avoid distracting physical behaviors or dress? (If "√" or "–," explain what was distracting to you in the notes below.)
+ √ – Was the speaker easy to hear and understand?
+ √ – *Did the speaker maintain good eye contact*?
+ √ – Was the speaker's material easy to follow?
+ √ – Did the speaker's arguments seem logically sound?
+ √ – Did the speaker have a clear presentation of a pro argument?
+ √ – Did the speaker have a clear presentation of a con argument?

Notes: Jot down briefly strong and weak points of the speaker's delivery so you will remember what to say during the feedback session.

Feedback: Jot down briefly things the speaker might do to improve.

Note: All feedback for Exercise 2 is to be given to the speaker orally in the twelve-minute feedback session. All feedback should be designed to *help* the speakers rather than to judge them. The feedback session is for learning and improving, not for criticizing.

Have the speakers practice the suggested new behavior so they can actually try to improve their eye contact, volume, and stance. Just to tell them about it is of little value for they can be passive. Make them actively work on suggested new behavior. This is a workshop session; make it worthwhile.

Two of these forms are for the class review session and six are for the group workshop session.

Your Name ______________________
No. ______ Group ______ Sec. ______

Exercise 2

SPEAKER FEEDBACK FORM

Feedback to Speaker______________ No. ______

Instructions: This form is for your own use. It is *not* to be turned in. As you listen to each speaker, use this form to take notes. A checklist is provided to help guide your listening and to allow you to devote time to listening rather than writing out comments. This checklist may also aid you in filling out the "Student Grading Form."

Checklist: (Circle One)

+ √ — Was the presentation interesting?
+ √ — Did the speaker avoid distracting physical behaviors or dress?
(If "√" or "—," explain what was distracting to you in the notes below.)
+ √ — Was the speaker easy to hear and understand?
+ √ — *Did the speaker maintain good eye contact*?
+ √ — Was the speaker's material easy to follow?
+ √ — Did the speaker's arguments seem logically sound?
+ √ — Did the speaker have a clear presentation of a pro argument?
+ √ — Did the speaker have a clear presentation of a con argument?

Notes: Jot down briefly strong and weak points of the speaker's delivery so you will remember what to say during the feedback session.

Feedback: Jot down briefly things the speaker might do to improve.

Note: All feedback for Exercise 2 is to be given to the speaker orally in the twelve-minute feedback session. All feedback should be designed to *help* the speakers rather than to judge them. The feedback session is for learning and improving, not for criticizing.

Have the speakers practice the suggested new behavior so they can actually try to improve their eye contact, volume, and stance. Just to tell them about it is of little value for they can be passive. Make them actively work on suggested new behavior. This is a workshop session; make it worthwhile.

Two of these forms are for the class review session and six are for the group workshop session.

Your Name ____________________
No. ________ Group ________ Sec. ________

Exercise 2

SPEAKER FEEDBACK FORM

Feedback to Speaker ________________ No. ______

Instructions: This form is for your own use. It is *not* to be turned in. As you listen to each speaker, use this form to take notes. A checklist is provided to help guide your listening and to allow you to devote time to listening rather than writing out comments. This checklist may also aid you in filling out the "Student Grading Form."

Checklist: (Circle One)

+ √ – Was the presentation interesting?
+ √ – Did the speaker avoid distracting physical behaviors or dress?
(If "√" or "–," explain what was distracting to you in the notes below.)
+ √ – Was the speaker easy to hear and understand?
+ √ – *Did the speaker maintain good eye contact?*
+ √ – Was the speaker's material easy to follow?
+ √ – Did the speaker's arguments seem logically sound?
+ √ – Did the speaker have a clear presentation of a pro argument?
+ √ – Did the speaker have a clear presentation of a con argument?

Notes: Jot down briefly strong and weak points of the speaker's delivery so you will remember what to say during the feedback session.

Feedback: Jot down briefly things the speaker might do to improve.

Note: All feedback for Exercise 2 is to be given to the speaker orally in the twelve-minute feedback session. All feedback should be designed to *help* the speakers rather than to judge them. The feedback session is for learning and improving, not for criticizing.

Have the speakers practice the suggested new behavior so they can actually try to improve their eye contact, volume, and stance. Just to tell them about it is of little value for they can be passive. Make them actively work on suggested new behavior. This is a workshop session; make it worthwhile.

Two of these forms are for the class review session and six are for the group workshop session.

Your Name ____________________
No.______ Group______ Sec.______

Exercise 2

SPEAKER FEEDBACK FORM

Feedback to Speaker______________ No. ______

Instructions: This form is for your own use. It is *not* to be turned in. As you listen to each speaker, use this form to take notes. A checklist is provided to help guide your listening and to allow you to devote time to listening rather than writing out comments. This checklist may also aid you in filling out the "Student Grading Form."

Checklist: (Circle One)

+ √ — Was the presentation interesting?
+ √ — Did the speaker avoid distracting physical behaviors or dress? (If "√" or "—," explain what was distracting to you in the notes below.)
+ √ — Was the speaker easy to hear and understand?
+ √ — *Did the speaker maintain good eye contact?*
+ √ — Was the speaker's material easy to follow?
+ √ — Did the speaker's arguments seem logically sound?
+ √ — Did the speaker have a clear presentation of a pro argument?
+ √ — Did the speaker have a clear presentation of a con argument?

Notes: Jot down briefly strong and weak points of the speaker's delivery so you will remember what to say during the feedback session.

Feedback: Jot down briefly things the speaker might do to improve.

Note: All feedback for Exercise 2 is to be given to the speaker orally in the twelve-minute feedback session. All feedback should be designed to *help* the speakers rather than to judge them. The feedback session is for learning and improving, not for criticizing.

Have the speakers practice the suggested new behavior so they can actually try to improve their eye contact, volume, and stance. Just to tell them about it is of little value for they can be passive. Make them actively work on suggested new behavior. This is a workshop session; make it worthwhile.

Two of these forms are for the class review session and six are for the group workshop session.

Your Name ______________________
No. ________ Group ________ Sec. ________

Exercise 2

SPEAKER FEEDBACK FORM

Feedback to Speaker ________________ No. ______

Instructions: This form is for your own use. It is *not* to be turned in. As you listen to each speaker, use this form to take notes. A checklist is provided to help guide your listening and to allow you to devote time to listening rather than writing out comments. This checklist may also aid you in filling out the "Student Grading Form."

Checklist: (Circle One)

+ √ – Was the presentation interesting?

+ √ – Did the speaker avoid distracting physical behaviors or dress?
(If "√" or "–," explain what was distracting to you in the notes below.)

+ √ – Was the speaker easy to hear and understand?

+ √ – *Did the speaker maintain good eye contact?*

+ √ – Was the speaker's material easy to follow?

+ √ – Did the speaker's arguments seem logically sound?

+ √ – Did the speaker have a clear presentation of a pro argument?

+ √ – Did the speaker have a clear presentation of a con argument?

Notes: Jot down briefly strong and weak points of the speaker's delivery so you will remember what to say during the feedback session.

Feedback: Jot down briefly things the speaker might do to improve.

Note: All feedback for Exercise 2 is to be given to the speaker orally in the twelve-minute feedback session. All feedback should be designed to *help* the speakers rather than to judge them. The feedback session is for learning and improving, not for criticizing.

Have the speakers practice the suggested new behavior so they can actually try to improve their eye contact, volume, and stance. Just to tell them about it is of little value for they can be passive. Make them actively work on suggested new behavior. This is a workshop session; make it worthwhile.

Two of these forms are for the class review session and six are for the group workshop session.

Your Name ______________________
No. ________ Group ________ Sec. ________

Exercise 2

FEEDBACK TO EVALUATORS

Feedback to Evaluator ______________________ No. ______

Instructions: On one of these forms rate each evaluator regarding how much the feedback will help you improve your next presentation. Use the same rating-ranking system as you used to rate speakers. Take two minutes to fill out the checklist, rating, and ranking sections of this form as soon as you finish receiving the feedback. After class, add written comments.

Rating: 1 = exceptional, 2 = excellent, 3 = good, 4 = fair, 5 = poor
Rank: 1st, 2nd, 3rd, with no ties permitted. All others are ranked 4th.

+ √ − The comments were specific rather than general.
+ √ − The feedback was constructive and contained suggestions on how to improve.
+ √ − He/She took this assignment seriously and really tried to be helpful.

Notes: Add any special comments that might help the evaluator to improve the quality of his/her feedback.

I rate and rank the feedback as: rating ______ + ranking ______ = total ______

Record the total on the bottom half of the Student Grading Form in the space labeled Feedback Grades. Then give this feedback form to the person being evaluated.

Your Name ____________________
No.________ Group________ Sec.________

Exercise 2

FEEDBACK TO EVALUATORS

Feedback to Evaluator ____________________ No.______

Instructions: On one of these forms rate each evaluator regarding how much the feedback will help you improve your next presentation. Use the same rating-ranking system as you used to rate speakers. Take two minutes to fill out the checklist, rating, and ranking sections of this form as soon as you finish receiving the feedback. After class, add written comments.

Rating: 1 = exceptional, 2 = excellent, 3 = good, 4 = fair, 5 = poor
Rank: 1st, 2nd, 3rd, with no ties permitted. All others are ranked 4th.

+ √ – The comments were specific rather than general.
+ √ – The feedback was constructive and contained suggestions on how to improve.
+ √ – He/She took this assignment seriously and really tried to be helpful.

Notes: Add any special comments that might help the evaluator to improve the quality of his/her feedback.

I rate and rank the feedback as: rating______ + ranking______ = total______

Record the total on the bottom half of the Student Grading Form in the space labeled Feedback Grades. Then give this feedback form to the person being evaluated.

Your Name ____________________
No.______ Group______ Sec.______

Exercise 2

FEEDBACK TO EVALUATORS

Feedback to Evaluator ____________________ No.______

Instructions: On one of these forms rate each evaluator regarding how much the feedback will help you improve your next presentation. Use the same rating-ranking system as you used to rate speakers. Take two minutes to fill out the checklist, rating, and ranking sections of this form as soon as you finish receiving the feedback. After class, add written comments.

Rating: 1 = exceptional, 2 = excellent, 3 = good, 4 = fair, 5 = poor
Rank: 1st, 2nd, 3rd, with no ties permitted. All others are ranked 4th.

+ √ – The comments were specific rather than general.
+ √ – The feedback was constructive and contained suggestions on how to improve.
+ √ – He/She took this assignment seriously and really tried to be helpful.

Notes: Add any special comments that might help the evaluator to improve the quality of his/her feedback.

I rate and rank the feedback as: rating______ + ranking______ = total______

Record the total on the bottom half of the Student Grading Form in the space labeled Feedback Grades. Then give this feedback form to the person being evaluated.

Your Name ______________________
No. ______ Group ______ Sec. ______

Exercise 2

FEEDBACK TO EVALUATORS

Feedback to Evaluator ____________________ No. ______

Instructions: On one of these forms rate each evaluator regarding how much the feedback will help you improve your next presentation. Use the same rating-ranking system as you used to rate speakers. Take two minutes to fill out the checklist, rating, and ranking sections of this form as soon as you finish receiving the feedback. After class, add written comments.

Rating: 1 = exceptional, 2 = excellent, 3 = good, 4 = fair, 5 = poor
Rank: 1st, 2nd, 3rd, with no ties permitted. All others are ranked 4th.

+ √ − The comments were specific rather than general.
+ √ − The feedback was constructive and contained suggestions on how to improve.
+ √ − He/She took this assignment seriously and really tried to be helpful.

Notes: Add any special comments that might help the evaluator to improve the quality of his/her feedback.

I rate and rank the feedback as: rating ______ + ranking ______ = total ______

Record the total on the bottom half of the Student Grading Form in the space labeled Feedback Grades. Then give this feedback form to the person being evaluated.

Your Name ______________________
No. _______ Group _______ Sec. _______

Exercise 2

FEEDBACK TO EVALUATORS

Feedback to Evaluator ____________________ No. ______

Instructions: On one of these forms rate each evaluator regarding how much the feedback will help you improve your next presentation. Use the same rating-ranking system as you used to rate speakers. Take two minutes to fill out the checklist, rating, and ranking sections of this form as soon as you finish receiving the feedback. After class, add written comments.

Rating: 1 = exceptional, 2 = excellent, 3 = good, 4 = fair, 5 = poor
Rank: 1st, 2nd, 3rd, with no ties permitted. All others are ranked 4th.

+ √ − The comments were specific rather than general.
+ √ − The feedback was constructive and contained suggestions on how to improve.
+ √ − He/She took this assignment seriously and really tried to be helpful.

Notes: Add any special comments that might help the evaluator to improve the quality of his/her feedback.

I rate and rank the feedback as: rating ______ + ranking ______ = total ______

Record the total on the bottom half of the Student Grading Form in the space labeled Feedback Grades. Then give this feedback form to the person being evaluated.

Your Name ____________________
No. ______ Group ______ Sec. ______

Exercise 2

FEEDBACK TO EVALUATORS

Feedback to Evaluator ____________________ No. ______

Instructions: On one of these forms rate each evaluator regarding how much the feedback will help you improve your next presentation. Use the same rating-ranking system as you used to rate speakers. Take two minutes to fill out the checklist, rating, and ranking sections of this form as soon as you finish receiving the feedback. After class, add written comments.

Rating: 1 = exceptional, 2 = excellent, 3 = good, 4 = fair, 5 = poor
Rank: 1st, 2nd, 3rd, with no ties permitted. All others are ranked 4th.

+ √ – The comments were specific rather than general.
+ √ – The feedback was constructive and contained suggestions on how to improve.
+ √ – He/She took this assignment seriously and really tried to be helpful.

Notes: Add any special comments that might help the evaluator to improve the quality of his/her feedback.

I rate and rank the feedback as: rating ______ + ranking ______ = total ______

Record the total on the bottom half of the Student Grading Form in the space labeled Feedback Grades. Then give this feedback form to the person being evaluated.

Your Name ____________________
No. ________ Group ________ Sec. ________

Exercise 2

FEEDBACK TO EVALUATORS

Feedback to Evaluator ____________________ No. ______

Instructions: On one of these forms rate each evaluator regarding how much the feedback will help you improve your next presentation. Use the same rating-ranking system as you used to rate speakers. Take two minutes to fill out the checklist, rating, and ranking sections of this form as soon as you finish receiving the feedback. After class, add written comments.

Rating: 1 = exceptional, 2 = excellent, 3 = good, 4 = fair, 5 = poor
Rank: 1st, 2nd, 3rd, with no ties permitted. All others are ranked 4th.

+ √ − The comments were specific rather than general.
+ √ − The feedback was constructive and contained suggestions on how to improve.
+ √ − He/She took this assignment seriously and really tried to be helpful.

Notes: Add any special comments that might help the evaluator to improve the quality of his/her feedback.

I rate and rank the feedback as: rating ______ + ranking ______ = total ______

Record the total on the bottom half of the Student Grading Form in the space labeled Feedback Grades. Then give this feedback form to the person being evaluated.

Your Name ____________________
No. ________ Group ________ Sec. ________

Exercise 2

FEEDBACK TO EVALUATORS

Feedback to Evaluator ____________________ No. ______

Instructions: On one of these forms rate each evaluator regarding how much the feedback will help you improve your next presentation. Use the same rating-ranking system as you used to rate speakers. Take two minutes to fill out the checklist, rating, and ranking sections of this form as soon as you finish receiving the feedback. After class, add written comments.

Rating: 1 = exceptional, 2 = excellent, 3 = good, 4 = fair, 5 = poor
Rank: 1st, 2nd, 3rd, with no ties permitted. All others are ranked 4th.

+ √ − The comments were specific rather than general.
+ √ − The feedback was constructive and contained suggestions on how to improve.
+ √ − He/She took this assignment seriously and really tried to be helpful.

Notes: Add any special comments that might help the evaluator to improve the quality of his/her feedback.

I rate and rank the feedback as: rating ______ + ranking ______ = total ______

Record the total on the bottom half of the Student Grading Form in the space labeled Feedback Grades. Then give this feedback form to the person being evaluated.

Your Name______________________
No._______ Group_______ Sec._______

Exercise 2

STUDENT GRADING FORM

Ratings should be made as soon as the speaker finishes and before any oral feedback is given. Do not consult with anyone else in your group before filling out this grading form. Do not let anyone else in your group see your grading.

Rating: 1 = exceptional, 2 = excellent, 3 = good, 4 = fair, 5 = poor.

After you have heard all of the speakers in your group, rank the 1st, 2nd, and 3rd best speakers. Give all of the other speakers a rank of 4th. No ties for 1st, 2nd, or 3rd are permitted.

After all ratings and rankings are completed for every student in the group SUM each student's rating and ranking to obtain his grade. The lower the score, the higher the grade.

The number-letter grade equivalents are: 2-3 = A, 4-5 = B, 6-8 = C, 9 = D.

Speaking Grades

Student's Number	Name	Rating	+	Ranking	=	Total	=	Letter Grade

Feedback Grades

Student's Number	Name	Rating	+	Ranking	=	Total	=	Letter Grade

When this sheet is completed, give it to the group coordinator, who will transfer the numbers in the boxes to the Group Coordinator's Grade Summary Sheet and Group Coordinator's Feedback Grade Summary Sheet.

Your Name________________________
No.________ Group________ Sec.________

Exercise 2

STUDENT'S GRADE RECORD SHEET

Record your grades on this sheet.

Grades received on speaking

From No.	rating	+	ranking	=	
______	______	+	______	=	______
______	______	+	______	=	______
______	______	+	______	=	______
______	______	+	______	=	______
______	______	+	______	=	______
______	______	+	______	=	______

Total	______	______	______	
÷ by Number of grade	______	______	______	
= your average grade	______	______	[ ]	= Sum Grade Average

Grades received on feedback

From No.	rating	+	ranking	=	
______	______	+	______	=	______
______	______	+	______	=	______
______	______	+	______	=	______
______	______	+	______	=	______
______	______	+	______	=	______
______	______	+	______	=	______

Total	______	______	______	
÷ by Number of grade	______	______	______	
= your average grade	______	______	[ ]	= Sum Grade Average

Group Coordinator's
Name ______________________
No.______ Group ______ Sec. ______

Exercise 2

GROUP COORDINATOR'S GRADE SUMMARY SHEET

Insert in the blanks the numbers in the boxes on the top half of the Student Grading Form filled out by each of the students in the group.

Student No.	____	____	____	____	____	____
Rater No.:						
____	____	____	____	____	____	____
____	____	____	____	____	____	____
____	____	____	____	____	____	____
____	____	____	____	____	____	____
____	____	____	____	____	____	____
____	____	____	____	____	____	____
Sum	====	====	====	====	====	====
÷ by	____	____	____	____	____	____
= Average Grade	☐	☐	☐	☐	☐	☐

After filling out this Grade Summary Sheet, record the students' average grades on the Class Grade Summary Sheet. Use the column headed Exercise 2 Speaker Grade. Then give this sheet to the instructor.

Coordinator's
Name ______________________________
No. _______ Group _______ Sec. _______

Exercise 2

GROUP COORDINATOR'S FEEDBACK GRADE SUMMARY SHEET

Record on the blanks the numbers in the boxes on the bottom half of the Student Grading Form. This information comes from the Feedback Grades section of the form.

Student No.	______	______	______	______	______	______
Evaluation by No.:						
______	______	______	______	______	______	______
______	______	______	______	______	______	______
______	______	______	______	______	______	______
______	______	______	______	______	______	______
______	______	______	______	______	______	______
______	______	______	______	______	______	______
Sum	======	======	======	======	======	======
÷ by	______	______	______	______	______	______
= Average Grade	☐	☐	☐	☐	☐	☐

After filling out this grade summary sheet, record the students' average grades on the Class Grade Summary Sheet. Use the column headed Exercise 2 Feedback Grade. Then give this sheet to the instructor.

List below the names of any group members who were absent or tardy for any group session.

Name ______________________ No. ___________ Name ______________________ No. _______

Excuse ______________________________________ Excuse ______________________________________

EXERCISE 3

Organizing and Supporting

PURPOSE OF ASSIGNMENT

The major purpose of this exercise is to learn what elements a presentation must contain and to learn how to organize those elements into an understandable and convincing presentation.

Introduction

The class has selected a topic, and you will use this topic for the remainder of the course. There are several reasons for using just one topic. Some of the reasons will become more apparent as you work on later exercises. A primary reason for using a single topic is that it allows you to focus on in-depth research on that one topic, rather than to treat many topics superficially. Although learning to do research is essential in this course, it is considered a by-product rather than a primary objective of the course. The primary objective is to learn to present the material you have researched and to be able to do so in a manner appropriate for a business setting. The major portion of class time will be devoted to identifying and improving the skills of organizing, presenting, and evaluating the material you have researched. Researching even one topic will require a great deal more time and effort than is commonly assumed by novices at this task.

In the Exercise 3 papers you are to present documented arguments favoring the proposition selected by the class. This means that the papers will be advocating some type of change. The first thing that you must do if you are to propose that someone change or that something be changed is to show *why* any change is needed. If a personnel manager proposes that the beginning salaries of new recruits should be raised, he must first show that there is a need to raise the salaries. He must next work out a plan for the raise. The plan should show such things as how much salaries should be raised and where the money would come from. Finally, he would need to show the benefits his firm would receive if they followed his plan to raise the salaries of new recruits.

In Exercise 3 papers you will be presenting only the first step of a proposal. You will present only arguments showing that there is a *need* for adopting the proposal selected by the class. Exercise 3 is a preparatory exercise which you will use to practice organizing your writing. In Exercise 4, you will go one step beyond showing a need for a change; you will present a proposed *plan* of change. Keep this in mind while doing your research for the present exercise.

Team Research

By having the entire class work on the same topic, you can learn to help each other do your research. This training in team research is most valuable for those who plan to go into the business world. In school, individual work is stressed. It is often considered cheating to work jointly on papers and certainly to help one another on exams. In the business world, people are much less concerned about how a paper or report is done. They are more concerned with the quality of the final product. If a manager turns in a quality report but had a staff of 20 research assistants to help him, he still gets the credit. He did a good job of managing the work of others.

The research for this class should be done in a cooperative manner. You are not competing for a grade in this course. You are all working together, as would the employees of a company, to help each other improve so as to maximize the over-all quality of the entire class. It is the over-all performance of the entire group that the instructor must finally evaluate, just as the success of a company is evaluated by its over-all performance. Individual efforts are only as valuable as their contribution to the group effort.

A cooperative system works only if each student does his share. *For Exercise 3, it is recommended that the research be done in groups of two or three, but each of you must write your own individual paper.* Groups larger than two or three require too much coordination for now. You may form your own group or ask the instructor to help you find a group.

How to Begin Teamwork

Each member of a group should begin by doing library work alone. Then when all members of the group have a basic knowledge of the topic, the group should meet for discussion. References should be shared so that other group members do not need to waste time re-searching through materials which their colleagues have already covered.

Following the group information sharing meetings, the individual members should return to the library and look up the materials suggested by others in the group. It is never safe to accept someone else's interpretation of what an article says. The meaning assigned to an article by one reader is usually quite different than that assigned by another. Remember, meaning is in people, not words. If you get the meaning second-hand, it has already been abstracted and edited by the limitations of the mind of the reader whose version you heard. (See Chapter Two in the second section of this text for a further explanation of this point.) It is wise to go back and read the original article; otherwise, you may end up quoting the author completely out of context.

PREASSIGNMENT INSTRUCTIONS

Step 1. Read at least 20* articles on the topic selected by the class. List all of these articles on the Basic Research Reference Forms (see example on page 75). Make three or four copies of the completed forms. Keep the original for your own use and *turn in one copy attached to the instructor's copy of your Exercise 3 paper.* Give one copy to each of the members of your research group.

Step 2. Articles considered valuable should be abstracted, using the Article Abstracting Forms (page 89). *At least 10* articles are to be abstracted using the format of the form provided* (sample form is on page 81). *Keep the originals. Turn in copies of the 10 abstracts. Attach them to the instructor's copy of the Exercise 3 paper.* You may wish to make other copies to share with the members of your research group.

Your research work should be completed and discussed with your group before any attempt is made at writing a paper. (Refer to Exercise 2 for guides to doing research.)

The instructions for the actual writing of Exercise 3 are detailed and specific. But before we cover them, there is some basic material we will review that explains (1) the basic parts that all presentations, oral or written, should contain, (2) the manner in which these parts should be organized, and (3) the basic techniques used to support proposals. This material is presented under headings that identify the three major parts of a presentation; (I) the introduction, (II) the supporting step or body, and (III) the conclusion. These instructions are also basic to all later exercises. This explanation begins on page 84 immediately following the preassignment exercise forms.

---

*Your instructor may modify this number, depending on the level of your class.

Exercise 3

BASIC RESEARCH REFERENCE FORMS COVER SHEET

On the following forms, list at least twenty (20) references of articles or books related to your class topic. For each reference include the following information:

Author's name

Article or chapter title

Book, magazine, or journal name

Date of publication; for books, add publisher and city (this information should be enclosed in parentheses)

Length of article

Rate the value of the article, using the following scale:
high medium low zero

Explain who the author is and why he is an authority.

Explain the key idea of the article.

Example:

Reference: Duncan, W. Jack "The Knowledge Utilization Process in Management and Organization," *Academy of Management Journal,* Vol. 15, No. 3, 273-287, (1972)

Value (circle one): high (medium) low zero

Author's background: J. Duncan is a Ph.D. from L. S. U. & is currently an Assoc. Prof. of Bus. Admin. at U. of Alabama. He has published several related articles.

Key idea: Discusses the linking together by communication of organizational subsystems.

The names of the other students in my informal research group are:

1. ____________________

2. ____________________

Reference 1: ____________________

Value (circle one): high medium low zero

Author's background: ____________________

Key idea: ____________________

Reference 2: ______________________________

____

____

Value (circle one): high medium low zero

Author's background: ______________________________

____

Key idea: ______________________________

____

Reference 3: ______________________________

____

____

Value (circle one): high medium low zero

Author's background: ______________________________

____

Key idea: ______________________________

____

Reference 4: ______________________________

____

____

Value (circle one): high medium low zero

Author's background: ______________________________

____

Key idea: ______________________________

____

Reference 5: ____________________

____

____

Value (circle one): high medium low zero

Author's background: ____________________

____

Key idea: ____________________

____

Reference 6: ____________________

____

____

Value (circle one): high medium low zero

Author's background: ____________________

____

Key idea: ____________________

____

Reference 7: ____________________

____

____

Value (circle one): high medium low zero

Author's background: ____________________

____

Key idea: ____________________

____

Reference 8: ____________________

____

____

Value (circle one): high medium low zero

Author's background: ____________________

____

Key idea: ____________________

____

Reference 9: ____________________

Value (circle one): high medium low zero

Author's background: ____________________

Key idea: ____________________

Reference 10: ____________________

Value (circle one): high medium low zero

Author's background: ____________________

Key idea: ____________________

Reference 11: ____________________

Value (circle one): high medium low zero

Author's background: ____________________

Key idea: ____________________

Reference 12: ____________________

Value (circle one): high medium low zero

Author's background: ____________________

Key idea: ____________________

Reference 13: ______________________________

____

____

Value (circle one): high medium low zero

Author's background: ______________________________

____

Key idea: ______________________________

____

Reference 14: ______________________________

____

____

Value (circle one): high medium low zero

Author's background: ______________________________

____

Key idea: ______________________________

____

Reference 15: ______________________________

____

____

Value (circle one): high medium low zero

Author's background: ______________________________

____

Key idea: ______________________________

____

Reference 16: ______________________________

____

____

Value (circle one): high medium low zero

Author's background: ______________________________

____

Key idea: ______________________________

____

Reference 17: ____________________

____

____

Value (circle one): high medium low zero

Author's background: ____________________

____

Key idea: ____________________

____

Reference 18: ____________________

____

____

Value (circle one): high medium low zero

Author's background: ____________________

____

Key idea: ____________________

____

Reference 19: ____________________

____

____

Value (circle one): high medium low zero

Author's background: ____________________

____

Key idea: ____________________

____

Reference 20: ____________________

____

____

Value (circle one): high medium low zero

Author's background: ____________________

____

Key idea: ____________________

____

Your Name ____________________
No. ______ Group ______ Sec. ______

Exercise 3
ARTICLE ABSTRACTING FORM

Bibliographic Reference: Author, Title, Publication, Date (book: place), Page. (type single space)

Bauer, Raymond A. and Dan H. Fenn, Jr., "What is a corporate social audit?" Harvard Business Review (January-February 1973), 37-48.

Authors' background: Mr. Bauer is a Professor of Business Administration at the Harvard Business School. Mr. Fenn is Director of the John F. Kennedy Library and Lecturer at Harvard Business School.

Summary of main points: (Type single space)
This article discusses methods and means for defining and reporting a company's activities that have a social impact. The authors suggest a "social audit" by independent auditors similar to a financial audit which includes an opinion of attestation.

The article discusses possible audit approaches and various sources of pressure which bring about activities for social good. Various organizations have gone about these activities in extremely different ways. Many questions were raised and discussed about how to decide what to audit, how to measure objectively, what criteria to use to measure success of an activity, and what accuracy can be obtained in such an audit.

Evaluation of the material and its relation to other articles or studies: (Type single space)
This article presented a systematic approach to conducting a social audit, without really designing a cookbook to social auditing. In all my readings, this was the most specific approach to an actual social audit. Bauer and Fenn go one step beyond Steiner's "Social Policies for Business." Steiner suggests a method to establish social programs; Bauer and Fenn suggest a method for conducting audits of the programs.

A dominant theme in most all of the social accounting articles is the limitation imposed by the difficulty in objectivity in measurement. This article was no exception. Some authors (Moskovitz and Francis) feel so strongly about this limitation they believe social accounting will never get off the ground.

Bauer and Fenn disagree with Alexander ("Why shouldn't the corporation account in social terms?") in that they feel attempting to reduce social performance to dollar terms is perverse while reducing costs to dollars is acceptable. Alexander felt that both benefits and costs should be quantified.

Steiner stated that publicity for social programs should not be done. Bauer and Fenn stated that such publicity is desirable for good public relations, product advertising, and stimulus for other companies to follow suit.

Your Name *Sample*

No.______ Group______ Sec.______

Exercise 3
ARTICLE ABSTRACTING FORM

Bibliographic Reference: Author, Title, Publication, Date (book: place), Page (type single space)

Alexander, Michael, O., "Why shouldn't the corporation account in social terms?" (Unpublished) 21 pages.

Author's background: Michael O. Alexander is a C.P.A. from Toronto, Canada. He has served as a member of the Committee on the Measurement of Social Costs for the American Accounting Association.

Summary of main points: (Type single space)
The corporation has three dimensions of accountability: (1) profits to stockholders; (2) useful goods and services to consumers and general public, and aesthetics and low pollution to society; and (3) pay, job security, and job satisfaction to employees. Traditionally, the corporation has only accounted to the stockholders with financial information. This article recognizes a need to account to society and employees, also. The author suggests devising means for measuring the effects, both benefits and costs, that the organization has on society and expanding the annual report to include sections reporting to society and employees. The greatest difficulty is in the measurement. The author offers suggestions on various means of communication between the organization and these groups for data (interviews, etc.), though objectivity is difficult to achieve.

Evaluation of the material and its relation to other articles or studies: (Type single space)
This was an excellent article outlining and explaining the need for accounting to extend beyond the traditional profit picture. The author recognizes that this traditional microanalysis of the firm ignores a larger system the firm is involved in. The firm is affected by and affects this larger system which includes the public and consumers as well as stockholders and employees. The organization should consider its responsibility to the entire system in planning new investments and conducting operations as well as reporting the results of operations.

A major problem in developing accounting data for these other groups is in objective measurement, communication, and feedback. All the articles I have read relating to social accounting recognize the problem in measurement. This appears to be the major barrier in accounting for social costs.

While Steiner in "Social Policies for Business" focuses on how the corporation should go about being responsible to all of society, Alexander goes one step further and discusses how one should account for the actions taken and report the results to society. Steiner's last specific action suggestion on page 24 was, "Develop cost/benefit analyses . . . which will serve to improve decision-making in the area of social responsibilities." This article suggests ways to develop the cost/benefit analysis.

Your Name ____________________
No. ______ Group ______ Sec. ______

(*Sample of Form To Use*)

Exercise 3
ARTICLE ABSTRACTING FORM

(Type Single Space)
Bibliographical References: Author, Title, Publication, (Date) (for books, include in the parentheses the name of the publisher and the city of publication), Page Numbers.

Author's background:

Summary of main points:

Evaluation of the material and its relation to other articles or studies:

THE BASICS

There are three basic steps to cover in preparing a presentation or paper. They are the introduction, body, and conclusion. Each of these steps can be further subdivided but rarely can one be omitted.

Introduction Step

Most papers or oral presentations require an introduction. There are several purposes an introduction serves, six of which will be discussed here.

1. *The first function of an introduction is to gain the attention of the reader or listener.* Messages sent but not received are of no value. Many people glance at the first line or two of a report and then drop it because it did not catch their attention. Likewise, many businessmen fail to get the other person's attention before they start to explain their ideas orally. They do not realize that the other person's mind may still be pondering some earlier problem. Talking to one who is not really listening is no more effective a means of communication than writing a report that will not be read.

To gain attention is an important, yet by itself inadequate, function. Dropping a firecracker beside a colleague will gain his attention. Putting a picture of a nude on a report cover will have the same effect on potential readers. But such attention-getters serve no function unless they focus that attention on a specified topic. The firecracker may work if the topic is noise pollution, but not for a talk on plant expansion or economic reform.

2. *The second function in the introduction is to focus attention on the topic you wish to discuss.* The firecracker would focus the attention on noise or fright or, possibly, even on consumer safety. The focus would depend upon what is said as follow-up. A possible follow-up for noise pollution might be: "The blast of that firecracker probably hurt your ears, but do you realize it was no louder than the average motocycle accelerating away from a stop light? Nor was it nearly as loud as the pile drivers working on the construction site next to our school."

Using such a gimmick as a firecracker to gain attention, even when appropriate to the topic, is likely to have several drawbacks. If the firecracker's noise is offensively loud, you may gain and focus the receiver's attention on your topic, but you may also gain and focus his displeasure against you. In writing and speaking, it is important to remember that your goal is *effective* communication, which is to gain a desired response. If the receiver understands what you want but is motivated by your message to take a contrary action, then the message, though understood by the receiver, was not effective communication. More than understanding is needed in effective communication.

3. *The third function of the introduction is to build rapport.* There must also be a relationship created between the sender and receiver that motivates the receiver to act in accordance with the sender's intent. *Rapport* is the term used to describe the positive relationship established between two individuals. This is a subtle action, for it involves the entire environment of a presentation. If the typing or copying of the written report is sloppy, that may be interpreted by the reader as indicating that the author's research or ideas are of the same shoddy quality. The impression a receiver gains from the first few introductory statements of a presentation will likewise have a tremendous effect on how he responds to the material that follows. The initial setting for a presentation must be right. In business meetings, even the temperature of the room or the setup of chairs may greatly affect how well the material presented is accepted. There are many research studies validating the strong impact of these first impressions on later responses. For a more detailed discussion of this point refer to Chapter Three in Part II of this book.

As important as it is to create a positive rapport in an introduction, it is even more important not to create a negative rapport. You must be careful when explaining why someone should pay attention to what you say that you do not offend that person. An example of such offensive behavior is the American diplomat who was speaking to a group of representatives from small nations. He began, "Because your farmers are uneducated, they are not able to produce enough crops to feed your people. That is why your countries are so poor and underdeveloped, and that is why we want to help you."

This diplomat certainly gained the attention of his listeners, but most likely he also gained their hostility towards anything else he had to say. Here is how he might have said the same thing without being offensive: "I have a deep respect for the proud farmers of your countries who work hard many long hours to raise enough crops to feed your people. But the population in your countries, as in ours, is increasing so fast that the farmers cannot keep up. Perhaps if we could combine some modern farming techniques that we have learned in our country with the knowledge your farmers have of the local soil and crops, we could work together to ease the task of your farmers and increase their production." This second statement stresses the "working together" rather than the "we will help you" attitude. This example also shows that the same message can be conveyed with a positive tone as easily as with a negative one. Be careful to word presentations positively so as to build rapport and to avoid offending.

4. *The fourth function to be achieved in the introduction of a presentation is to clearly state the topic in terms the receiver will understand.* Many presentations are confusing because the message senders get so involved in their topics that they forget to tell the receivers what they are talking about. A legislator once gave a speech in which he presented volumes of data on no-fault insurance, but he failed to state what he was trying to show by the data. Some listeners thought he was for no-fault (which he was not) and listened to see how his data supported it. By the end of his presentation, almost everyone was confused. They did not know how to interpret the data because they did not know the legislator's intent. When a topic is clearly stated, it helps the receiver to narrow the focus of his attention so that he knows what to read or listen for. This normally aids understanding.

There are some situations in which it is advisable not to clearly define the topic in your introduction. One such situation is when the receivers are believed to be hostile to the topic. Then it is often best to present supporting material which is acceptable to the group before the true nature of the topic is revealed.

5. *The fifth function of an introduction is to operationally define ambiguous terms used in the topic.* This will help focus the receivers' minds even more accurately. It aids understanding, especially if the topic is technical. Operational definitions must be worked out by each individual. Before going further, it is advisable to define the term *operational definition.*

An *operational definition* is one that explains the meaning of a word or phrase by describing observable, measurable activities that the word or phrase represents in a specific context. For example, if the topic statement proposes that people be made to be happy, you must operationally define what is happiness. Since the internal state of mind happiness cannot be measured, one must define it operationally in terms of something that can be observed and measured. You may define happiness operationally as a person smiling. You can observe whether or not people are smiling, and you can time how long or how often they smile. If you try a new management style and people smile more, you can conclude that since you operationally defined happiness as smiling people, the employees are happier. All operational definitions are of necessity limited. Someone may say that people are not really happier when they smile. Instead of that causing a long argument over what real happiness is, we can, instead, at least agree that people are happier as the term was operationally defined for your study.

Before one can intelligently talk or write about a topic, the vague terms must be operationally defined and limited to specific meanings. Listeners need only accept your operational meaning. Then they can understand what you mean when you use a specific term at a specific time. They do not have to accept your definition as being an ultimate or even correct use of the term. They must only accept it as your definition at that time for that report.

6. *The final function of an introduction is to provide the listeners or readers with a road map of the areas to be covered and the order in which the material will be covered.* This road map is usually referred to as a *presummary* or *forecasting summary*. It is simply a description of the subareas or subarguments to be developed under the main topic. The purpose of stating the main topic and its subarguments clearly in the beginning of a presentation is to help the receivers focus their attention even further. If a topic is broad, like "labor relations," the listener may be expecting to receive material on unions when the presen-

tation actually deals with benefit plans. The receiver will keep wondering when the sender is going to relate the material to unions. Because he is listening or reading for one thing and receiving something else, he becomes confused. He may completely misunderstand the message because his attention is focused in one area while it should be in another.

The presentation to be given in Exercise 3, and also the most common type of presentation in business, is one in which someone is making a proposal. Businessmen are constantly proposing that a bank lend them money, that a client buy their new products, that their firm be awarded a contract, that a new accounting procedure be adopted, and so on. Such proposals all advocate a change and thus must be supported by arguments that show there is a need to change.

The initial statement of purpose of such a presentation usually is in the form of an assumption, such as, "The State should adopt a no-fault auto insurance program." Such a statement is an assumption until it can be supported.

With most proposals, there are usually several reasons why they should or should not be adopted. If these reasons are brought up in a random order, people will likely become confused. Thus, most good presentations are carefully organized and divided into subsections. The forecast summary lists these subcategories, or subarguments, at the beginning of a presentation. Using as an example the topic of no-fault auto insurance, we might list the following statement of our topic and forecast summary of the subarguments to be developed:

Topic: The State should adopt a no-fault auto insurance program. (Because)

Subargument 1. It would enable accident victims to receive compensation more rapidly.

Subargument 2. It would reduce the insurance companies' legal costs and thus allow premiums to be lowered.

Subargument 3. It would permit mass marketing of insurance and thus allow premiums to be lowered.

Note that the topic as well as the three subarguments are stated as assumptions that must be supported. Note also that when each of these subarguments is supported, it will in turn support the main argument. If we can show that a no-fault program will save on insurance companies' legal costs and thus lower premiums, we have in turn shown a reason why a no-fault program should be adopted. This, of course, would be only one argument out of many which must be considered before the main argument would be accepted. Once the receivers understand this first argument, they are ready for the sender to move on and develop his next argument.

Subarguments must be tested for one main characteristic before they are accepted as appropriate subarguments. This characteristic is called *inherency*. Look at the third subargument under the no-fault proposal. We will rephrase it to see if a no-fault plan is necessary to achieve mass marketing of insurance. "*Can the state mass market insurance other than no-fault insurance*?" If the answer is yes, then the subargument does not necessarily show a need to adopt a no-fault plan. Since the state could adopt an insurance mass marketing program without adopting no-fault, the argument is not an inherent reason to adopt the no-fault plan. Because the subargument is not inherently related to the main argument, it requires both evidence to prove the subargument and evidence to show that the subargument actually does in some way support the main argument. The subargument in our example may still be used if it can be shown that it will be substantially easier to mass market no-fault insurance than fault insurance. Subarguments should generally be inherently tied to the main argument. Those that are not are highly suspect and should be examined carefully.

The number of subarguments in the forecast summary should be limited. Usually the number of subarguments in oral presentations is limited to three or four. The number can be somewhat larger for written proposals. Psychological studies of memory have shown that people can remember a series of up to five items rather easily, but that when the number is more than seven, they tend to forget items in the middle of the series. When we need to present an argument with more than five subpoints, we should consider grouping some of the subpoints into general categories. For example, on the no-fault topic, all subarguments that show that no-fault would cost less could be grouped under the subargument: "No-fault will cost consumers less." When this argument is developed, it might be organized with several sub-subarguments supporting the cost-less subargument. Of course, each of the sub-sub-subarguments of the sub-subarguments of the subarguments can be further subdivided. In fact, this is the way almost any textbook is organized. Textbooks have parts, units, chapters, and sections. Note that most books with many chapters group the chapters under parts. Rarely will books have more than six chapters in a part or more than four parts in a book. Likewise, a paper should use a limited number of arguments. The ideal number of subarguments is usually between two and four for a proposal of the length used in this exercise.

Written and oral reports differ in their needs for a forecasting summary. Forecasting summaries are much more important in an oral than in a written presentation. In a written presentation the reader can glance ahead and read the major topic headings. (The use of headings is described in Exercise 5.) If a reader is not mentally set to read the topic written about when he begins his reading, he can, when he discovers his misconception, go back and reread the paper. Listeners have no such opportunity to glance ahead or to reread. Therefore, they need more advance clues as to how to prepare their mental frame of reference so they can understand the material on the first try.

Forecast summaries can be used to avoid many misunderstandings and to save much follow-up discussion time in business meetings. Meeting agendas and book tables of contents are forms of forecast summaries. They are written presummaries of what is planned to be covered in the meeting or the book. A forecast summary in a speech serves the same purpose of guiding the audience. *For Exercise 3 a forecast summary is required to be used in the paper.*

There are many times when you would not use a forecast summary even in an oral presentation. We will not be concerned with these exceptions now. The goal now is to learn to write one type of paper in a structured form. You are not learning "the correct" way to write a paper; you are learning one of many acceptable ways. This course format can be compared to competitive figure skating. The contestants must perfect the rigidly structured school figures to show that they have basic skills before they are allowed to go on and develop their own free style. This exercise is to be considered as a school figure. You will follow a very structured format. Later you can develop and use your own free style.

In summary, the introduction of a paper or of an oral presentation should achieve six things:

1. Gain attention.
2. Focus attention on the topic (interest the audience).
3. Build rapport.
4. Identify the topic clearly.
5. Define operationally the vague terms in the topic.
6. Outline the subarguments to be developed.

Supporting Step or Body

In the body of a presentation, the assumptions outlined in the introduction are to be clarified and supported with evidence. The support section of a paper can be subdivided many ways. For Exercise 3, it is required that the support section be divided into subarguments supporting a need to adopt the change proposed in the topic selected by the class.

The support section of a paper begins with a statement of the first subargument. Each of the subarguments in a presentation can be presented almost as though it were a separate paper. That is, each subargument has its own introduction, body, and conclusion. The introduction of a subargument usually is brief since the introduction to the over-all paper should have already gained attention, focused the attention, established rapport, and introduced the topic to be discussed. Often all that is needed in the subargument's introduction is to state the subargument and to define any vague or controversial terms used. Of course, if the subargument has its own sub-subarguments, these should be outlined in a forecast summary of the sub-subarguments of that subargument. *Because of the short length of the Exercise 3 papers, you are to use for this exercise no less than two nor more than four subarguments, and none of these is to be further subdivided into sub-subarguments.*

Once the first subargument is introduced, it is time to start offering support to back up the assumption stated in that subargument.

Forms of Support

When asked to support their ideas, most students seem to have only a vague idea of what is expected. They have obviously never learned what various forms of support are available for them to choose from. If basketball were taught the way communication has typically been taught, the coaches would probably all be fired. In high school English classes, students are given a rule book that tells them about spelling, punctuation, and grammar, and they are told to write. This is as if a basketball coach drilled his team on the rule book and then had team members practice until they could play a complete game without violating any rules. If he assumed his team was good because it did not break any rules, he would be evaluating the team in much the same fashion as many English themes are often graded. The basketball coaches are fortunately not as concerned with rules as they are with teaching players to perfect basic skills. They teach their players that there are many ways to shoot. When the players perfect each of these various ways of shooting, he teaches them to recognize situations that call for each kind of shot. He teaches the players to anticipate what the opponent's response is likely to be, to try to block a shot, and how to counter the blocks. This text is designed to teach communication the same way a coach trains his team. You will learn which different forms of support are available to choose from. When you have learned to use each of these, you will attempt to learn to recognize the type of situations that call for each form of support. You will try to become aware of the type of response each form of support is likely to generate in the reader or listener and how to deal with these responses.

There are seven forms of support described in this section. This is not an ultimate list. It is simply a useful list to help categorize the different types of support material available. The seven forms of support are grouped into three subcategories: first, forms of support used primarily to inform or arouse emotion; second, forms of support used primarily to convince; and third, a single form of support which is used to present an historical background or a frame of reference.

Forms of Support Used Primarily to Inform or Arouse Emotion

The first group of forms of support is used primarily to inform or arouse emotional responses so that the receiver is favorably disposed to listen to convincing material that follows. These forms of support are *analogies*, *explanations of logic*, and *detailed examples*.

1. Analogies. The term *analogies* is used here very broadly to include all forms of comparisons in which one explains the unknown by comparing it to the known. The previous explanation that compared the teaching of management communication to the teaching of basketball is an analogy.

Simple comparisons such as "he looked like a ball" have some of the characteristics of an analogy but are more of a style of speech than a means of support that is designed to clarify the listener's understanding. Such a style of speech is not considered a form of support. Analogies are ideal for explaining concepts to an audience that has little prior knowledge of a subject. An analogy is used in Chapter Two to explain the human binomial (on-off) nervous transmission system. The nervous system's means of stimulating the re-creations of reality in the brain is compared to the Ranger moon rocket binomial system's ability to stimulate the re-creations of a picture of the moon by an earth-stationed computer and printer. The system of the brain is far too complex to explain in one class period. The system in the Ranger rocket program is very similar to that in the brain but much less complex. By explaining the simpler Ranger system and showing how it is analogous to the human perceptual system, it is possible in a short period of time to explain the basic concept of a binomial information transmission system of the brain. The complex is thereby explained in terms of the similar but less complex.

Analogies also can be very effective as a means of arousing an audience. They can make vivid a situation with which the receiver would not normally identify. For example, few Americans are emotionally aware of what was happening in the north of Thailand in the early 1970s. Village chiefs were being systematically killed by guerilla troops. To bring this home emotionally, one might create a hypothetical analogy by saying, "Many of you have heard of the beginnings of guerilla fighting in northern Thailand, but I would like to bring this closer to you by explaining how such action might affect this class if we were in Thailand right now. Imagine someone breaking into class right this minute and aiming a machine gun at you." This analogy could go into great detail explaining what happens in Thailand by describing how the guerillas would treat the class. One way to do this would be to select individuals in the class by name to be shot and to explain why from the guerilla's point of view this is necessary. The emotional impact of this type of analogy on the receiver is much greater than if he were just told about what happened to some people thousands of miles away.

In summary, analogies are designed to help explain complex concepts by comparing them to simpler concepts, to explain the unknown by comparing it to the known, and to raise emotional responses by explaining things the audience does not identify with in terms of events with which they can identify.

2. Explanations of logic. This form of support is closely related to formal logic. It involves the process of explaining to the audience the logic by which one goes from facts A and B to conclusion C. In formal logic, this would be an explanation of the steps in a syllogism. For example: Step A, major premise, "All boys have red hair." Step B, minor premise, "Pat has red hair." Step C, conclusion, "Pat is a boy." When the logical steps in this syllogism are explained, the audience can clearly see how we reached our conclusion. They are then in a position to accept or reject it. In the case cited the major premise (the basic assumption we started from) could be challenged, for the premise said that all boys have red hair. It did not say that all persons with red hair are boys. So, the conclusion that "Pat is a boy" is not logical. A better example of logic might be: (A) Only men have beards. (B) John has a beard. (C) Therefore, John is a man. If we accept the premise that only men have beards, then this syllogism is logical. That is an example of *deductive logic.* The logic was based on a general assumption. A conclusion about a specific example was drawn from that general rule.

There is another major form of logic called *inductive logic.* Inductive logic uses many specific examples and then draws a general conclusion based upon them. For example, a boy drank bourbon and water and got drunk. He later drank scotch and water and got drunk. We can use inductive logic to conclude that water is intoxicating. From this example, one can see that inductive logic can lead one astray about as easily as deductive logic. Both examples used here were misuses of logic. This was done to stress that *explanations of logic* are tools for revealing poor logic as well as means of clarifying and gaining support for sound, logical arguments. Logic is simply a system of putting things together much like mathematics. The system is good and can be very exact, but the quality of the conclusion is no better than the quality of the original input. As computer people say, "Garbage in, garbage out."

Explanations of logic as means of support are not limited to formal logic. They are simply a process of explaining each step we went through to reach any logical conclusion. When those in the audience understand how the sender arrived at this conclusion, they are in a better position to know whether or not they agree with him. This form of support is useful for explaining complex material. When conclusions are based on complexities, the receiver must follow one step at a time, or he will become lost and quit listening. If the logic is not understood, the audience is not likely to accept the conclusion. This is especially true if another person who disagrees can make his logic understandable.

Explanations of logic are, likewise, important to use when the material being presented is contrary to what the audience already believes. If the steps in the logic are not clearly explained, such an audience may easily use this as an excuse to reject what is said.

In summary, explanations of logic are most important in explaining complex arguments, especially if those arguments draw conclusions contrary to the beliefs of the audience.

3. Detailed examples. It is hard for humans to conceive abstracts. We need examples. Examples are used for two major purposes: to clarify and to gain an emotional response. For example, when we try to explain a complex new tax law, examples are generally needed. The tax laws are usually so broad that before people can understand them, they require examples of how the law would apply in a specific situation. Tax guides almost always use detailed examples following each description of a law.

Detailed examples are generally the most effective means of arousing an audience emotionally. Detailed examples are stories. To have maximum impact, they should contain the following three characteristics: (1) specific as to person, (2) specific as to time, and (3) specific as to place. The reason to be specific as to person is that it is easiest for humans to identify with a single human being. We cannot easily identify with the people of Russia, but we can identify with the problems of Ivan Stovich who is an eleven-year-old boy living in Irkutsk, a city of 100,000, located on the shores of Lake Baykal in Western Siberia. "Ivan is waiting for his mother to be released from the Siberian work camp where she was sent for five years. She was arrested at her home in Estonia for attending a subversive meeting. . ." The more details that are told about Ivan, the easier it is to identify with him. As we identify with him, we become emotionally concerned over the problems affecting his life. As we become more concerned, we become more willing to listen to his plight and to take actions that may help him.

The reason for being specific as to time is that if people know something is happening right now, it is easier for them to identify with the event than if it happened at some earlier or unspecified time. If Ivan's example is about an event in 1945, it has much less impact than if it is happening while we are reading this paper. If Ivan is still waiting for his mother, right now at this very moment, we are likely to be more concerned than if the event is one of history.

The reason for being specific as to place is that it is easier for people to identify with places that they know. If the example is about unfamiliar places like Siberia, detailed descriptions may make them easier to visualize and thus identify with. To give a detailed description, one cannot talk about such large and diversified places as Russia or Texas. We must talk about one small section of one specific city or other area small enough to be described in detail. When *Life* magazine described Lyndon Johnson's Texas, it did so by doing a story on a nine-year-old boy who lived on a farm near the Johnson's home in Texas. By telling what this boy did on Saturdays, where he went fishing, and other details of his daily life, an otherwise dull description of a ranch became a fascinating story about a boy like the one who grew up to be President.

An additional ingredient is necessary for a detailed example to have full emotional impact. The ingredient is *imagery*. Imagery is the process of describing in words a sensed response and doing so with so much detail that those in the audience vicariously experience the sensed response as though they were there. For example, we could describe the eruption of a volcano with such clarity and detail that the readers begin to actually visualize the eruption. We could describe a snake bite so that when the snake strikes, the readers feel the pain.

In summary, detailed examples should be stories—true or hypothetical—that are specific as to person, time, and place and should contain enough imagery so that the receivers actually feel as though they are eyewitnesses to the events.

Obviously, all examples cannot contain this much detail, imagery, or specificity. The explanations given describe an ideal detailed example. Examples that are not detailed are constantly used in writing. (Those types of examples are classified later under specific instances and background data.) Detailed examples are excellent to use whenever it is important to gain the emotional response of the audience. They are also the easiest way to make a paper or speech more interesting.

The three preceding forms of support have as their main functions to increase the reader's or listener's understanding of, awareness of, interest in, and concern for the topic being presented. The next three forms of support may also serve some of these same functions, but their primary function is different.

Forms of Support Used Primarily to Convince

The second group of forms of support are those used primarily to convince the audience to accept an idea. These forms are called *specific instances, statistics,* and *use of authorities.*

4. Specific instances. These are very similar to detailed examples and are commonly used to follow up detailed examples. One example by itself may raise interest, but it does not show how common the event is. To become a form of support to convince, the detailed example should be followed up by several additional examples. These show that the first example is not just an isolated instance. Showing several examples and drawing a general conclusion is a type of inductive logic. Follow-up examples usually do not need to be as detailed, because the first example has already created the emotional response and set the scene. Follow-up examples are called specific instances. Note the plural "s" on instances. These instances must always be used in groups to be inductive proof. They usually follow a detailed example and ride on the emotion created by it. Specific instances should be stories which are specific as to person, time, and place. The instances add to a detailed example the extra cases which show that the event is a common one from which one can, through inductive logic, draw a conclusion. For example, we might follow up the detailed example, used earlier, of Ivan Stovich with an example of a thirteen-year-old girl named Natasha, who also is waiting for her parents who are prisoners. It is not necessary to tell all of the details of her case to build the audience's empathy. The empathy was already developed with the story of Ivan. The story of Natasha can be brief. Its only purpose is to show that there are other cases similar to the first one. A story of a third such child could be even shorter. Thus, specific instances, through the use of inductive logic, turn examples into a form of support to convince.

5. Statistics. The term *statistics* is used here broadly. There are two major types of data commonly referred to as statistics. The first is *raw data,* and the second is data that have in some way been *modified by statistical analysis.*

Raw data are free of interpretive distortion but often too detailed to be understandable, especially for comparisons. For example, if one were to write, "The population of state A is 4,134,186 people, and it has an average of 7,413 serious traffic accidents per month, whereas state B with a population of 3,971,243 has an average of 7,241 serious traffic accidents per month. From this, we can clearly see that state ______ has the better driving record." Most people would not have the vaguest idea of the answer from reading this raw data. To make raw data more understandable, one might perform a statistical analysis of the data and then report the number of traffic deaths as a percentage or a ratio of death to the population. Then it would be simple to compare the traffic records of the two states. In this case, state A has 17 and state B has 18 traffic accidents per month per 10,000 population.

The danger with reporting the results of statistical analysis is that often neither the writer nor the reader understands the limitations of the statistics. For example, a common deceiver is to talk about percentage increases. One argument published in a magazine a few years ago talked about how the Russians, at their present rate of growth, would soon be outproducing the United States in refrigerators. Let us assume that the USSR was producing about 1,000 refrigerators a year, and the United States was producing about 100,000 per year. A 5% increase in the United States would be (5% of 100,000 = 5,000) to 105,000 per year. A 500% increase in the USSR would be (500% of 1,000 = 5,000) to 6,000 per year. Now comes the deceptive statement, "If the USSR continues at its current rate of increase, it will surpass the United States production within five years." Not only would it surpass the United States production, but at that rate of increase it would within a dozen years bury the entire continent of Asia in refrigerators.

Year one	1,000 + 500% = 6,000
Year two	6,000 + 500% = 36,000
Year three	36,000 + 500% = 216,000
Year four	216,000 + 500% = 1,296,000
Year five	1,296,000 + 500% = 7,776,000
Year twelve	2.14 trillion refrigerators per year (about 900 for every person in the world)

When the implications of such a statement are figured out, they become ridiculous; but how often do people stop to figure them out? You must be careful as a speaker, writer, listener, or reader not to be deceived by statistical manipulations. To project percentage increases into the future is very misleading.

Another common deceptive statistic is "average." The average income in the United States may be the highest in the world, but the typical American has less income than the typical Swede. The fact that average income is a deceptive statistic can be seen by calculating the average income of a one-factory town. The owner of the factory makes one million dollars a year. His 100 employees are 50 married couples. Each employee receives $3,000 per year. One might be surprised to figure that the average family income in the town is more than $25,000 per year. This average income figure of $25,000 does not reveal that only one person in the town makes in excess of $3,000 per year.*

Statistics are often based on polls or samples of opinion. The validity of these statistics depends not only on how the data is statistically manipulated but also on the quality of the poll from which they were obtained. The sample may be too small, too homogeneous, or too biased. The questions asked may be too vague, misleading, or biased. The interviewers may bias, intimidate, misunderstand, or misrecord. To explain all the limitations of statistical analysis or survey research would require a lengthy book. The point to understand is that neither the writer nor the reader should blindly accept statistical data. They should find out how the data were obtained and how the data were analyzed.

Statistical data are among the strongest forms of support one can use to back up arguments. They are also the most difficult form of support to communicate. Statistics are usually boring to listen to and difficult to understand. To make large figures understandable, analogies are often used. For example, some technicians at IBM, working on miniaturizing computer parts, were trying to explain how small one-millionth of an inch is. They described it this way, "If you made a stack of dimes as high as the Empire State Building, and you placed another stack of dimes that high on top of it, and then you placed a third stack on top of that, and finally, a fourth stack on top of that, and then pulled out the bottom dime, it would represent one-millionth part of the stack." Such an analogy certainly makes a millionth sound much more minute than it did before.

We often become immune to hearing figures. When people hear statements such as, "There were 50,000 people killed in automobile deaths last year," they have little response. Yet, they can be brought to tears hearing the story of one little girl in one traffic accident. For this reason, statistics are often used following detailed examples while the audience is still emotionally receptive. After hearing about one incident in detail, the receivers are upset by the larger figures showing that such things occur over 50,000 times a year, or hundreds of times every day, or several times every hour.

In summary, statistics are a persuasive form of support if they can be presented in an interesting and understandable fashion. Statistics are also potentially the most misleading of the forms of support.

6. Testimonies of Authorities. When presenting material to support an argument, it is usually desirable to show that someone else who is an authority on the topic agrees with us. When presenting statistics, it is often more persuasive to state that the research was conducted by a qualified authority than to try to describe the actual experimental design. Most of us would not understand the design but will accept the word of a noted authority who says the research is valid. When historical or research data are presented, telling the source of the information will make it much more acceptable for it can be checked and validated.

Whenever using resource material, be sure to identify the source. This is called *documenting* your presentation.

The most important thing to be aware of when quoting authorities is to make sure they really are honest and informed sources and, if possible, are unbiased. It must be assumed that a military general explaining why the military needs more money is a biased source, even though he may be honest and informed. He will tend to look at the facts from the point of view that is best for the military. He may not consider

*This example is based on an actual situation. A rural county with much poverty was denied federal help because the average income in the county was too high. The average income was high because about 20 millionaires lived in one little exclusive area of the county. Because the average income was high, the poor could not receive federal help.

other means of international power besides military power. A senator who is quoted as an expert on air pollution may not be more informed than the man on the street. He is quoted as an expert only because he is a senator. Being a senator may make him an expert on politics but not necessarily on air pollution. The trial lawyer who opposes a no-fault auto insurance plan may have reasons to be less than honest in his testimony about no-fault. If a no-fault plan were adopted, he might lose 80% of his income which comes from automobile fault cases.

When giving a quote, be sure to tell *who* the authority is, *why* he is an authority, *when* he made the statements, and the conditions under which the statements were made. The importance of the "who" and "why" has already been discussed. The reason for the "when" should be obvious; former Attorney General John Mitchell in 1968 would almost certainly sound different from citizen John Mitchell speaking on law and order after his indictment in 1973. It is also important to explain the conditions under which the statements were made. Court testimony under oath often sounds much different than the description of the same event by the same person at a political rally.

In summary, it can be said that specific instances, statistics, and testimony are strong means of supporting an argument. but they generally lack the audience appeal necessary for an effective presentation. For this reason, forms of support used primarily to convince are usually presented jointly with the forms of support used primarily to arouse or increase understanding.

There is one last form of support which is used to present historical background or create a frame of reference. We will call this form *background data*.

7. Background Data. This form of support is frequently backed up by a reference or is based on the author's personal knowledge. This is one of the most frequently used forms of support. It often contains within it other forms of support, such as specific instances, detailed examples, and statistics. This form of support is the explanation of past, present, and possible future conditions and events that one desires the receiver to understand as basic to a presentation. For example, when talking about the need for welfare reform, we might point out that many welfare recipients whom we know are the third generation of families on welfare. Background data is a form of support that lays a groundwork of knowledge on which to base arguments. This form of support can be used to inform and/or to convince the audience. It is often a series of short bits of information that need to be tied together with explanations of logic.

Historical data is used to set the frame of reference that the listener or reader should use if he is to understand the message in context. It is material that gives the background and knowledge of events that the sender has that has led him to believe as he does.

Interrelatedness of forms of support. These seven forms of support often overlap each other. Statistics are often clarified by analogies. There is no clear line between where specific instances end and detailed examples begin. Historical data often contain statistics, explanations of logic, and detailed examples. We should not be too concerned if we cannot always distinguish between two forms of support. These seven categories are not mutually exclusive. They are guides to help you select the type of material you need to use to gain the response you desire from your readers or listeners.

These seven forms of support are techniques which the speaker or writer has at his disposal to back up his ideas and arguments. You should become aware of the effect each may have on an audience. Then when the time comes to design a presentation, you can systematically analyze the audience and the responses you want the presentation to generate in that audience. You can then select the forms of support that are most appropriate.

Organization of Subarguments

Now that we have reviewed what forms of support are available to back subarguments, we will turn our attention to how to combine or organize the support. Each of the subarguments in a presentation is developed almost as a separate presentation. Each has an introduction, but, as was explained earlier, often parts of the introduction to a subargument can be omitted. Once the subargument is introduced, you can begin presenting the support material.

To back an argument, there are many ways to combine forms of support. If you are supporting an issue over which the audience is already aroused, you might use only forms of support designed to convince them that your position is right. If the audience is already convinced of the validity of your basic arguments, you might simply include forms of support designed to arouse them to action. An example of the latter would be a paper on traffic safety. We all believe in it, so statistics or testimony (convincing forms of support) are of little value. Detailed examples, analogies, and specific instances would be much more appropriate because they are more arousing.

A topic about which the audience is neither aroused nor informed could be completely supported by using all seven forms of support. For example, the argument might be that we should help the children in Laos who were injured by the United States bombs. There is little awareness of the war that went on in Laos, so the audience is not likely to be informed, aroused, or convinced. We might start with some *background data* on the war, then follow with a *detailed example* of an eight-year-old girl. We could tell who she is, her hopes and dreams, and then describe how a bomb killed her parents and crushed one of her legs. This will build emotion and interest. We might capitalize on this emotion by following it with several *specific instances* of other injured children. This shows that the first example was not an isolated one. Next, we might follow up with *statistics* to show how many thousands of children were similarly injured. We could use an *analogy* to make those in the audience visualize how many children that would be in their own town. We could use *testimony* to back up the statement that these children could be helped if money for medication were available. We could use *background data* to show how the United States has not yet taken appropriate action to help these children. If you support a presentation using all seven forms of support, you are not likely to read on a paper, "your arguments are not adequately supported."

After presenting all of your support material for your first subargument, you must be sure to draw a conclusion as to what all of that material has shown. You cannot assume that those in the audience will draw the conclusion you wish them to; you must lead them into that conclusion. This is often done by using *explanations of logic.* The logic should also show how the subargument related to and supports the main argument. This explanation of logic may be the summary for the subargument, or you may wish to follow it with more summary material that is designed to make the audience reflect over the ideas just presented.

Once the first subargument is completed, the second, third, and any other subarguments are developed in the same way. When the last subargument is developed, you are ready to begin the conclusion of the presentation.

The Conclusion Step

The conclusion is similar to the introduction of a presentation. The introduction focuses attention forward to what is going to be said. A conclusion should focus attention backward over what has just been said. In the introduction there is a forecast summary outlining what is to be covered. In the conclusion there is a final summary to show the audience that you have covered all that you said you would. This final summary is used to point out how each subargument was supported and to show those in the audience that they should agree with your position on the topic and, if requested, take some action.

The conclusion for Exercise 3 must contain a restatement of each of the subarguments used and must point out how the subarguments support the main argument. The conclusion must also contain a restatement of the topic and conclude that since support has been offered to back up all of the arguments, the audience should now accept the proposal. Such a complete conclusion is not always needed in a regular presentation, especially in written presentations, but it is to be used in this practice exercise. The completeness of the conclusion depends upon the topic, the audience, and the objective of the presentation. The following is an example of a possible conclusion to a presentation on no-fault auto insurance:

The evidence indicates that our state needs a no-fault plan. As the Acme research report showed, victims typically receive compensation under no-fault in less than one-third the time that they do under other insurance programs. In addition, it has been shown that this savings of time and the removal of the need for court action has actually lowered the insurance companies' overhead by nearly forty percent. It has been pointed out that companies in states which have no-fault plans have passed this saving on to the consumers in the form of lower premiums. Finally, it has been pointed out that though other forms of automobile insurance could be mass marketed, no-fault makes mass marketing even less expensive because it removes the need for evaluating each driver's personal record before setting his premium. Thus, the evidence seems to clearly indicate that since a no-fault plan would get compensation to victims when they need it the most and at the same time lower court costs and marketing costs of the insurance companies and premium cost to insurance buyers, this state should adopt a no-fault auto insurance policy. Remember John Atkin, the man I mentioned in the beginning of this paper? He would not have had to file bankruptcy if he had been covered by no-fault. Think of your own situation. Could you afford to stay out of work for two years with no compensation while you waited for an insurance claim to be paid? If not, then you should support no-fault.

Following is a list of the key essentials that must be included in the conclusion section of Exercise 3 papers:

1. A summary of the subarguments of your presentation. If possible, include references to key pieces of support material to remind the readers of how each argument was supported.
2. A concluding statement making it clear that each subargument has been supported and in turn supports the main argument.
3. A statement telling the readers what conclusion you wish them to draw or what action you wish them to take as a result of the material presented in your paper.
4. A concluding statement that is designed to make the audience focus attention back over your main arguments.

Summary

These three basic parts of a paper—the introduction, the body, and the conclusion—are described as guides to help you subdivide your work. The order in which to prepare each of these steps is usually (1) body, (2) introduction, and (3) conclusion. The introduction and conclusion should be written only after the body is pretty well developed. That is because the introduction and conclusion both contain summaries of the body.

A brief outline of the organization of a short presentation is shown in Figure 3-1.

ASSIGNMENT INSTRUCTIONS

The paper for Exercise 3 is a practice drill. It is not a paper giving a complete proposal, as will be done in Exercise 7. The goal in this assignment is to do the drill correctly. Following are detailed and specific instructions on how to (1) write, (2) read, and (3) evaluate the papers. Also included are instructions on how to give feedback to those who evaluated your paper to let them know how helpful they were as evaluators.

Paper Size

The paper for Exercise 3, including references, is to be no shorter than 3½ nor longer than 4½ pages in length. All papers are to be typed, single space on 8½ X 11″ paper. (If the copy machine uses longer paper, cut it.) All pages are to use 1″ margins on the right side and bottom of the paper and a 1¼″ margin at the top. The left-hand margin for Exercise 3 is to be 2″ wide. The reason for this is explained later. For all later assignments, the left-hand margin will be 1″ wide.

FIGURE 3-1. Outline of Exercise 3

Introduction

Introduction (Gain and focus attention on material to be presented; build rapport.)
Statement of topic
 Define terms in statement
Forecast Summary
 Statement of subargument 1
 Statement of subargument 2
 Statement of subargument . . . *n*

Body

Restatement of subargument 1
 Support subargument 1 using appropriate forms of support
  Summarize subargument 1
Restatement of subargument 2
 Support subargument 2 using appropriate forms of support
  Summarize subargument 2
Restatement of subargument . . . *n*
 Support subargument . . . *n* using appropriate forms of support
 (*Note*: the last subargument is summarized in the conclusion.)

Conclusion

Final summary
 Restatement of subargument 1 and brief summary of how it was supported
 Restatement of subargument 2 and brief summary of how it was supported
 Restatement of subargument . . . *n* and brief summary of how it was supported
Restatement of topic showing how subarguments 1, 2, . . . *n* support the topic statement
Statement that the reader should now accept the supported topic proposal and/or should take some action
Conclusion statement (focus attention back over material presented)

Paper Heading

In the upper right-hand corner of the margin on the first page, type your name and class number. Directly below, type "Evaluator No.______." Below that, type "Copy No.______." Make sure that you number your copies from 0 to 14 *before* bringing them to class.

In the center of the paper, 1¼" below the top, type "Exercise 3" and then the semester and year. Skip two spaces and type your paper title.

FIGURE 3-2. Exercise 3 Paper Heading

John Doe No. 25
Evaluator No. ______
Copy No. ______

Exercise 3, Fall 19--
(Title)

Paper References and Bibliography

Exercise 3 requires a minimum of eight references footnoted in the paper. For papers in this course, list all footnote references in alphabetical order at the end of the paper. Number each reference, and use that number at the end of the sentence being documented. References should use the same format as that shown on the Basic Research Reference Form (page 75). This style is the same as is used in the *Academy of Management Journal.* Note that in this style of referencing, the footnotes and bibliography are the same list, located at the end of the paper. No reference-type footnotes are used at the bottom of the page.

Example:

Union elections often involve as much campaigning as political elections. The readability of the campaign material can be a major deciding factor in the outcome of the election (4). The union must carefully. . .

(reference list at the end of the article)

REFERENCES

1. Argyris, Chris. *Interpersonal Competence and Organizational Effectiveness* (Homewood, Ill.: Richard D. Irwin, Inc., 1962).
2. Blau, Peter M. "Cooperation and Competition in Bureaucracy," *American Journal of Sociology,* Vol. 56 (1954), 520-525.
3. Deutsch, Morton. "Trust and Suspicion," *Journal of Conflict Resolution,* Vol. 2 (1958), 265-79.
4. Edison, Dan S. "A Union Authorization Election," *Personnel Journal,* Vol. 51 (1972), 246-254.

If you need to refer to a specific page (or pages) in an article or book, insert the page number in parenthesis along with the footnote reference number. Always refer to a specific page when using a direct quote.

Example:

The readability index suggests that many of the messages and statistics used by the union were simply not understood, even if they were read. The author states, "The union made the messages even less readable by combining several messages and several pictures on a single handout, thus making the messages appear to be longer than most workers would read." (4, p. 253).

Margin Outline

In the 2″ margin on the left side of the Exercise 3 paper, there is to be an outline identifying the various parts of the paper. The parts to be identified are those listed in the outline in Figure 3-1. In addition, each form of support that is used must be named in the margin.

The forms of support are as follows:

Detailed Examples	Background Data	Specific Instances
Explanations of Logic		Statistics
Analogies		Testimonies of authorities

The margin outline may be done in pen.

Forms of Support Required

You are required to use each of the seven forms of support at least once in the Exercise 3 paper. Under each subargument include at least one form of support that is primarily to inform or arouse, that is, a detailed example, explanation of logic, or analogy. Under each subargument also use at least one form of support that is primarily to convince, such as specific instances, statistics, or testimony.

Outline Cards

On the day the assignment is due for review in class, bring in a set of 5 X 8″ cards. On the first card have written out the exact statement of the class topic and the exact statements of the two, three, or four subarguments that you are using. The subarguments should be simple declarative sentences. For examples, refer to page 86. Do not use compound or complex sentences or interrogative sentences.

On the second card, write out the forms of support used to support your first subargument. Do not include any transitions or introductions. For examples, see Figure 3-3.

FIGURE 3-3. Exercise 3 Sample Card Showing Forms of Support

Forms of Support Used For Subargument 1

1. Analogy:
   To make an auto accident victim wait for payment during a lengthy trial is like asking the victim of a robbery to wait in jail while the robber is waiting for trial. The person who caused the accident can be compared to the robber. He has taken something from you, your health, car, and so on. Yet, it is you, not him, who must suffer while the courts decide who is at fault and how much should be paid.
2. Statistics:
   There are more than 50,000 auto accidents in the United States every year. The average length of time that the victims of these accidents wait to collect insurance is in excess of 10 months. Of these, . . .

On the next cards, write out the forms of support you used to support your subarguments 2, 3 or 4. In class discussions, we will discuss whether or not each of these forms of support is the type of support you think it is and whether or not it is an appropriate form of support to back the subargument.

These cards will be collected at the end of class and checked by the instructor. If these cards are not turned in on time, Exercise 3 will be considered late.

Passing Out Papers

On the day Exercise 3 is due, bring to class an original and 14* copies of your paper. If, for some reason, you cannot make class on this day, you must arrange for someone else to pass out your papers and collect the papers you are to grade. Bring your Paper Number Record Form (page 103) to class on the day you are to pass out your papers. Fill it out before passing out any papers. The instructor will explain how and to whom the papers are to be distributed. It is best that you do not know in advance whose papers you are grading.

Evaluation and Grading of Papers

Copies 1-14 of your paper will be passed out to your classmates for them to study and evaluate. The "0" copy will be collected for the instructor's records.

You will receive 14 of your classmates' papers. For the first eight papers (copies 1-8), completely fill out the Feedback Form (page 105) with written evaluations and suggestions. For papers 9-14**, fill out only the checklist and grading section of the Feedback Form.

There are three general criteria to use in grading these papers:

Criterion I. Presentation of paper. Consider under Criterion I neatness, spelling, grammar, layout of page, readability of sentences, or any other factor that affects your response to the paper apart from the organization or content of the message.

Criterion II. Organization of paper. Consider under Criterion II how accurately the author conformed to the exact layout specified for this paper. This criterion is the main focus of Exercise 3 and is graded more heavily than it will be on later papers. Use the checklists on the Feedback Form as a guide to show whether or not the author included all that he was supposed to in the layout of his paper.

Criterion III. Content of paper. Consider under Criterion III the logic of the author's arguments and the adequacy of the material used to support them. Check the inherency of each subargument and the appropriateness and adequacy of the forms of support used to substantiate them.

Some Grading Guides. In Exercise 1, the writers could use any form of organization they desired. The main concern in grading that paper was to see if the student could, in an unstructured situation, turn in a paper with writing of acceptable quality. In grading Exercise 3, it should be assumed that the students as a minimum will use writing of acceptable quality. That is, the paper will be neat, the spelling will be corrected, the punctuation will be acceptable, grammar will be correct, and the correct size of paper will be used. These are all technical skills that if the authors cannot correct themselves, they should at least have others correct for them before the paper is distributed. If any of these mechanical problems are noticed on a paper, be sure to call them to the author's attention on the Feedback Form, and grade accordingly.

The main new focus in grading Exercise 3 is on organization. This assignmnet is a drill, not a complete

*This number may be modified by your instructor.

**Grading of these paper 9-14 may be omitted at the option of the instructor. This reduction is recommended for less advanced or short courses.

paper. It is like a basketball practice drill. The goal is to do the exercise correctly, rather than to show off a beautiful free style. To grade the organization of these papers, follow carefully the checklist on the Feedback Form.

The grading of the next paper will focus on the area of logic and content. Although that is not the main focus of the grading of this paper, you are still encouraged to give each author some feedback regarding how acceptable and convincing his arguments are. The meaning of number grades is shown in Figure 3-4 by comparing them to letter grades and percentile ranks.

FIGURE 3-4. Meaning of Number Grades

14% 55% 20% 10% 1%

F D C– C C+ B A A+

1 2 3 4 5 6 7 8 9 10

poor OK good excellent perfect

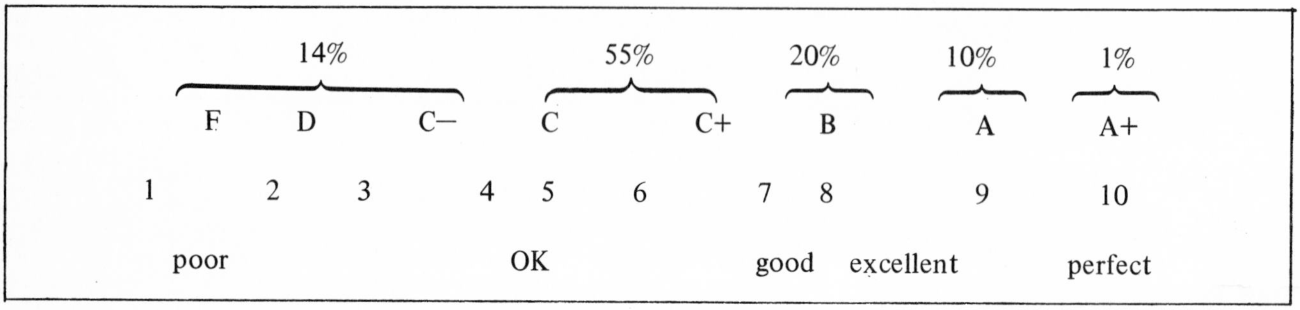

Recording Grades

1. When all papers have been graded, record the grades on the Exercise 3 Grading Form (page 135). *The form is to be given to the instructor on the day the graded papers are returned to the authors.*

2. When your graded papers are returned to you, record your grades on the Author's Grade Record Form (page 137). Use this form to compute your Sum Grade Average.

3. The Author's Grade Record Form is to be completed and given to the instructor no later than one class period after you have received your graded papers. Record your Sum Grade Average on the Class Grade Summary Sheet. This sheet will be provided by the instructor.

4. If you have two or more ratings of 1 on Criterion II, bring your Author's Grade Record Form and your set of Exercise 3 papers to the instructor no later than one class period after you have received your graded papers. The instructor will determine what you must do before you can go on to Exercise 5. If you fail to contact the instructor, you may not be permitted to do Exercise 5.

Grading of the Feedback

Communication is rarely only a two-step process. Most communication involves many steps. The message sender sends a message. The receiver receives the message. Then the receiver becomes a sender, transmitting feedback to the original speaker. The original sender thus becomes the new receiver; he, in turn, might send feedback on the feedback and so on. To help us become good listeners and readers, we all need feedback on the quality of the feedback we give others. We will call this second-level feedback.

Second-level feedback is especially useful to managers, for most of their time is spent giving subordinates first-level feedback. Rarely do managers have a chance to check on their skill at giving this feedback. Second-level feedback also enables you to work on our listening and reading skills. Just knowing that your feedback will be graded is often an incentive to do a better job of reading and listening so that you can give good feedback.

Recording Feedback Grades

1. The second-level feedback grade for Exercise 3 is to be recorded on the Grader Quality Report (page 139). As soon as your graded papers are returned, read the Feedback Forms and the comments written on your papers. Then grade the evaluators on the quality and helpfulness of the feedback they gave to you.
2. A master chart containing each student's number may be provided by your instructor. This enables you to compare yourself with other students by recording all ratings from your Grader Quality Report on that master chart.
3. Some graders may not be aware that their feedback to you is incomplete or superficial. An "x" rating is used to identify these students that need special help. (The x rating is explained further on the Grader Quality Report.)
4. If you receive an "x" rating, you should redo the evaluation of the paper of the person who gave you the "x."

EXERCISE 3 CHECKLIST

Check Yourself First

Before duplicating your Exercise 3 paper, it would be wise to check yourself on the following:

1. Spelling
2. Punctuation
3. Grammar
4. Neatness
5. Margins

} If you are not sure of any of these items, ask a friend to proofread your paper.

6. Margin Outline: Refer to Figure 3-1. Make sure that all items covered in that outline are covered in your margin outline. Also, be sure you have identified forms of support in your margin outline.
7. Read the four "yes-no" questions at the top of the Feedback Form. Remember, just one "no" means your paper must be redone. These questions are as follows:
   a. Does this paper contain at least 8 references?
   b. Is this paper between 3½ and 4½ pages in length?
   c. Are all seven forms of support used at least once?
   d. Does this paper have a complete outline in the margin?
8. Go down each item on the Feedback Form and grade your own paper. If you would give your paper any minuses, rewrite that part of your paper.
9. Readability: Check your paper for readability. A simple test is to count the number of words in each sentence. If there are many sentences with more than 25 words, your paper is probably not clearly written.

There is one important difference between a manager's and a student's writing. Students' papers are graded by someone else. Managers must be able to grade their own work, or it is sent out full of errors for everyone to see. Start practicing now to grade your own work.

FINAL CHECKLIST

Checklist of Things to Do for Exercise 3

Preassignment Preparation

_______ 1. Fill out the Basic Research Reference Form (pp. 75–81).

_______ 2. Write 10* abstracts following the form shown on the Article Abstracting Forms (page 83).

The Assignment

_______ 3. Write your paper.

_______ 4. Use the checklist on page 101 to check your own paper before bringing it to class.

_______ 5. Draft of Paper due for in-class review: (Date) ____________________

_______ Bring one copy of a draft of your paper to class on that date.

_______ Bring to class one set of outline cards (see page 98).

_______ 6. Papers due for distribution: (Date) ____________________

_______ Bring to class the "0" copy of your paper with the Basic Research Reference Form and 10* Article Abstracting Forms attached.

_______ Bring to class copies 1-14* of your paper to distribute.

_______ Bring to class your Paper Number Record Form (page 103).

_______ 7. Graded papers are to be returned: (Date) ____________________

_______ Bring to class the papers you graded.

_______ Bring to class your completed Exercise 3 Grading Form (page 135)

_______ 8. Record all grades you received on your Author's Grade Record Form (page 137), and compute your Sum Grade Average.

_______ 9. Complete the Grader Quality Report. To evaluate your graders.

_______ 10. Grades are to be Recorded by: (Date) ____________________

_______ Record your Sum Grade Average on the Class Grade Summary Sheet.

_______ Record the Grader Quality scores on the Grader Quality Master Chart.**

---

*The number required may be modified by your instructor, depending on the level of your class.

**Your class may or may not use this chart.

Your Name______________________

No.________ Group________ Sec.________

Exercise 3

PAPER NUMBER RECORD FORM

My papers are to be passed out to:
(information to be provided by your instructor)

I am to receive papers from:

Paper No.	Student No.	Check When Returned Graded	Paper No.	Student No.
1	______	______	______	______
2	______	______	______	______
3	______	______	______	______
4	______	______	______	______
5	______	______	______	______
6	______	______	______	______
7	______	______	______	______
8	______	______	______	______
9	______	______	______	______
10	______	______	______	______
11	______	______	______	______
12	______	______	______	______
13	______	______	______	______
14	______	______	______	______
extras	______	______	______	______

Papers from the following students were not returned graded:

Copy No.	Student No.
______	______
______	______
______	______

Check with these students. If you still do not find your paper, report the loss to the instructor.

I should have but did not receive papers from:

Copy No.	Student No.
______	______
______	______
______	______

Please report to your instructor if any papers are not received in time to be graded.

Before distributing your paper, record on each the class number of the student who is to receive and evaluate that paper. For example, if student 25 is to receive your copy No. 2 paper, write:

Evaluator No. __25__
Copy No. __2__

Name______________________________ No._______ Sec. _______

EXERCISE 3: Feedback Form to Author ____________________________ **No.** ________

Circle One

Yes No — Does this paper contain at least 8 references?
Yes No — Is this paper between 3½ and 4½ pages in length?
Yes No — Are all seven forms of support used at least once in this paper?
Yes No — Does this paper have a complete outline in the left-hand margin?

If the answer to any of these questions is no, the paper is unacceptable and must be redone. Give it a grade of 1 on Criteria II. Then continue grading the paper.

I. The Introduction:

+ √ − 1. Did it gain your attention?
+ √ − 2. Did it focus your interest toward the topic?
+ √ − 3. Did the over-all writing style and appearance make you feel this would be a good paper (rapport)? Or, was there anything in the introduction to make you feel this paper was going to be worth reading?

Write what specific things you felt were good about the introduction.

____
____
____
____
____

(Write additional comments on the student's paper)

+ √ − Is the topic clearly stated in the introduction?
+ √ − Are terms adequately defined?
+ √ − Are the subarguments clearly stated in the forecast summary?
Yes No — Is subargument one inherently related to the main argument?
Yes No — Is subargument two inherently related to the main argument?
Yes No — Is subargument three inherently related to the main argument?

Write out an explanation for any "minuses" or "no's" in the preceding list.
Add other comments you feel may help the writer improve.

____
____
____
____
____

(Write additional comments on the student's paper)

II. The Body or Support Section:

Yes No — Is subargument one clearly stated?

Which of the following forms of support are used to support it? (circle)

detailed examples background data specific instances analogies
statistics explanations of logic testimonies of authorities

+ √ − Is this argument backed with enough informative support?
+ √ − Is this argument backed with enough convincing support?
+ √ − Is the evidence supported by adequate documentation?

What do you feel needs to be added to support this argument? Explain below.

____
____
____

(Write additional comments on the student's paper)

Yes No — Is subargument two clearly stated?
Which of the following forms of support are used to support it? (circle)

detailed examples background data specific instances analogies

statistics explanations of logic testimonies of authorities

+ √ − Is this argument backed with enough informative support?
+ √ − Is this argument backed with enough convincing support?
+ √ − Is the evidence supported by adequate documentation?
What do you feel needs to be added to support this argument?

____

____

____

____

____

(Write additional comments on the student's paper)

Yes No — Is subargument three clearly stated?
Which of the following forms of support are used to support it? (circle)

detailed examples background data specific instances analogies

statistics explanations of logic testimonies of authorities

+ √ − Is this argument backed with enough informative support?
+ √ − Is this argument backed with enough convincing support?
+ √ − Is the evidence supported by adequate documentation?
What do you feel needs to be added to support this argument?

____

____

____

____

____

(Write additional comments on the student's paper)

III. The Conclusion: Does the conclusion:

+ √ − 1. Summarize the arguments effectively?
+ √ − 2. Restate the topic proposal?
+ √ − 3. Draw a conclusion for the reader that the proposal had been supported and should be accepted and/or acted upon?
+ √ − 4. Do something to make the reader reflect over the logic?

Grades (see criteria explanation on page 99 and in Figure 3-4)
(Circle one and record it as the raw score)

	F	D	C−		C		C+	B	A	A+	Raw Score	Weight	Weighted Grades
Criteria I	1	2	3	4	5	6	7	8	9	10 =	______	X 1 =	______
Criteria II	1	2	3	4	5	6	7	8	9	10 =	______	X 6 =	______
Criteria III	1	2	3	4	5	6	7	8	9	10 =	______	X 3 =	______
												Sum Grade	______

Transfer the weighted grades to the Exercise 3 Grading Form (page 000).

Note: This Feedback Form is to be attached (staple or paper clip) to the front of the student's paper and returned to him with the graded paper.

Name ______________________ No. ______ Sec. ______

EXERCISE 3: Feedback Form to Author ______________________ No. ______

Circle One

Yes No Does this paper contain at least 8 references?
Yes No Is this paper between 3½ and 4½ pages in length?
Yes No Are all seven forms of support used at least once in this paper?
Yes No Does this paper have a complete outline in the left-hand margin?

If the answer to any of these questions is no, the paper is unacceptable and must be redone. Give it a grade of 1 on Criteria II. Then continue grading the paper.

I. The Introduction:

\+ √ − 1. Did it gain your attention?
\+ √ − 2. Did it focus your interest toward the topic?
\+ √ − 3. Did the over-all writing style and appearance make you feel this would be a good paper (rapport)? Or, was there anything in the introduction to make you feel this paper was going to be worth reading?

Write what specific things you felt were good about the introduction.

____

____

____

____

____

____

(Write additional comments on the student's paper)

\+ √ − Is the topic clearly stated in the introduction?
\+ √ − Are terms adequately defined?
\+ √ − Are the subarguments clearly stated in the forecast summary?
Yes No Is subargument one inherently related to the main argument?
Yes No Is subargument two inherently related to the main argument?
Yes No Is subargument three inherently related to the main argument?

Write out an explanation for any "minuses" or "no's" in the preceding list. Add other comments you feel may help the writer improve.

____

____

____

____

____

____

(Write additional comments on the student's paper)

II. The Body or Support Section:

Yes No Is subargument one clearly stated?

Which of the following forms of support are used to support it? (circle)

detailed examples background data specific instances analogies
statistics explanations of logic testimonies of authorities

\+ √ − Is this argument backed with enough informative support?
\+ √ − Is this argument backed with enough convincing support?
\+ √ − Is the evidence supported by adequate documentation?

What do you feel needs to be added to support this argument? Explain below.

____

____

____

____

(Write additional comments on the student's paper)

Yes No Is subargument two clearly stated?

Which of the following forms of support are used to support it? (circle)

detailed examples background data specific instances analogies

statistics explanations of logic testimonies of authorities

+ √ − Is this argument backed with enough informative support?

+ √ − Is this argument backed with enough convincing support?

+ √ − Is the evidence supported by adequate documentation?

What do you feel needs to be added to support this argument?

____

____

____

____

____

____

(Write additional comments on the student's paper)

Yes No Is subargument three clearly stated?

Which of the following forms of support are used to support it? (circle)

detailed examples background data specific instances analogies

statistics explanations of logic testimonies of authorities

+ √ − Is this argument backed with enough informative support?

+ √ − Is this argument backed with enough convincing support?

+ √ − Is the evidence supported by adequate documentation?

What do you feel needs to be added to support this argument?

____

____

____

____

____

____

(Write additional comments on the student's paper)

III. The Conclusion: Does the conclusion:

+ √ − 1. Summarize the arguments effectively?

+ √ − 2. Restate the topic proposal?

+ √ − 3. Draw a conclusion for the reader that the proposal had been supported and should be accepted and/or acted upon?

+ √ − 4. Do something to make the reader reflect over the logic?

Grades (see criteria explanation on page 99 and in Figure 3-4)
(Circle one and record it as the raw score)

	F	D	C−		C	C+		B	A	A+	Raw Score	Weight	Weighted Grades
Criteria I	1	2	3	4	5	6	7	8	9	10 =	________	X 1 =	________
Criteria II	1	2	3	4	5	6	7	8	9	10 =	________	X 6 =	________
Criteria III	1	2	3	4	5	6	7	8	9	10 =	________	X 3 =	________
												Sum Grade	________

Transfer the weighted grades to the Exercise 3 Grading Form (page 000).

Note: This Feedback Form is to be attached (staple or paper clip) to the front of the student's paper and returned to him with the graded paper.

Name ______________________ No. ______ Sec. ______

EXERCISE 3: Feedback Form to Author ______________________ **No.** ______

Circle One

Yes No Does this paper contain at least 8 references?
Yes No Is this paper between 3½ and 4½ pages in length?
Yes No Are all seven forms of support used at least once in this paper?
Yes No Does this paper have a complete outline in the left-hand margin?

If the answer to any of these questions is no, the paper is unacceptable and must be redone. Give it a grade of 1 on Criteria II. Then continue grading the paper.

I. The Introduction:

+ √ − 1. Did it gain your attention?
+ √ − 2. Did it focus your interest toward the topic?
+ √ − 3. Did the over-all writing style and appearance make you feel this would be a good paper (rapport)? Or, was there anything in the introduction to make you feel this paper was going to be worth reading?

Write what specific things you felt were good about the introduction.

____

____

____

____

____

____

(Write additional comments on the student's paper)

+ √ − Is the topic clearly stated in the introduction?
+ √ − Are terms adequately defined?
+ √ − Are the subarguments clearly stated in the forecast summary?
Yes No Is subargument one inherently related to the main argument?
Yes No Is subargument two inherently related to the main argument?
Yes No Is subargument three inherently related to the main argument?

Write out an explanation for any "minuses" or "no's" in the preceding list. Add other comments you feel may help the writer improve.

____

____

____

____

____

____

(Write additional comments on the student's paper)

II. The Body or Support Section:

Yes No Is subargument one clearly stated?

Which of the following forms of support are used to support it? (circle)

detailed examples background data specific instances analogies
statistics explanations of logic testimonies of authorities

+ √ − Is this argument backed with enough informative support?
+ √ − Is this argument backed with enough convincing support?
+ √ − Is the evidence supported by adequate documentation?

What do you feel needs to be added to support this argument? Explain below.

____

____

____

____

(Write additional comments on the student's paper)

Yes No Is subargument two clearly stated?

Which of the following forms of support are used to support it? (circle)

detailed examples background data specific instances analogies

statistics explanations of logic testimonies of authorities

+ √ − Is this argument backed with enough informative support?

+ √ − Is this argument backed with enough convincing support?

+ √ − Is the evidence supported by adequate documentation?

What do you feel needs to be added to support this argument?

____

____

____

____

____

____

(Write additional comments on the student's paper)

Yes No Is subargument three clearly stated?

Which of the following forms of support are used to support it? (circle)

detailed examples background data specific instances analogies

statistics explanations of logic testimonies of authorities

+ √ − Is this argument backed with enough informative support?

+ √ − Is this argument backed with enough convincing support?

+ √ − Is the evidence supported by adequate documentation?

What do you feel needs to be added to support this argument?

____

____

____

____

____

____

(Write additional comments on the student's paper)

III. The Conclusion: Does the conclusion:

+ √ − 1. Summarize the arguments effectively?

+ √ − 2. Restate the topic proposal?

+ √ − 3. Draw a conclusion for the reader that the proposal had been supported and should be accepted and/or acted upon?

+ √ − 4. Do something to make the reader reflect over the logic?

Grades (see criteria explanation on page 99 and in Figure 3-4)
(Circle one and record it as the raw score)

	F	D	C−		C	C+		B	A	A+		Raw Score	Weight	Weighted Grades
Criteria I	1	2	3	4	5	6	7	8	9	10	=	________	X 1 =	________
Criteria II	1	2	3	4	5	6	7	8	9	10	=	________	X 6 =	________
Criteria III	1	2	3	4	5	6	7	8	9	10	=	________	X 3 =	________
													Sum Grade	________

Transfer the weighted grades to the Exercise 3 Grading Form (page 000).

Note: This Feedback Form is to be attached (staple or paper clip) to the front of the student's paper and returned to him with the graded paper.

Name ______________________ No. ______ Sec. ______

EXERCISE 3: Feedback Form to Author ______________________ No. ______

Circle One

Yes No Does this paper contain at least 8 references?
Yes No Is this paper between 3½ and 4½ pages in length?
Yes No Are all seven forms of support used at least once in this paper?
Yes No Does this paper have a complete outline in the left-hand margin?

If the answer to any of these questions is no, the paper is unacceptable and must be redone. Give it a grade of 1 on Criteria II. Then continue grading the paper.

I. The Introduction:

+ √ − 1. Did it gain your attention?
+ √ − 2. Did it focus your interest toward the topic?
+ √ − 3. Did the over-all writing style and appearance make you feel this would be a good paper (rapport)? Or, was there anything in the introduction to make you feel this paper was going to be worth reading?

Write what specific things you felt were good about the introduction.

____

____

____

____

____

____

(Write additional comments on the student's paper)

+ √ − Is the topic clearly stated in the introduction?
+ √ − Are terms adequately defined?
+ √ − Are the subarguments clearly stated in the forecast summary?
Yes No Is subargument one inherently related to the main argument?
Yes No Is subargument two inherently related to the main argument?
Yes No Is subargument three inherently related to the main argument?

Write out an explanation for any "minuses" or "no's" in the preceding list. Add other comments you feel may help the writer improve.

____

____

____

____

____

____

(Write additional comments on the student's paper)

II. The Body or Support Section:

Yes No Is subargument one clearly stated?

Which of the following forms of support are used to support it? (circle)

detailed examples background data specific instances analogies
statistics explanations of logic testimonies of authorities

+ √ − Is this argument backed with enough informative support?
+ √ − Is this argument backed with enough convincing support?
+ √ − Is the evidence supported by adequate documentation?

What do you feel needs to be added to support this argument? Explain below.

____

____

____

____

(Write additional comments on the student's paper)

Yes No Is subargument two clearly stated?

Which of the following forms of support are used to support it? (circle)

detailed examples background data specific instances analogies

statistics explanations of logic testimonies of authorities

\+ √ − Is this argument backed with enough informative support?

\+ √ − Is this argument backed with enough convincing support?

\+ √ − Is the evidence supported by adequate documentation?

What do you feel needs to be added to support this argument?

____

____

____

____

____

____

(Write additional comments on the student's paper)

Yes No Is subargument three clearly stated?

Which of the following forms of support are used to support it? (circle)

detailed examples background data specific instances analogies

statistics explanations of logic testimonies of authorities

\+ √ − Is this argument backed with enough informative support?

\+ √ − Is this argument backed with enough convincing support?

\+ √ − Is the evidence supported by adequate documentation?

What do you feel needs to be added to support this argument?

____

____

____

____

____

____

(Write additional comments on the student's paper)

III. The Conclusion: Does the conclusion:

\+ √ − 1. Summarize the arguments effectively?

\+ √ − 2. Restate the topic proposal?

\+ √ − 3. Draw a conclusion for the reader that the proposal had been supported and should be accepted and/or acted upon?

\+ √ − 4. Do something to make the reader reflect over the logic?

Grades (see criteria explanation on page 99 and in Figure 3-4)
(Circle one and record it as the raw score)

	F	D	C−		C		C+		B	A	A+	Raw Score	Weight	Weighted Grades
Criteria I	1	2	3	4	5	6	7	8	9	10	=	________	X 1 =	________
Criteria II	1	2	3	4	5	6	7	8	9	10	=	________	X 6 =	________
Criteria III	1	2	3	4	5	6	7	8	9	10	=	________	X 3 =	________
													Sum Grade	________

Transfer the weighted grades to the Exercise 3 Grading Form (page 000).

Note: This Feedback Form is to be attached (staple or paper clip) to the front of the student's paper and returned to him with the graded paper.

Name ______________________ No. ______ Sec. ______

EXERCISE 3: Feedback Form to Author ______________________ No. ______

Circle One

Yes No — Does this paper contain at least 8 references?
Yes No — Is this paper between 3½ and 4½ pages in length?
Yes No — Are all seven forms of support used at least once in this paper?
Yes No — Does this paper have a complete outline in the left-hand margin?

If the answer to any of these questions is no, the paper is unacceptable and must be redone. Give it a grade of 1 on Criteria II. Then continue grading the paper.

I. The Introduction:

+ √ − 1. Did it gain your attention?
+ √ − 2. Did it focus your interest toward the topic?
+ √ − 3. Did the over-all writing style and appearance make you feel this would be a good paper (rapport)? Or, was there anything in the introduction to make you feel this paper was going to be worth reading?

Write what specific things you felt were good about the introduction.

____
____
____
____
____
____

(Write additional comments on the student's paper)

+ √ − Is the topic clearly stated in the introduction?
+ √ − Are terms adequately defined?
+ √ − Are the subarguments clearly stated in the forecast summary?
Yes No — Is subargument one inherently related to the main argument?
Yes No — Is subargument two inherently related to the main argument?
Yes No — Is subargument three inherently related to the main argument?

Write out an explanation for any "minuses" or "no's" in the preceding list. Add other comments you feel may help the writer improve.

____
____
____
____
____
____

(Write additional comments on the student's paper)

II. The Body or Support Section:

Yes No — Is subargument one clearly stated?

Which of the following forms of support are used to support it? (circle)

detailed examples background data specific instances analogies
statistics explanations of logic testimonies of authorities

+ √ − Is this argument backed with enough informative support?
+ √ − Is this argument backed with enough convincing support?
+ √ − Is the evidence supported by adequate documentation?

What do you feel needs to be added to support this argument? Explain below.

____
____
____
____

(Write additional comments on the student's paper)

Yes No — Is subargument two clearly stated?

Which of the following forms of support are used to support it? (circle)

detailed examples   background data   specific instances   analogies

statistics   explanations of logic   testimonies of authorities

+ √ − Is this argument backed with enough informative support?
+ √ − Is this argument backed with enough convincing support?
+ √ − Is the evidence supported by adequate documentation?

What do you feel needs to be added to support this argument?

____

____

____

____

____

____

(Write additional comments on the student's paper)

Yes No — Is subargument three clearly stated?

Which of the following forms of support are used to support it? (circle)

detailed examples   background data   specific instances   analogies

statistics   explanations of logic   testimonies of authorities

+ √ − Is this argument backed with enough informative support?
+ √ − Is this argument backed with enough convincing support?
+ √ − Is the evidence supported by adequate documentation?

What do you feel needs to be added to support this argument?

____

____

____

____

____

____

(Write additional comments on the student's paper)

III. The Conclusion: Does the conclusion:

+ √ − 1. Summarize the arguments effectively?
+ √ − 2. Restate the topic proposal?
+ √ − 3. Draw a conclusion for the reader that the proposal had been supported and should be accepted and/or acted upon?
+ √ − 4. Do something to make the reader reflect over the logic?

Grades (see criteria explanation on page 99 and in Figure 3-4)
(Circle one and record it as the raw score)

	F	D	C−		C		C+		B	A	A+	Raw Score	Weight	Weighted Grades
Criteria I	1	2	3	4	5	6	7	8	9	10 =	________	X 1 =	________
Criteria II	1	2	3	4	5	6	7	8	9	10 =	________	X 6 =	________
Criteria III	1	2	3	4	5	6	7	8	9	10 =	________	X 3 =	________

Sum Grade ________

Transfer the weighted grades to the Exercise 3 Grading Form (page 000).

Note: This Feedback Form is to be attached (staple or paper clip) to the front of the student's paper and returned to him with the graded paper.

Name ______________________ No.______ Sec.______

EXERCISE 3: Feedback Form to Author ______________________ No. ______

Circle One

Yes No Does this paper contain at least 8 references?
Yes No Is this paper between 3½ and 4½ pages in length?
Yes No Are all seven forms of support used at least once in this paper?
Yes No Does this paper have a complete outline in the left-hand margin?

If the answer to any of these questions is no, the paper is unacceptable and must be redone. Give it a grade of 1 on Criteria II. Then continue grading the paper.

I. The Introduction:

+ √ − 1. Did it gain your attention?
+ √ − 2. Did it focus your interest toward the topic?
+ √ − 3. Did the over-all writing style and appearance make you feel this would be a good paper (rapport)? Or, was there anything in the introduction to make you feel this paper was going to be worth reading?

Write what specific things you felt were good about the introduction.

____

____

____

____

____

____

(Write additional comments on the student's paper)

+ √ − Is the topic clearly stated in the introduction?
+ √ − Are terms adequately defined?
+ √ − Are the subarguments clearly stated in the forecast summary?
Yes No Is subargument one inherently related to the main argument?
Yes No Is subargument two inherently related to the main argument?
Yes No Is subargument three inherently related to the main argument?

Write out an explanation for any "minuses" or "no's" in the preceding list. Add other comments you feel may help the writer improve.

____

____

____

____

____

____

(Write additional comments on the student's paper)

II. The Body or Support Section:

Yes No Is subargument one clearly stated?

Which of the following forms of support are used to support it? (circle)

detailed examples background data specific instances analogies
statistics explanations of logic testimonies of authorities

+ √ − Is this argument backed with enough informative support?
+ √ − Is this argument backed with enough convincing support?
+ √ − Is the evidence supported by adequate documentation?

What do you feel needs to be added to support this argument? Explain below.

____

____

____

____

(Write additional comments on the student's paper)

Yes No Is subargument two clearly stated?

Which of the following forms of support are used to support it? (circle)

detailed examples   background data   specific instances   analogies

statistics   explanations of logic   testimonies of authorities

+ √ − Is this argument backed with enough informative support?

+ √ − Is this argument backed with enough convincing support?

+ √ − Is the evidence supported by adequate documentation?

What do you feel needs to be added to support this argument?

____

____

____

____

____

____

(Write additional comments on the student's paper)

Yes No Is subargument three clearly stated?

Which of the following forms of support are used to support it? (circle)

detailed examples   background data   specific instances   analogies

statistics   explanations of logic   testimonies of authorities

+ √ − Is this argument backed with enough informative support?

+ √ − Is this argument backed with enough convincing support?

+ √ − Is the evidence supported by adequate documentation?

What do you feel needs to be added to support this argument?

____

____

____

____

____

____

(Write additional comments on the student's paper)

III. The Conclusion: Does the conclusion:

+ √ − 1. Summarize the arguments effectively?

+ √ − 2. Restate the topic proposal?

+ √ − 3. Draw a conclusion for the reader that the proposal had been supported and should be accepted and/or acted upon?

+ √ − 4. Do something to make the reader reflect over the logic?

Grades (see criteria explanation on page 99 and in Figure 3-4)
(Circle one and record it as the raw score)

	F		D	C−		C	C+		B	A	A+		Raw Score	Weight	Weighted Grades
Criteria I	1	2	3	4	5	6	7	8	9		10	=	________	X 1 =	________
Criteria II	1	2	3	4	5	6	7	8	9		10	=	________	X 6 =	________
Criteria III	1	2	3	4	5	6	7	8	9		10	=	________	X 3 =	________
														Sum Grade	________

Transfer the weighted grades to the Exercise 3 Grading Form (page 000).

Note: This Feedback Form is to be attached (staple or paper clip) to the front of the student's paper and returned to him with the graded paper.

Name ______________________ No.______ Sec.______

EXERCISE 3: Feedback Form to Author ______________________ No. ______

Circle One

Yes No Does this paper contain at least 8 references?
Yes No Is this paper between 3½ and 4½ pages in length?
Yes No Are all seven forms of support used at least once in this paper?
Yes No Does this paper have a complete outline in the left-hand margin?

If the answer to any of these questions is no, the paper is unacceptable and must be redone. Give it a grade of 1 on Criteria II. Then continue grading the paper.

I. The Introduction:

+ √ − 1. Did it gain your attention?
+ √ − 2. Did it focus your interest toward the topic?
+ √ − 3. Did the over-all writing style and appearance make you feel this would be a good paper (rapport)? Or, was there anything in the introduction to make you feel this paper was going to be worth reading?

Write what specific things you felt were good about the introduction.

____
____
____
____
____
____
______________________ (Write additional comments on the student's paper)

+ √ − Is the topic clearly stated in the introduction?
+ √ − Are terms adequately defined?
+ √ − Are the subarguments clearly stated in the forecast summary?
Yes No Is subargument one inherently related to the main argument?
Yes No Is subargument two inherently related to the main argument?
Yes No Is subargument three inherently related to the main argument?

Write out an explanation for any "minuses" or "no's" in the preceding list. Add other comments you feel may help the writer improve.

____
____
____
____
____
____
______________________ (Write additional comments on the student's paper)

II. The Body or Support Section:

Yes No Is subargument one clearly stated?

Which of the following forms of support are used to support it? (circle)

detailed examples background data specific instances analogies
statistics explanations of logic testimonies of authorities

+ √ − Is this argument backed with enough informative support?
+ √ − Is this argument backed with enough convincing support?
+ √ − Is the evidence supported by adequate documentation?

What do you feel needs to be added to support this argument? Explain below.

____
____
____
____
______________________ (Write additional comments on the student's paper)

Yes No Is subargument two clearly stated?

Which of the following forms of support are used to support it? (circle)

detailed examples background data specific instances analogies

statistics explanations of logic testimonies of authorities

+ √ − Is this argument backed with enough informative support?

+ √ − Is this argument backed with enough convincing support?

+ √ − Is the evidence supported by adequate documentation?

What do you feel needs to be added to support this argument?

____

____

____

____

____

____

(Write additional comments on the student's paper)

Yes No Is subargument three clearly stated?

Which of the following forms of support are used to support it? (circle)

detailed examples background data specific instances analogies

statistics explanations of logic testimonies of authorities

+ √ − Is this argument backed with enough informative support?

+ √ − Is this argument backed with enough convincing support?

+ √ − Is the evidence supported by adequate documentation?

What do you feel needs to be added to support this argument?

____

____

____

____

____

____

(Write additional comments on the student's paper)

III. The Conclusion: Does the conclusion:

+ √ − 1. Summarize the arguments effectively?

+ √ − 2. Restate the topic proposal?

+ √ − 3. Draw a conclusion for the reader that the proposal had been supported and should be accepted and/or acted upon?

+ √ − 4. Do something to make the reader reflect over the logic?

Grades (see criteria explanation on page 99 and in Figure 3-4)
(Circle one and record it as the raw score)

	F	D	C−		C		C+	B	A	A+	Raw Score	Weight	Weighted Grades
Criteria I	1	2	3	4	5	6	7	8	9	10 =	________	X 1 =	________
Criteria II	1	2	3	4	5	6	7	8	9	10 =	________	X 6 =	________
Criteria III	1	2	3	4	5	6	7	8	9	10 =	________	X 3 =	________
												Sum Grade	________

Transfer the weighted grades to the Exercise 3 Grading Form (page 000).

Note: This Feedback Form is to be attached (staple or paper clip) to the front of the student's paper and returned to him with the graded paper.

Name ______________________ No. ______ Sec. ______

EXERCISE 3: Feedback Form to Author ______________________ No. ______

Circle One

Yes	No	Does this paper contain at least 8 references?
Yes	No	Is this paper between 3½ and 4½ pages in length?
Yes	No	Are all seven forms of support used at least once in this paper?
Yes	No	Does this paper have a complete outline in the left-hand margin?

If the answer to any of these questions is no, the paper is unacceptable and must be redone. Give it a grade of 1 on Criteria II. Then continue grading the paper.

I. The Introduction:

+ √ − 1. Did it gain your attention?

+ √ − 2. Did it focus your interest toward the topic?

+ √ − 3. Did the over-all writing style and appearance make you feel this would be a good paper (rapport)? Or, was there anything in the introduction to make you feel this paper was going to be worth reading?

Write what specific things you felt were good about the introduction.

____

____

____

____

____

____

(Write additional comments on the student's paper)

+ √ −		Is the topic clearly stated in the introduction?
+ √ −		Are terms adequately defined?
+ √ −		Are the subarguments clearly stated in the forecast summary?
Yes	No	Is subargument one inherently related to the main argument?
Yes	No	Is subargument two inherently related to the main argument?
Yes	No	Is subargument three inherently related to the main argument?

Write out an explanation for any "minuses" or "no's" in the preceding list. Add other comments you feel may help the writer improve.

____

____

____

____

____

____

(Write additional comments on the student's paper)

II. The Body or Support Section:

Yes No Is subargument one clearly stated?

Which of the following forms of support are used to support it? (circle)

detailed examples background data specific instances analogies
statistics explanations of logic testimonies of authorities

+ √ − Is this argument backed with enough informative support?

+ √ − Is this argument backed with enough convincing support?

+ √ − Is the evidence supported by adequate documentation?

What do you feel needs to be added to support this argument? Explain below.

____

____

____

____

(Write additional comments on the student's paper)

Yes No Is subargument two clearly stated?

Which of the following forms of support are used to support it? (circle)

detailed examples background data specific instances analogies

statistics explanations of logic testimonies of authorities

\+ √ − Is this argument backed with enough informative support?

\+ √ − Is this argument backed with enough convincing support?

\+ √ − Is the evidence supported by adequate documentation?

What do you feel needs to be added to support this argument?

____

____

____

____

____

____

(Write additional comments on the student's paper)

Yes No Is subargument three clearly stated?

Which of the following forms of support are used to support it? (circle)

detailed examples background data specific instances analogies

statistics explanations of logic testimonies of authorities

\+ √ − Is this argument backed with enough informative support?

\+ √ − Is this argument backed with enough convincing support?

\+ √ − Is the evidence supported by adequate documentation?

What do you feel needs to be added to support this argument?

____

____

____

____

____

____

(Write additional comments on the student's paper)

III. The Conclusion: Does the conclusion:

\+ √ − 1. Summarize the arguments effectively?

\+ √ − 2. Restate the topic proposal?

\+ √ − 3. Draw a conclusion for the reader that the proposal had been supported and should be accepted and/or acted upon?

\+ √ − 4. Do something to make the reader reflect over the logic?

Grades (see criteria explanation on page 99 and in Figure 3-4)
(Circle one and record it as the raw score)

	F	D	C−		C		C+	B	A	A+	Raw Score	Weight	Weighted Grades
Criteria I	1	2	3	4	5	6	7	8	9	10 =	________	X 1 =	________
Criteria II	1	2	3	4	5	6	7	8	9	10 =	________	X 6 =	________
Criteria III	1	2	3	4	5	6	7	8	9	10 =	________	X 3 =	________
												Sum Grade	________

Transfer the weighted grades to the Exercise 3 Grading Form (page 000).

Note: This Feedback Form is to be attached (staple or paper clip) to the front of the student's paper and returned to him with the graded paper.

Name ______________________________ No.________ Sec.________

EXERCISE 3: Feedback Form to Author ____________________________ **No.** ________

Circle One

Yes	No	Does this paper contain at least 8 references?
Yes	No	Is this paper between 3½ and 4½ pages in length?
Yes	No	Are all seven forms of support used at least once in this paper?
Yes	No	Does this paper have a complete outline in the left-hand margin?

If the answer to any of these questions is no, the paper is unacceptable and must be redone. Give it a grade of 1 on Criteria II. Then continue grading the paper.

I. The Introduction:

+ √ − 1. Did it gain your attention?

+ √ − 2. Did it focus your interest toward the topic?

+ √ − 3. Did the over-all writing style and appearance make you feel this would be a good paper (rapport)? Or, was there anything in the introduction to make you feel this paper was going to be worth reading?

Write what specific things you felt were good about the introduction.

____

____

____

____

____

____

(Write additional comments on the student's paper)

+ √ −		Is the topic clearly stated in the introduction?
+ √ −		Are terms adequately defined?
+ √ −		Are the subarguments clearly stated in the forecast summary?
Yes	No	Is subargument one inherently related to the main argument?
Yes	No	Is subargument two inherently related to the main argument?
Yes	No	Is subargument three inherently related to the main argument?

Write out an explanation for any "minuses" or "no's" in the preceding list. Add other comments you feel may help the writer improve.

____

____

____

____

____

____

(Write additional comments on the student's paper)

II. The Body or Support Section:

Yes No Is subargument one clearly stated?

Which of the following forms of support are used to support it? (circle)

detailed examples background data specific instances analogies
statistics explanations of logic testimonies of authorities

+ √ − Is this argument backed with enough informative support?

+ √ − Is this argument backed with enough convincing support?

+ √ − Is the evidence supported by adequate documentation?

What do you feel needs to be added to support this argument? Explain below.

____

____

____

____

(Write additional comments on the student's paper)

Yes No Is subargument two clearly stated?

Which of the following forms of support are used to support it? (circle)

detailed examples background data specific instances analogies

statistics explanations of logic testimonies of authorities

+ √ − Is this argument backed with enough informative support?

+ √ − Is this argument backed with enough convincing support?

+ √ − Is the evidence supported by adequate documentation?

What do you feel needs to be added to support this argument?

(Write additional comments on the student's paper)

Yes No Is subargument three clearly stated?

Which of the following forms of support are used to support it? (circle)

detailed examples background data specific instances analogies

statistics explanations of logic testimonies of authorities

+ √ − Is this argument backed with enough informative support?

+ √ − Is this argument backed with enough convincing support?

+ √ − Is the evidence supported by adequate documentation?

What do you feel needs to be added to support this argument?

(Write additional comments on the student's paper)

III. The Conclusion: Does the conclusion:

+ √ − 1. Summarize the arguments effectively?

+ √ − 2. Restate the topic proposal?

+ √ − 3. Draw a conclusion for the reader that the proposal had been supported and should be accepted and/or acted upon?

+ √ − 4. Do something to make the reader reflect over the logic?

Grades (see criteria explanation on page 99 and in Figure 3-4)
(Circle one and record it as the raw score)

	F	D	C−		C	C+		B	A	A+	Raw Score	Weight	Weighted Grades
Criteria I	1	2	3	4	5	6	7	8	9	10 =	______	X 1 =	______
Criteria II	1	2	3	4	5	6	7	8	9	10 =	______	X 6 =	______
Criteria III	1	2	3	4	5	6	7	8	9	10 =	______	X 3 =	______
												Sum Grade	______

Transfer the weighted grades to the Exercise 3 Grading Form (page 000).

Note: This Feedback Form is to be attached (staple or paper clip) to the front of the student's paper and returned to him with the graded paper.

Name ______________________ No.______ Sec.______

EXERCISE 3: Feedback Form to Author ______________________ **No.** ______

Circle One

Yes	No	Does this paper contain at least 8 references?
Yes	No	Is this paper between 3½ and 4½ pages in length?
Yes	No	Are all seven forms of support used at least once in this paper?
Yes	No	Does this paper have a complete outline in the left-hand margin?

If the answer to any of these questions is no, the paper is unacceptable and must be redone. Give it a grade of 1 on Criteria II. Then continue grading the paper.

I. The Introduction:

+	√	–	1. Did it gain your attention?
+	√	–	2. Did it focus your interest toward the topic?
+	√	–	3. Did the over-all writing style and appearance make you feel this would be a good paper (rapport)? Or, was there anything in the introduction to make you feel this paper was going to be worth reading?

Write what specific things you felt were good about the introduction.

____

____

____

____

____

____

______________________ (Write additional comments on the student's paper)

+	√	–	Is the topic clearly stated in the introduction?
+	√	–	Are terms adequately defined?
+	√	–	Are the subarguments clearly stated in the forecast summary?
Yes	No		Is subargument one inherently related to the main argument?
Yes	No		Is subargument two inherently related to the main argument?
Yes	No		Is subargument three inherently related to the main argument?

Write out an explanation for any "minuses" or "no's" in the preceding list. Add other comments you feel may help the writer improve.

____

____

____

____

____

____

______________________ (Write additional comments on the student's paper)

II. The Body or Support Section:

Yes No — Is subargument one clearly stated?

Which of the following forms of support are used to support it? (circle)

detailed examples — background data — specific instances — analogies
statistics — explanations of logic — testimonies of authorities

+	√	–	Is this argument backed with enough informative support?
+	√	–	Is this argument backed with enough convincing support?
+	√	–	Is the evidence supported by adequate documentation?

What do you feel needs to be added to support this argument? Explain below.

____

____

____

____

______________________ (Write additional comments on the student's paper)

Yes No Is subargument two clearly stated?

Which of the following forms of support are used to support it? (circle)

detailed examples   background data   specific instances   analogies

statistics   explanations of logic   testimonies of authorities

+ √ − Is this argument backed with enough informative support?

+ √ − Is this argument backed with enough convincing support?

+ √ − Is the evidence supported by adequate documentation?

What do you feel needs to be added to support this argument?

____

____

____

____

____

(Write additional comments on the student's paper)

Yes No Is subargument three clearly stated?

Which of the following forms of support are used to support it? (circle)

detailed examples   background data   specific instances   analogies

statistics   explanations of logic   testimonies of authorities

+ √ − Is this argument backed with enough informative support?

+ √ − Is this argument backed with enough convincing support?

+ √ − Is the evidence supported by adequate documentation?

What do you feel needs to be added to support this argument?

____

____

____

____

____

(Write additional comments on the student's paper)

III. The Conclusion: Does the conclusion:

+ √ − 1. Summarize the arguments effectively?

+ √ − 2. Restate the topic proposal?

+ √ − 3. Draw a conclusion for the reader that the proposal had been supported and should be accepted and/or acted upon?

+ √ − 4. Do something to make the reader reflect over the logic?

Grades (see criteria explanation on page 99 and in Figure 3-4)
(Circle one and record it as the raw score)

	F	D	C−		C	C+		B	A	A+	Raw Score	Weight	Weighted Grades
Criteria I	1	2	3	4	5	6	7	8	9	10 =	______	X 1 =	______
Criteria II	1	2	3	4	5	6	7	8	9	10 =	______	X 6 =	______
Criteria III	1	2	3	4	5	6	7	8	9	10 =	______	X 3 =	______
												Sum Grade	______

Transfer the weighted grades to the Exercise 3 Grading Form (page 000).

Note: This Feedback Form is to be attached (staple or paper clip) to the front of the student's paper and returned to him with the graded paper.

Name ____________________ No. ______ Sec. ______

EXERCISE 3: **Feedback Form to Author** ____________________ No. ______

Circle One

Yes No Does this paper contain at least 8 references?
Yes No Is this paper between 3½ and 4½ pages in length?
Yes No Are all seven forms of support used at least once in this paper?
Yes No Does this paper have a complete outline in the left-hand margin?

If the answer to any of these questions is no, the paper is unacceptable and must be redone. Give it a grade of 1 on Criteria II. Then continue grading the paper.

I. The Introduction:

+ √ − 1. Did it gain your attention?
+ √ − 2. Did it focus your interest toward the topic?
+ √ − 3. Did the over-all writing style and appearance make you feel this would be a good paper (rapport)? Or, was there anything in the introduction to make you feel this paper was going to be worth reading?

Write what specific things you felt were good about the introduction.

____

____

____

____

____

____

(Write additional comments on the student's paper)

+ √ − Is the topic clearly stated in the introduction?
+ √ − Are terms adequately defined?
+ √ − Are the subarguments clearly stated in the forecast summary?
Yes No Is subargument one inherently related to the main argument?
Yes No Is subargument two inherently related to the main argument?
Yes No Is subargument three inherently related to the main argument?

Write out an explanation for any "minuses" or "no's" in the preceding list. Add other comments you feel may help the writer improve.

____

____

____

____

____

____

(Write additional comments on the student's paper)

II. The Body or Support Section:

Yes No Is subargument one clearly stated?

Which of the following forms of support are used to support it? (circle)

detailed examples background data specific instances analogies
statistics explanations of logic testimonies of authorities

+ √ − Is this argument backed with enough informative support?
+ √ − Is this argument backed with enough convincing support?
+ √ − Is the evidence supported by adequate documentation?

What do you feel needs to be added to support this argument? Explain below.

____

____

____

____

(Write additional comments on the student's paper)

Yes No Is subargument two clearly stated?

Which of the following forms of support are used to support it? (circle)

detailed examples background data specific instances analogies

statistics explanations of logic testimonies of authorities

+ √ − Is this argument backed with enough informative support?

+ √ − Is this argument backed with enough convincing support?

+ √ − Is the evidence supported by adequate documentation?

What do you feel needs to be added to support this argument?

____

____

____

____

____

____

(Write additional comments on the student's paper)

Yes No Is subargument three clearly stated?

Which of the following forms of support are used to support it? (circle)

detailed examples background data specific instances analogies

statistics explanations of logic testimonies of authorities

+ √ − Is this argument backed with enough informative support?

+ √ − Is this argument backed with enough convincing support?

+ √ − Is the evidence supported by adequate documentation?

What do you feel needs to be added to support this argument?

____

____

____

____

____

____

(Write additional comments on the student's paper)

III. The Conclusion: Does the conclusion:

+ √ − 1. Summarize the arguments effectively?

+ √ − 2. Restate the topic proposal?

+ √ − 3. Draw a conclusion for the reader that the proposal had been supported and should be accepted and/or acted upon?

+ √ − 4. Do something to make the reader reflect over the logic?

Grades (see criteria explanation on page 99 and in Figure 3-4)
(Circle one and record it as the raw score)

	F	D	C−		C		C+	B	A	A+	Raw Score	Weight	Weighted Grades
Criteria I	1	2	3	4	5	6	7	8	9	10 =	________	X 1 =	________
Criteria II	1	2	3	4	5	6	7	8	9	10 =	________	X 6 =	________
Criteria III	1	2	3	4	5	6	7	8	9	10 =	________	X 3 =	________
												Sum Grade	________

Transfer the weighted grades to the Exercise 3 Grading Form (page 000).

Note: This Feedback Form is to be attached (staple or paper clip) to the front of the student's paper and returned to him with the graded paper.

Name ______________________ No. ______ Sec. ______

EXERCISE 3: Feedback Form to Author ______________________ No. ______

Circle One

Yes	No	Does this paper contain at least 8 references?
Yes	No	Is this paper between 3½ and 4½ pages in length?
Yes	No	Are all seven forms of support used at least once in this paper?
Yes	No	Does this paper have a complete outline in the left-hand margin?

If the answer to any of these questions is no, the paper is unacceptable and must be redone. Give it a grade of 1 on Criteria II. Then continue grading the paper.

I. The Introduction:

+ √ − 1. Did it gain your attention?

+ √ − 2. Did it focus your interest toward the topic?

+ √ − 3. Did the over-all writing style and appearance make you feel this would be a good paper (rapport)? Or, was there anything in the introduction to make you feel this paper was going to be worth reading?

Write what specific things you felt were good about the introduction.

____

____

____

____

____

____

(Write additional comments on the student's paper)

+ √ −		Is the topic clearly stated in the introduction?
+ √ −		Are terms adequately defined?
+ √ −		Are the subarguments clearly stated in the forecast summary?
Yes	No	Is subargument one inherently related to the main argument?
Yes	No	Is subargument two inherently related to the main argument?
Yes	No	Is subargument three inherently related to the main argument?

Write out an explanation for any "minuses" or "no's" in the preceding list. Add other comments you feel may help the writer improve.

____

____

____

____

____

____

(Write additional comments on the student's paper)

II. The Body or Support Section:

Yes No Is subargument one clearly stated?

Which of the following forms of support are used to support it? (circle)

detailed examples background data specific instances analogies
statistics explanations of logic testimonies of authorities

+ √ − Is this argument backed with enough informative support?

+ √ − Is this argument backed with enough convincing support?

+ √ − Is the evidence supported by adequate documentation?

What do you feel needs to be added to support this argument? Explain below.

____

____

____

____

(Write additional comments on the student's paper)

Yes No Is subargument two clearly stated?

Which of the following forms of support are used to support it? (circle)

detailed examples background data specific instances analogies

statistics explanations of logic testimonies of authorities

+ √ – Is this argument backed with enough informative support?

+ √ – Is this argument backed with enough convincing support?

+ √ – Is the evidence supported by adequate documentation?

What do you feel needs to be added to support this argument?

____

____

____

____

____

(Write additional comments on the student's paper)

Yes No Is subargument three clearly stated?

Which of the following forms of support are used to support it? (circle)

detailed examples background data specific instances analogies

statistics explanations of logic testimonies of authorities

+ √ – Is this argument backed with enough informative support?

+ √ – Is this argument backed with enough convincing support?

+ √ – Is the evidence supported by adequate documentation?

What do you feel needs to be added to support this argument?

____

____

____

____

____

(Write additional comments on the student's paper)

III. The Conclusion: Does the conclusion:

+ √ – 1. Summarize the arguments effectively?

+ √ – 2. Restate the topic proposal?

+ √ – 3. Draw a conclusion for the reader that the proposal had been supported and should be accepted and/or acted upon?

+ √ – 4. Do something to make the reader reflect over the logic?

Grades (see criteria explanation on page 99 and in Figure 3-4)
(Circle one and record it as the raw score)

	F	D	C–		C		C+		B	A	A+	Raw Score	Weight	Weighted Grades
Criteria I	1	2	3	4	5	6	7	8	9	10 =	______	X 1 =	______
Criteria II	1	2	3	4	5	6	7	8	9	10 =	______	X 6 =	______
Criteria III	1	2	3	4	5	6	7	8	9	10 =	______	X 3 =	______

Sum Grade ______

Transfer the weighted grades to the Exercise 3 Grading Form (page 000).

Note: This Feedback Form is to be attached (staple or paper clip) to the front of the student's paper and returned to him with the graded paper.

Name ______________________ No. ______ Sec. ______

EXERCISE 3: Feedback Form to Author ______________________ No. ______

Circle One

Yes	No	Does this paper contain at least 8 references?
Yes	No	Is this paper between 3½ and 4½ pages in length?
Yes	No	Are all seven forms of support used at least once in this paper?
Yes	No	Does this paper have a complete outline in the left-hand margin?

If the answer to any of these questions is no, the paper is unacceptable and must be redone. Give it a grade of 1 on Criteria II. Then continue grading the paper.

I. The Introduction:

+ √ − 1. Did it gain your attention?
+ √ − 2. Did it focus your interest toward the topic?
+ √ − 3. Did the over-all writing style and appearance make you feel this would be a good paper (rapport)? Or, was there anything in the introduction to make you feel this paper was going to be worth reading?

Write what specific things you felt were good about the introduction.

____

____

____

____

____

____

(Write additional comments on the student's paper)

+ √ − Is the topic clearly stated in the introduction?
+ √ − Are terms adequately defined?
+ √ − Are the subarguments clearly stated in the forecast summary?
Yes No Is subargument one inherently related to the main argument?
Yes No Is subargument two inherently related to the main argument?
Yes No Is subargument three inherently related to the main argument?

Write out an explanation for any "minuses" or "no's" in the preceding list. Add other comments you feel may help the writer improve.

____

____

____

____

____

____

(Write additional comments on the student's paper)

II. The Body or Support Section:

Yes No Is subargument one clearly stated?

Which of the following forms of support are used to support it? (circle)

detailed examples   background data   specific instances   analogies
statistics   explanations of logic   testimonies of authorities

+ √ − Is this argument backed with enough informative support?
+ √ − Is this argument backed with enough convincing support?
+ √ − Is the evidence supported by adequate documentation?

What do you feel needs to be added to support this argument? Explain below.

____

____

____

____

(Write additional comments on the student's paper)

Yes	No	Is subargument two clearly stated?

Which of the following forms of support are used to support it? (circle)

detailed examples   background data   specific instances   analogies

statistics   explanations of logic   testimonies of authorities

+ √ − Is this argument backed with enough informative support?
+ √ − Is this argument backed with enough convincing support?
+ √ − Is the evidence supported by adequate documentation?

What do you feel needs to be added to support this argument?

____

____

____

____

____

____

(Write additional comments on the student's paper)

Yes   No   Is subargument three clearly stated?

Which of the following forms of support are used to support it? (circle)

detailed examples   background data   specific instances   analogies

statistics   explanations of logic   testimonies of authorities

+ √ − Is this argument backed with enough informative support?
+ √ − Is this argument backed with enough convincing support?
+ √ − Is the evidence supported by adequate documentation?

What do you feel needs to be added to support this argument?

____

____

____

____

____

____

(Write additional comments on the student's paper)

III. The Conclusion: Does the conclusion:

+ √ − 1. Summarize the arguments effectively?
+ √ − 2. Restate the topic proposal?
+ √ − 3. Draw a conclusion for the reader that the proposal had been supported and should be accepted and/or acted upon?
+ √ − 4. Do something to make the reader reflect over the logic?

Grades (see criteria explanation on page 99 and in Figure 3-4)
(Circle one and record it as the raw score)

	F	D	C−		C		C+	B	A	A+	Raw Score	Weight	Weighted Grades
Criteria I	1	2	3	4	5	6	7	8	9	10 =	________	X 1 =	________
Criteria II	1	2	3	4	5	6	7	8	9	10 =	________	X 6 =	________
Criteria III	1	2	3	4	5	6	7	8	9	10 =	________	X 3 =	________
												Sum Grade	________

Transfer the weighted grades to the Exercise 3 Grading Form (page 000).

Note: This Feedback Form is to be attached (staple or paper clip) to the front of the student's paper and returned to him with the graded paper.

Name ______________________ No. ______ Sec. ______

EXERCISE 3: Feedback Form to Author ______________________ **No.** ______

Circle One

Yes	No	Does this paper contain at least 8 references?
Yes	No	Is this paper between 3½ and 4½ pages in length?
Yes	No	Are all seven forms of support used at least once in this paper?
Yes	No	Does this paper have a complete outline in the left-hand margin?

If the answer to any of these questions is no, the paper is unacceptable and must be redone. Give it a grade of 1 on Criteria II. Then continue grading the paper.

I. The Introduction:

+ √ –	1. Did it gain your attention?
+ √ –	2. Did it focus your interest toward the topic?
+ √ –	3. Did the over-all writing style and appearance make you feel this would be a good paper (rapport)? Or, was there anything in the introduction to make you feel this paper was going to be worth reading?

Write what specific things you felt were good about the introduction.

____

____

____

____

____

(Write additional comments on the student's paper)

____

+ √ –		Is the topic clearly stated in the introduction?
+ √ –		Are terms adequately defined?
+ √ –		Are the subarguments clearly stated in the forecast summary?
Yes	No	Is subargument one inherently related to the main argument?
Yes	No	Is subargument two inherently related to the main argument?
Yes	No	Is subargument three inherently related to the main argument?

Write out an explanation for any "minuses" or "no's" in the preceding list.
Add other comments you feel may help the writer improve.

____

____

____

____

____

(Write additional comments on the student's paper)

____

II. The Body or Support Section:

Yes No — Is subargument one clearly stated?

Which of the following forms of support are used to support it? (circle)

detailed examples background data specific instances analogies
statistics explanations of logic testimonies of authorities

+ √ –	Is this argument backed with enough informative support?
+ √ –	Is this argument backed with enough convincing support?
+ √ –	Is the evidence supported by adequate documentation?

What do you feel needs to be added to support this argument? Explain below.

____

____

____

(Write additional comments on the student's paper)

____

Yes No — Is subargument two clearly stated?
Which of the following forms of support are used to support it? (circle)

detailed examples — background data — specific instances — analogies

statistics — explanations of logic — testimonies of authorities

+ √ − Is this argument backed with enough informative support?
+ √ − Is this argument backed with enough convincing support?
+ √ − Is the evidence supported by adequate documentation?
What do you feel needs to be added to support this argument?

____
____
____
____
____
____

(Write additional comments on the student's paper)

Yes No — Is subargument three clearly stated?
Which of the following forms of support are used to support it? (circle)

detailed examples — background data — specific instances — analogies

statistics — explanations of logic — testimonies of authorities

+ √ − Is this argument backed with enough informative support?
+ √ − Is this argument backed with enough convincing support?
+ √ − Is the evidence supported by adequate documentation?
What do you feel needs to be added to support this argument?

____
____
____
____
____
____

(Write additional comments on the student's paper)

III. The Conclusion: Does the conclusion:

+ √ − 1. Summarize the arguments effectively?
+ √ − 2. Restate the topic proposal?
+ √ − 3. Draw a conclusion for the reader that the proposal had been supported and should be accepted and/or acted upon?
+ √ − 4. Do something to make the reader reflect over the logic?

Grades (see criteria explanation on page 99 and in Figure 3-4)
(Circle one and record it as the raw score)

	F	D	C−		C		C+	B	A	A+	Raw Score	Weight	Weighted Grades
Criteria I	1	2	3	4	5	6	7	8	9	10 =	________	X 1 =	________
Criteria II	1	2	3	4	5	6	7	8	9	10 =	________	X 6 =	________
Criteria III	1	2	3	4	5	6	7	8	9	10 =	________	X 3 =	________
												Sum Grade	________

Transfer the weighted grades to the Exercise 3 Grading Form (page 000).

Note: This Feedback Form is to be attached (staple or paper clip) to the front of the student's paper and returned to him with the graded paper.

Name ______________________ No. ______ Sec. ______

EXERCISE 3: Feedback Form to Author ______________________ No. ______

Circle One

Yes No Does this paper contain at least 8 references?
Yes No Is this paper between 3½ and 4½ pages in length?
Yes No Are all seven forms of support used at least once in this paper?
Yes No Does this paper have a complete outline in the left-hand margin?

If the answer to any of these questions is no, the paper is unacceptable and must be redone. Give it a grade of 1 on Criteria II. Then continue grading the paper.

I. The Introduction:

+ √ − 1. Did it gain your attention?
+ √ − 2. Did it focus your interest toward the topic?
+ √ − 3. Did the over-all writing style and appearance make you feel this would be a good paper (rapport)? Or, was there anything in the introduction to make you feel this paper was going to be worth reading?

Write what specific things you felt were good about the introduction.

____

____

____

____

____

____

(Write additional comments on the student's paper)

+ √ − Is the topic clearly stated in the introduction?
+ √ − Are terms adequately defined?
+ √ − Are the subarguments clearly stated in the forecast summary?
Yes No Is subargument one inherently related to the main argument?
Yes No Is subargument two inherently related to the main argument?
Yes No Is subargument three inherently related to the main argument?

Write out an explanation for any "minuses" or "no's" in the preceding list. Add other comments you feel may help the writer improve.

____

____

____

____

____

____

(Write additional comments on the student's paper)

II. The Body or Support Section:

Yes No Is subargument one clearly stated?

Which of the following forms of support are used to support it? (circle)

detailed examples background data specific instances analogies
statistics explanations of logic testimonies of authorities

+ √ − Is this argument backed with enough informative support?
+ √ − Is this argument backed with enough convincing support?
+ √ − Is the evidence supported by adequate documentation?

What do you feel needs to be added to support this argument? Explain below.

____

____

____

____

(Write additional comments on the student's paper)

Yes No Is subargument two clearly stated?

Which of the following forms of support are used to support it? (circle)

detailed examples background data specific instances analogies

statistics explanations of logic testimonies of authorities

+ √ − Is this argument backed with enough informative support?

+ √ − Is this argument backed with enough convincing support?

+ √ − Is the evidence supported by adequate documentation?

What do you feel needs to be added to support this argument?

____

____

____

____

____

____

(Write additional comments on the student's paper)

Yes No Is subargument three clearly stated?

Which of the following forms of support are used to support it? (circle)

detailed examples background data specific instances analogies

statistics explanations of logic testimonies of authorities

+ √ − Is this argument backed with enough informative support?

+ √ − Is this argument backed with enough convincing support?

+ √ − Is the evidence supported by adequate documentation?

What do you feel needs to be added to support this argument?

____

____

____

____

____

____

(Write additional comments on the student's paper)

III. The Conclusion: Does the conclusion:

+ √ − 1. Summarize the arguments effectively?

+ √ − 2. Restate the topic proposal?

+ √ − 3. Draw a conclusion for the reader that the proposal had been supported and should be accepted and/or acted upon?

+ √ − 4. Do something to make the reader reflect over the logic?

Grades (see criteria explanation on page 99 and in Figure 3-4)
(Circle one and record it as the raw score)

	F	D	C−		C		C+		B	A	A+	Raw Score	Weight	Weighted Grades
Criteria I	1	2	3	4	5	6	7	8	9		10 =	________	X 1 =	________
Criteria II	1	2	3	4	5	6	7	8	9		10 =	________	X 6 =	________
Criteria III	1	2	3	4	5	6	7	8	9		10 =	________	X 3 =	________
													Sum Grade	________

Transfer the weighted grades to the Exercise 3 Grading Form (page 000).

Note: This Feedback Form is to be attached (staple or paper clip) to the front of the student's paper and returned to him with the graded paper.

Your Name ____________________
No. ________ Sec. ____________

Exercise 3

GRADING FORM

Paper Copy No.	Author's Name and	No.	Weighted Grade on Criteria				Sum Grade
1	________	No. ____	I ____	II ____	III ____	=	☐
2	________	No. ____	I ____	II ____	III ____	=	☐
3	________	No. ____	I ____	II ____	III ____	=	☐
4	________	No. ____	I ____	II ____	III ____	=	☐
5	________	No. ____	I ____	II ____	III ____	=	☐
6	________	No. ____	I ____	II ____	III ____	=	☐
7	________	No. ____	I ____	II ____	III ____	=	☐
8	________	No. ____	I ____	II ____	III ____	=	☐
9	________	No. ____	I ____	II ____	III ____	=	☐
10	________	No. ____	I ____	II ____	III ____	=	☐
11	________	No. ____	I ____	II ____	III ____	=	☐
12	________	No. ____	I ____	II ____	III ____	=	☐
13	________	No. ____	I ____	II ____	III ____	=	☐
14	________	No. ____	I ____	II ____	III ____	=	☐
	________	No. ____	I ____	II ____	III ____	=	☐
	________	No. ____	I ____	II ____	III ____	=	☐

Totals	I ____	II ____	III ____	=	____
divided by number graded	____	____	____	=	____
equals the average grade given by you	I ____	II ____	III ____	=	____

Return this form to your instructor on the day the graded papers are returned to the authors.
That due date is: ____/____/____

Your Name ____________________
No.________ Sec.______________

Exercise 3

AUTHOR'S GRADE RECORD FORM

Your Copy No.	Evaluator No.		Weighted Grade on Criteria:						Sum Grade
1.	______	I	______	II	______	III	______	=	______
2.	______	I	______	II	______	III	______	=	______
3.	______	I	______	II	______	III	______	=	______
4.	______	I	______	II	______	III	______	=	______
5.	______	I	______	II	______	III	______	=	______
6.	______	I	______	II	______	III	______	=	______
7.	______	I	______	II	______	III	______	=	______
8.	______	I	______	II	______	III	______	=	______
9.	______	I	______	II	______	III	______	=	______
10.	______	I	______	II	______	III	______	=	______
11.	______	I	______	II	______	III	______	=	______
12.	______	I	______	II	______	III	______	=	______
13.	______	I	______	II	______	III	______	=	______
14.	______	I	______	II	______	III	______	=	______
	______	I	______	II	______	III	______	=	______
	______	I	______	II	______	III	______	=	______
	Sum of Grades:	I	______	II	______	III	______	=	______
	divided by number of graders		______		______		______		______
	= your average grade =	I	______	II	______	III	______		[ ] This is your Sum Grade Average

When this form is completed, record your Sum Grade Average on the Class Grade Summary Sheet. Use the column headed Exercise 3 Paper Grades. This sheet is to be completed and given to the instructor no later than the second period after you receive your graded papers.

This form is due on ________________.

Note: If you have 2 or more ratings of "1" on Criteria II (weighted grades of 6), you are to bring this form and your set of papers and rating sheets to the instructor before you do Exercise 5. The instructor will determine whether or not you must do this exercise over. If you fail to check with the instructor, you may not be permitted to do Exercise 5.

Your Name ______________________

No. ____________ Sec. ____________

Exercise 3

GRADER QUALITY REPORT

This written assignment requires a great deal of effort on the part of the graders. If they do not carefully read and evaluate your paper, they cannot give you proper feedback on how to improve. Some graders may not be aware that their feedback is either incomplete or superficial. This form is designed to provide such information to each grader. Go over each feedback sheet before filling out this form. Then use this form to grade the quality of the feedback to you.

Rate each category 1 = very superior 2 = excellent 3 = O.K. 4 = below average X = very poor

Paper Copy No.	Grader No.	Category A The completeness of the job of filling out the checklist was?	Category B The quantity of suggestions on how to improve was?	Category C The quality of the suggestions on how to improve was?
1	____	____	____	____
2	____	____	____	____
3	____	____	____	____
4	____	____	____	____
5	____	____	____	____
6	____	____	____	____
7	____	____	____	____
8	____	____	____	____
9	____	____		
10	____	____	(Do not rate 9-14 on Categories B or C)	
11	____	____		
12	____	____		
13	____	____		
14	____	____		

Note: The X rating is designed to identify students who need special help. It is not a punishment. If you give an evaluator an "X" rating, take your paper which he graded and his Feedback Form to the instructor. The instructor will return these to the evaluator and will show him how to improve the quality of his feedback. When the reevaluation is done, the paper is to be returned to the instructor so the X can be removed. All X's should be removed before the student grades Exercise 5.

A master chart containing each student's number may be posted. If this is used, record your ratings on that chart. The column on the left of the chart will contain the number of the evaluator you are rating. The top of the chart lists your number as the rater.

	1	2	3	4
1				
2		223		
3		334		
4		32X		

If you are student No. 2 and you gave evaluator No. 4 an O.K. (3) in category A, an excellent (2) in category B, and a very poor (X) in category C, his grade would be recorded as shown in the sample chart as 32X. *Due Date*: These ratings are to be recorded on the master chart by the end of the period following the one in which your graded papers are returned.

EXERCISE 4

Creating an Atmosphere for Listening

PURPOSE OF ASSIGNMENT

In this assignment we will first work on developing an atmosphere for positive listening. We will review how to organize and support a presentation stressing how organization of oral and written material differ. Finally we will discuss the development of the "How to change" section of a proposal.

Introduction

In Exercise 4 you will further develop the presentation prepared for Exercise 3. This time, however, the presentation will be given orally and will contain a plan of how to change. In the business world, most proposals are presented first in written form and then, if they generate enough interest, the authors are asked to come in to a meeting to give an oral presentation. The presentation is almost always followed by a question-and-answer session.

In this exercise, we will first focus on learning to create a proper atmosphere for an oral presentation. Actions speak so loud it is often impossible to hear what one is saying; thus, to be effective communicators, we must learn to control not only what we say but also the impression we make on others by our nonverbal behavior. We never can deal with all of the behaviors which affect the audience's response to us. That would involve a total analysis of all of our past associations with each person in the audience. We will focus only on behaviors that we can easily control: those which affect listeners' attitudes during an actual communication event. These behaviors are often referred to as our *silent language*. In Exercise 2, you worked on avoiding behaviors that were distracting. In this assignment, you will go one step further and work on creating behaviors that reinforce your verbal messages.

THE NONVERBAL ATMOSPHERE

From the second we meet another person, our silent language stimulates communication. The way we dress, the way we speak (regardless of the content of the conversation), the way we stand, and even the type of car we drive contain potential messages about us. Most people are consciously or subconsciously aware of much of this silent language. We behave in expedient ways because of our total past experience in our culture. We observe our own behavior and give ourselves feedback that certain acts convey a message that we do or do not wish to convey. This is the type of feedback that tells us to shine our shoes before going to a formal party in our culture. As we enter each new environment (or culture), we must learn which actions convey which messages in that new environment. Then we can attempt to modify our behavior to convey the message we desire.

There is no correct nonverbal behavior to fit all occasions anymore than there is one correct way to organize or to write. The nonverbal messages which are appropriate are as variable as the verbal messages we may wish to convey. We may wish to appear poised to impress those in the audience or coy and bashful to gain their sympathy. The important consideration is that the nonverbal message must be controlled and integrated with the verbal message to achieve the effect desired.

Although there is no set rule to govern nonverbal behavior, there are certain behaviors that are generally valuable for persons giving presentations in which the goal is to gain acceptance of a proposal. Since that is the goal of Exercise 4, we will practice these. We will refer to these behaviors as the acts of creating an air or atmosphere which makes the audience want to listen. They will generally want to listen only after we have conveyed to them that we are competent persons with something to say which they may benefit by hearing. There are three basic traits of speakers that aid in creating such attitudes. These traits are preparedness, confidence, and enthusiasm. Although all of these are created by both verbal and nonverbal behaviors, they are created predominantly by the nonverbal behaviors. Following are descriptions of some techniques used to create a proper air for successfully presenting a proposal:

1. ***Create an air of preparedness.*** You should let the audience know you are worth listening to. If you appear to be unprepared, then why should people listen to you? It is important to appear to be prepared and knowledgeable. There are many ways to do this. The type and amount of material you bring with you to a meeting can show that you have done your research. It is often important to have material available and well organized so that when questions are asked you can quickly find the information to support the answers. Mentioning the source of your information is one of the best ways of giving an air of preparedness, for it shows that you have done your research. You must also make sure that your material is organized so as to avoid forgetting and leaving things out.

The presentations must be carefully thought out. They should be approached somewhat like a chess game. You must think not only of your move or proposal, but you must also look at the other side. You must anticipate objections or questions and be prepared in advance to answer them. Once a presentation is completely thought out and answers to possible objections are prepared, it is time to start rehearsing. Rehearsals often reveal that things which you thought were carefully worked out do not always come across when you attempt to explain them. There is a difference between being prepared to think an idea through and being able to present it to someone else. Practicing a presentation before giving it will help you to appear to be as prepared as you actually are. This air of preparedness cannot be easily faked; to create it, you must be prepared. Just being prepared is still not enough. Many well-prepared persons fail to convey the image of being prepared and, consequently, they and their message are taken less seriously. You must both be prepared and convey an air of preparedness to the listener.

2. ***Create an air of confidence.*** If you appear unsure of your ideas and data, you cannot expect your listeners to be too convinced. Of course, confidence and preparedness go hand in hand. It is hard to be confident if one is unprepared. But the problem is that many who are prepared and confident do not appear to be. There are several traits that can help a person to appear to be more confident. One of the most important is that of maintaining good eye contact. When speakers are constantly looking at the ceiling or reading notes, they appear unsure and nervous, regardless of how confident they actually are. Another important trait is to speak up clearly. When volume is very low or speech is slow or hesitant, it sounds as if the speaker is unsure of what he is saying. A little embarrassed laugh after stating a point is a behavior that should be avoided. Such a laugh is a plea for sympathy from the listeners. It is more common in a classroom setting where students have little to lose than it is in a real business meeting. It has no place in either.

The line between confidence and overconfidence is very thin. You must be careful not to act like a know-it-all. You should always avoid being glib or talking down to people. A truly confident person has no need to belittle others by talking down to them or by refusing to treat their ideas respectfully. The goal of acting confident is simply to let others know that you understand and believe in the material that you are asking them to accept. Being confident is not enough if others think you are afraid. You must not only be confident; you must create an air of confidence about you.

3. ***Create an air of enthusiasm.*** You should show the listeners that you are truly interested in the proposal and in their response to it. Why should they respond to you if you show no interest in their response? Speakers give silent messages of disinterest in many ways. Dressing sloppily might convey that you do not

care enough about the listeners' response to bother to clean up. Leaning away from the audience while speaking might convey that you are disinterested. Whenever someone is really trying to convince us, he or she tends to lean forward and to add expression to his or her voice. Normally, our enthusiasm for an idea will be obvious. The danger is that when you are tired or overworked, you may have to give an important presentation. You may, without knowing it, be communicating to the audience that you do not care. The truth may be that you are only fatigued, but how is the audience to know? It is up to you to let them know that you really are concerned. You must always try to put a little emotion into your voice. Emotions are contagious. The audience will tend to respond at the same emotional level as that at which you are speaking. No matter how you feel inside, you must learn to appear enthusiastic; you may even fool yourself.

The three traits of preparedness, confidence, and enthusiasm are revealed in verbal and nonverbal behavior to create an over-all impression or atmosphere. That atmosphere can work for or against you. When the listeners walk away saying, "I cannot put my finger on it, but that proposal just does not strike me right," that is a pretty good sign the atmosphere created was not right. When the listeners walk away saying, "That sounds interesting; get me more data on it," that is the best sign that the atmosphere was right.

This discussion of how to create the airs of preparedness, confidence, and enthusiasm is brief, for until one actually sees a person's presentation, it is hard to pin down specific things that a person should or should not do to create these airs. Therefore, the main discussion of what each of you must do to create a favorable atmosphere for listening must come out in the workshop sessions for Exercise 4.

PREJUDICE AND THE FIRST IMPRESSION

Your nonverbal behavior begins communicating to the audience long before you begin to speak. Research studies over a period of many years have shown that first impressions, based on appearance, vocal quality, sex, or any of a number of traits, can and do bias listeners' later response. For further discussion of this point refer to chapter 3 in Part II of this book. The three airs already described are behaviors you can control to create a favorable initial bias. There are many other traits you cannot control. For these, you can only try to identify the prejudices of your audience in advance and try to compensate for them. It is nice to say that all people should be treated equal, but a fact of life is that they are not. Women often are still paid less than men for doing the same work. Married veterans on the GI bill receive more than single veterans. Members of racial minorities still have trouble joining some craft unions. Short basketball players have more trouble getting pro contracts than tall players. When you possess a trait which your listeners are likely to be prejudiced against, your best defense is to surprise them by being even better than you need to be, by being more prepared, more enthusiastic, and more confident than anyone else. This will help not only to get your proposals adopted but may help to remove the prejudice.

Pointing

There is one additional technique that can often greatly increase the audience's level of interest in a presentation. When giving a presentation, it is important to make the readers or listeners see how the topic relates to them personally. This is called *pointing*. Pointing is often one of the most important tasks to perform in a presentation in which a change is proposed. People do not get easily excited about things they know only in the abstract. The energy crisis of 1973 was written about and predicted for three or four years before it occurred. Yet, few people took it seriously until they pulled up to a service station that summer and found out they could not buy gas. To talk in the abstract about the problems facing the world does not motivate many people to take action. Pointing is telling people specifically what effect a specific problem like the energy crisis is going to have on them personally. For example, if we were giving a speech on the energy crisis in 1972, we might have pointed out the problem to the audience in the following manner:

Mr. Jones, how many miles do you drive a week? You say about 200. And how many miles do you get per gallon? About 8. So you use about 25 gallons of gas a week. By the figures we have just presented to you, by 1980 there may only be 10 gallons of gas available for you to use. What are you going to cut out? Do you go for Sunday drives? You may have to stop. They may even be made illegal. Do you drive to town to see movies or for dinner? This may have to stop. In short, Mr. Jones, the quality of your life and the lives of each of the rest of you sitting in this audience is going to be lowered unless new sources of energy are developed. And I do not mean in the 1990s. I am talking about what will happen to you next year or the year after. We cannot delay action even a week—in fact, it is probably already too late to prevent a crisis. Our best effort will make that crisis only less painful.

In the example, the speaker focused on one specific person in the audience. Personal interaction with an individual adds to the impact of the presentation. Specific things that could happen were mentioned, so those in the audience would realize that this was not an abstract problem but one that would actually affect their lives. This is the goal of pointing: to let people see that they will be personally affected.

ORGANIZING ORAL PRESENTATIONS

Exercise 4 will consist of workshop sessions in which each person will give a 7- to 8-minute oral presentation, followed by a 12- to 15-minute discussion of the impact of that presentation. The oral presentation is a further practice of the written presentation given in Exercise 3. However, in addition to showing that there is a need for the proposal, you are to go one step further and present a plan of how to bring about the proposed change. Before discussing how to develop the plan, we will review the basics of organization of an oral presentation.

Introduction Step

Special care must be taken in the introduction of an oral presentation to prepare the listener's mental set—to create a positive atmosphere for listening. This can be done partially by what is said and partially by the nonverbal behaviors discussed earlier. In the write-up of Exercise 3, there is a discussion of what should be accomplished in the introduction to a written presentation. All of these elements are also necessary for an oral presentation. The speaker should (1) gain attention, (2) focus attention, (3) build rapport, (4) state the topic, (5) operationally define any vague terms in the topic, and (6) give a forecast summary listing the main subsections of the presentation. In Exercise 3, the instructions focused on what words to say or write in an introduction. This is because a written presentation is pretty much limited to verbal messages (though there are a few nonverbal messages that can aid a written report, such as neat typing, attractive covers, letterheads, and quality paper.) In introducing oral presentations, we must control not just the words, but also the nonverbal messages and atmosphere. The nonverbal portion of an introduction must be considered as important as the verbal. From the moment you enter the room for Exercise 4, your nonverbal introduction begins with the way you dress, the way you walk, and so on. Especially be aware of creating the airs of preparedness, confidence, and enthusiasm, discussed earlier.

The verbal content of the introduction of an oral presentation does not differ greatly from that of a written one. The initial attention getter is sometimes a little longer. This is because those in the audience may need time to relax or to get their minds shifted to thinking about the topic. There is no one correct length for an introduction. It should simply be long enough to achieve the six goals listed earlier.

Forecast Summary. The forecast summary in the introduction of Exercise 4 is one part that will differ from that in Exercise 3 for two reasons: the presentation is to be given orally, and a plan of how to change is included in this exercise.

The forecast summary is much more important in oral presentations because it provides the listeners with their only road map of what they are to be listening for. In a written presentation, there are tables of contents and section headings to assist readers in discovering the over-all point of the presentation. Listeners, on the other hand, have no way to glance ahead or to refer to previous material. They must depend upon the speaker to keep them aware of the over-all picture. Therefore, oral presentations need more clear and more frequent summaries than do written presentations.

The forecasting summary in this assignment must prepare the listener to expect to hear a proposed plan of action as well as a need for a change. In Exercise 3, there was no plan of how to change, so the forecasting summary outlined only the subarguments which showed a need for a change. The forecast summary for Exercise 4 must be modified to adapt to the expanded content of this exercise. The forecast summary for Exercise 4 should state that you are going to present *first*, material showing why we need to change our present system, and *second*, a plan of action by which the proposed change could be brought about.

Note that the subarguments under the need are not included in this forecast summary. They will be presented as part of the need argument. They are no longer the major sections of the presentation. They are now only subsections of the need section. This is further clarified in Figure 4-1.

Subpoint Order. There are two main reasons for proposing changes. Some proposals are made because the need for a change is so great that almost any plan that will work is acceptable. An example would be when a dam is about to break. Any workable plan of action is better than none. With such a topic, the need for a change is presented first and then the proposed change is explained.

For many topics, the need for change is neither obvious nor pressing. This is the case when the present system is working at an acceptable level. Then, the argument is not that we must change or face disaster; it is, rather, that we should change from what is acceptable to something that is superior. An example would be a proposal that a successful company change its investment policy. In such a situation, just any workable plan is not necessarily acceptable. The need to change is shown only by comparing the advantages of the proposed change to those of the present system. The proposed plan of change must then be presented before any needs to change can be discussed.

Many topics fall in between these two extremes. An example would be the no-fault auto insurance proposal described in Exercise 3. There are problems with the present insurance system, but the system is not a total disaster. There are also advantages of the no-fault system over the present system. With such topics, the arguments showing needs to change are usually presented first. They are followed by the proposal of how to change. Finally, arguments showing the advantage of the new proposal over the present system are presented. You must analyze your class topic to see which order of presentation is most appropriate. The assignment instructions are written as though the order for the topic is the common sequence of need, plan, and benefits. You will need to make some adjustments if the selected topic is not suited to that order. Whichever order the topic calls for is the order you should use for the arguments in your forecast summary.

Supporting Step or Body

The development of the body of the presentation of Exercise 4 is similar to that of Exercise 3, but a little more complex because the arguments showing a need to change have become merely a part of the body instead of being the whole body as they were in Exercise 3. However, when you begin actually developing these arguments, you will develop them just as you did for Exercise 3.

Need for Change. The first subpoint in Exercise 4 will be that there is a need to change. If we once again use the no-fault auto insurance topic as an example, we might begin the body of our presentation as follows:

> There is a need to abandon our present fault auto insurance system and adopt a no-fault system. There are three main reasons that will be presented to show why a no-fault system of automobile insurance is superior: first, it would enable accident victims to receive compensation more rapidly; second, it would allow premiums to be lowered because it would lower insurance companies' legal costs; and, last, it would allow premiums to be lowered because it would facilitate low-cost mass marketing of insurance.
>
> Let's look at that first point. Accident victims are suffering unduly under our fault system because of the long delays in court settlements. In the recent issue of. . .

Note that the first item in the example is an introduction to the need arguments. A forecast summary of the subargument supporting the need is included in that introduction. The development of these need arguments would be the same as in Exercise 3.

Plan of Change. The major new element in Exercise 4 is the proposal or plan showing how to bring about a change. This plan of change can be organized in much the same fashion as the rest of the presentation; however, headings that are more appropriate will be main points and subpoints rather than main arguments and subarguments.

The main objectives in developing a plan are (1) to inform the audience of how it will work, and (2) to convince the audience that it is feasible. Not too much can be said about how to structure a plan of change. Different situations call for completely different kinds of plans. There are, however, two key ideas to remember. First, a plan of change must remove or substantially reduce the problems described in the need for change arguments. For example, if one of those arguments is that the present system is too expensive, you must show how your new proposal will be less expensive. That point may seem obvious, but experience has shown that a high percentage of the presentations given for Exercise 4 fail in this regard. To prevent this from happening, after you have prepared your proposal on how to bring about the change, check your plan against each subargument showing a need for a change. Make sure that the problems discussed under each need for change argument are either removed or substantially reduced by your proposed plan for change.

Second, the plan must be feasible. A plan that costs more to implement than it will save is not feasible. A plan that simply appoints a committee to work out all the problems is also not feasible. What if the committee cannot work out the problems? Then the plan offers no solution at all. The plan must contain enough detail to show that it actually can solve the problems raised in the need arguments.

Running Summaries. More repetition is needed in an oral presentation than in a written presentation. Readers can glance back over a written presentation, something they cannot do with an oral one. To aid the listener, running summaries are often used. They are required for Exercise 4. A *running summary* is a series of summaries located between subarguments or subpoints.

When you finish developing the first subargument, summarize that argument for the listeners. The summary should remind the audience of some of the key pieces of support used and should point out that the argument has been substantiated. Summaries are usually followed by transitions which lead into the next subargument. After developing subargument two, you should again summarize for the listeners. This time, summarize subarguments one and two and then make a transition to subargument three. In this way, you keep presenting running summaries of all of your previous subarguments until you are ready to summarize the main argument. After presenting subargument three, summarize subarguments one, two, and three. If subargument three is the last subargument, then that summary of all three subarguments becomes the summary for the main argument.

There should be summaries between any two main segments of a presentation as well as between subarguments. Once the need arguments are completed, there needs to be a summary of those arguments, followed by a transition from the need arguments to the proposed plan of change. Following the presentation of the plan of change, a running summary is again needed. It should summarize briefly the arguments for the need for change and for the proposed plan of change. If these are the only two major sections of the paper, then that summary is the final summary and is part of the conclusion.

If the plan of change contains many subsections, you may need to use summaries and transitions between the subsections of the plan. Usually, the proposed plans are not so complicated or detailed as to require such internal summaries.

Figure 4-1 contains a skeleton outline of Exercises 3 and 4, showing how the two compare and also showing where transitions and summaries should be located.

Use of Documentation. In a written presentation, documentation is supplied by footnotes. Since no footnotes can be attached to a verbal message, all documentation must be contained in the presentation. Following is an example of how a footnote from Exercise 3 would be used in an oral report:

FIGURE 4-1 Comparison of Outlines of Exercises 3 and 4 Presentations

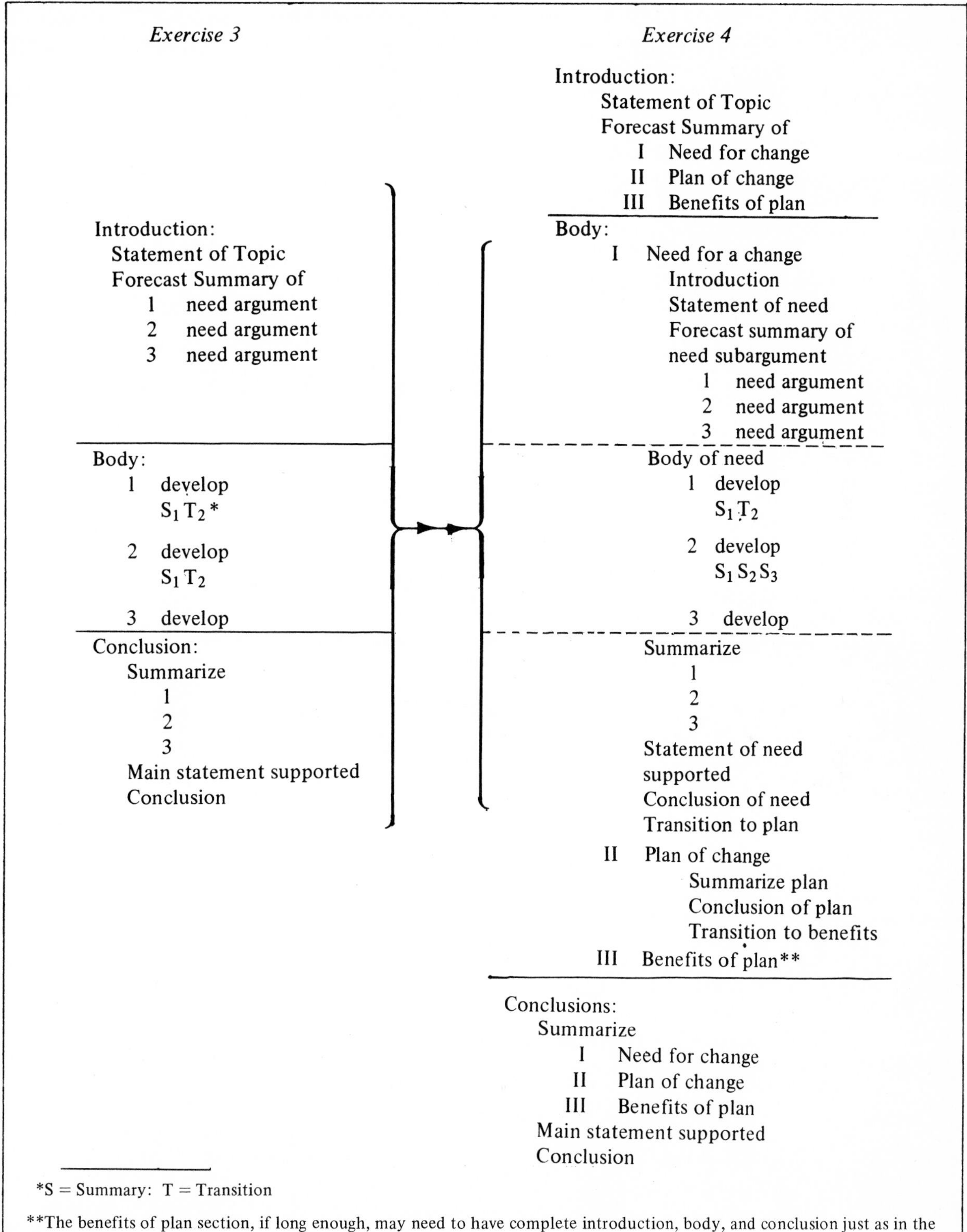

*S = Summary: T = Transition

**The benefits of plan section, if long enough, may need to have complete introduction, body, and conclusion just as in the need for a change section.

In a recent study by Dan Edison, an Associate Professor of Management and Marketing at the University of Hawaii and a specialist in organizational communications, it was reported that the readability of campaign material in union elections can be a major deciding factor in the final vote for representation.

Compare this to the way the written reference was used in Exercise 3 (see page 97).

The documentation and quotes for Exercise 4 should be on cards or on regular sheets of paper. The use and format of quote cards is explained in Exercise 2 (see page 29) and later in this exercise. Much of your quoted material is likely to be on Xeroxed sheets or in magazines. Be careful to organize these sheets and to put headings at the top of each so you can locate them quickly when you need them. These sheets or cards should be used for quotes and outlines only; they should *not* be used to write out a speech. *Do not attempt to write out or memorize your presentation.*

The Conclusion Step

There is very little difference in the conclusion step of oral and written reports, except that the summary should be a little more detailed in an oral presentation. Reread the instruction for the conclusion step in Exercise 3 (see page 94).

ASSIGNMENT INSTRUCTIONS

Prepare a 7-to 8-minute oral presentation on the class topic. In this presentation, show that there is a need for a change and present a plan of how this needed change could be brought about. You will each give your presentations before a group of peers as in Exercise 2. The presentation is to be documented and supported, using the same requirements as outlined for Exercise 3. That is, all seven forms of support must be used at least once. Each need for a change subargument must contain at least one form of support that is designed primarily to inform or to arouse emotion, and one form of support designed primarily to convince.

Pointing

Pointing must be used at least once in the presentation. The pointing may be used either to show how those in the audience will be harmed by a continuation of the present system or to show how they would be helped if the proposed plan of change were adopted.

Running Summaries

Running summaries must be used between subarguments and subpoints. Remember that listeners depend upon summaries to keep them aware of how all the parts of a presentation hang together. Listeners cannot flip ahead or glance back to refresh their memories as a reader can.

The format the presentations should follow is outlined in Figure 4-1.

Speaking Notes

This presentation is to be given extemporaneously from notes. It is *not* to be written out nor is it to be memorized.

Note cards or sheets are to contain only the following:

Card 1. Statement of topic and definition of terms
Card 2. Statements of need for a change subarguments
Card 3. Brief outline of development of subargument 1
Card 4. Brief outline of development of subargument 2
Card 5. Brief outline of development of subargument 3
Card 6. Brief outline of plan

Card 7. Brief outline of benefits (optional)
Card 8+ Direct quotes which you intend to read

These cards or sheets (other than the direct quote cards) should contain only outlines of ideas. They should not contain complete statements or parts of the speech. Do *NOT* use or read from forms of support cards which you developed for Exercise 3.

NOTE: You are to bring to the class review session a duplicate copy of your speaking notes containing items 1-6. Staple or clip these cards or sheets together and make sure your name is on the top of each card or sheet. They will be checked in class and returned.

Evaluation and Feedback

Listening is a key element in this exercise. As speakers, you are each trying to create an atmosphere, by your behavior and words, that is conducive to attentive listening. As audience members you must carefully observe each presentation so that you can learn to help each other improve. You must note whether or not each speaker did in fact create an air of confidence, preparedness, and enthusiasm. If they did not, you must try to pinpoint why they failed. By carefully listening to and observing others, you often become aware of similar traits of your own that need correcting.

The second thing to listen for is organization. To aid you in following the organization of this exercise, a set of Feedback Forms is provided (page 155). On these forms is an outline of the exercise with a checklist down the side. You should become familiar with this checklist so that during an actual presentation you can simply check off points without having to study the Feedback Form. By using the checklist, you will not need to write out so many notes. Writing notes can be distracting to the speaker, and it interferes with listening.

PROCEDURE FOR PRESENTATIONS

Practice

It takes much practice to be able to create a proper atmosphere while speaking. Before the class review session, practice giving your presentation in front of a mirror or to a friend, if possible. Practice giving the presentation from your notes and while standing. Time each practice presentation to be certain that the speech will run between 7 and 8 minutes.

Use a copy of the Exercise 4 Feedback Form checklist while you practice. It will help you know whether or not you have included all of the necessary parts in your presentation. You should practice at least ten times before trying to give a presentation in class.

Class Review

You will spend one to two days in class reviewing this assignment before you break up into small workshop groups. The first thing you will do during the review session is make sure all students are assigned to a workshop group and that each group has a coordinator.

Next, you will check each other's speaking notes to see if any changes are needed. To assist in reviewing these, use the Exercise 4 Feedback Form. This will also help you to become familiar with the use of that form.

For the final review session activity, at least one of the workshop groups will come before the class and go through one complete presentation and feedback session. Then, you will discuss how members of the group conducted themselves. You should mainly be looking to see if their feedback was accurate and constructive.

The key things to be listening for in the feedback are (1) Did the group discuss the atmosphere that the speaker created and offer suggestions on how to improve it? (2) Did the group identify any missing parts or weaknesses in the organization and support of the proposal? (3) Did the group identify any inconsistencies between the need for a change arguments and.the proposed plan of change? By observing a practice group and discussing its behavior, you can each get ideas on what to do and what to avoid doing in your own group.

Operation of Workshop Groups*

For Exercise 4, you will be divided into groups of five. You can determine the group you are in by your class number. The groups are formed in numerical order, counting by fives. That is, Nos. 5, 10, 15, 20, 25 make group one. The next group begins with No. 30. Let us assume there are 40 in the class. Group two would be Nos. 30, 35, 40, 1, 6. Group three would be Nos. 11, 16, 21, 26, 31. Write down the number of students in your class _____. On the following chart make a list of the students by number for each group. Extra students are to be added to groups as a sixth member. This will be done by the instructor. The instructor will also assign each group to a meeting place.

Group (A)	(B)	(C)	(D)	(E)	(F)	(G)	(H)	(I)	(J)	(K)	(L)
___	___	___	___	___	___	___	___	___	___	___	___
___	___	___	___	___	___	___	___	___	___	___	___
___	___	___	___	___	___	___	___	___	___	___	___
___	___	___	___	___	___	___	___	___	___	___	___
___	___	___	___	___	___	___	___	___	___	___	___

My group letter is ______.
We will meet in room ______.

Group Coordinators. The person at the top of each column in the preceding chart is to act as the group's coordinator. The coordinator will be responsible for seeing that his group is conducted according to the instruction for this exercise. He will also collect all Feedback Forms and summarize the data on these forms, using the Exercise 4 Group Coordinator's Grade Summary Sheet and the Exercise 4 Group Coordinator's Feedback Grade Summary Sheet. The group coordinator is also to record each student's average grade on the Class Grade Summary Sheet (to be provided by the instructor). The speaking grades are to be posted on the Class Grade Summary Sheet under the heading Exercise 4 Speaker Grades, and the feedback grades go under the heading Exercise 4 Feedback Grades. The group coordinator is also to keep records of group attendance and tardiness and will give that report to the instructor along with the Group Coordinator's Grade Summary Sheets.

The group coordinator will time the first speaker. The person listed at the bottom of each column will be the first speaker in the group. The others will follow, proceeding up the column in order. The first speaker will become the timer for all remaining speakers. The room should be arranged so that the speaker can present his material while standing and facing the entire group. Try to avoid the round-table setting in which several members of the group will be turned sideways to the speaker. No presentations are to be given from a sitting position. The stmosphere for the presentations should be rather formal. The feedback sessions should be informal. It is the group coordinator's duty to enforce the rules of conduct for the group.

---

* Your instructor may vary the way in which you are assigned to groups.

Time Limits. The time for these presentations is 7 to 8 minutes. Speeches less than 6½ or more than 9 minutes in length must be redone to fit the time limits. This is to be done at a later time to be arranged by the group. The feedback discussion that follows each presentation should be from 12 to 15 minutes. These time limits allow for two or three speakers to perform each day. Groups of six speakers may have to arrange for an extra 20 minutes either before or after one of the allotted class periods. Time the feedback periods carefully or you are likely to run out of time.

Feedback Sessions. The group coordinators should not allow any oral feedback until the speaker's grading has been completed. The timer should allow no more than 2 minutes for this grading. *Be sure all grading is done independently*. The grading criteria are described below.

The feedback in each group can take many forms. The group can use a structured session in which a different person begins the oral feedback each time, or the group can use an unstructured session in which anyone can speak at any time. Either approach is acceptable, but the group should decide in advance how its feedback session will be conducted. It is suggested that the feedback sessions be flexible enough that they do not turn into a series of five little feedback speeches. The session should stress interaction between the speaker and his evaluators and interaction among the various evaluators as they probe each other to try to come up with the best ideas on how the speaker can improve. The group coordinator must be careful to avoid letting one person dominate the feedback session.

Rating of Feedback. Following the feedback session and while the next speaker is getting ready to begin, the speaker who has just received the feedback should rate the other five members of his group on how helpful their feedback was and why. Allow several minutes (not over 4 minutes) for each speaker to do this. The speaker may wish to expand his feedback comments after class, but he should at least fill out the ratings *immediately*.

The feedback you give is as important as the presentation. The ratings received for it are considered equal in weight to those for presentation. In business meetings, two-way communication is vital. The rating on feedback is a rating on your skill in two-way communication and, in effect, on your management ability. Try to help those in the workshop group who are quiet. Ask them questions to draw out their opinions. If one person is very talkative and tends to dominate, tell him in a nice way that he is taking a disproportionate amount of the group's time. This is a workshop learning session. Help each other learn by making others aware of their good traits and, when necessary, their bad ones. If you do not tell a student he is too talkative, how is he to know? And, if he does not know what his problem is, how is he to correct it?

When rating students on their ability to give feedback, add special notes for those students who are especially good and for those who have special problems. Be careful to make sure that all feedback is constructive. Remember there is no value in exposing someone's weakness unless you have the means to help him overcome it.

Grading Criteria

Fill out a Feedback Form (page 155) for each speaker. Then transfer the grades on the feedback form to your Grading Sheet (page 181). These grades will be recorded on the Group Coordinator's Grade Summary Sheet.

There are three general criteria to use in grading Exercise 4 presentations:

Criterion I. Presentation. Consider the over-all atmosphere the speaker created; the three key items in creating atmosphere are (1) creating an air of preparedness, (2) creating an air of confidence, and (3) creating an air of enthusiasm. Also evaluate the speaker's eye contact, vocal quality, stance, dress, volume, and any other factor which affects your response to the speaker, apart from the organization or content of his message.

Criterion II. Organization of presentation. Consider how accurately the author conformed to the exact directions specified for this presentation. This criterion is one of the main focuses of Exercise 4 and is graded more heavily than it will be on later presentations. Use the checklist on the Feedback Form as a guide to see whether or not the speaker included all that he was supposed to in the organization of this presentation.

Criterion III. Content of presentation. Consider the logic of the author's argument and the adequacy of the material used to support them. Check the inherency of each subargument and the appropriateness and adequacy of the forms of support used to substantiate them.

Some Grading Guides. In grading this presentation, it should be assumed that the student, as a minimum, will have acceptable delivery. That is, his stance, eye contact, and vocal quality will be acceptable. If any of these delivery problems is noticed, be sure to call it to the speaker's attention during the feedback session. If delivery is a serious problem, the speaker should be given no higher than a "2" on Criterion I. This informs the instructor that a student needs special help.

There are two main elements to watch for in grading these presentations: atmosphere and organization. This presentation is a drill and the goal is to do the exercise correctly rather than to show off a beautiful free style. To grade the organization of these presentations, use the checklist on the Assignment 4 Feedback Form. If the organization is very weak, give the student no higher than a "2" on Criterion II. This alerts the instructor that a student needs special help.

The areas in which the grading for the next presentation will focus are logic and content. Although that is not the main focus of the grading of this presentation, you are still encouraged to give each speaker some feedback regarding how acceptable and convincing you find his arguments.

The meaning of number grades is shown in Figure 4-2 by comparing the number grades to letter grades and percentile ranks.

FIGURE 4-2 Meaning of Number Grades

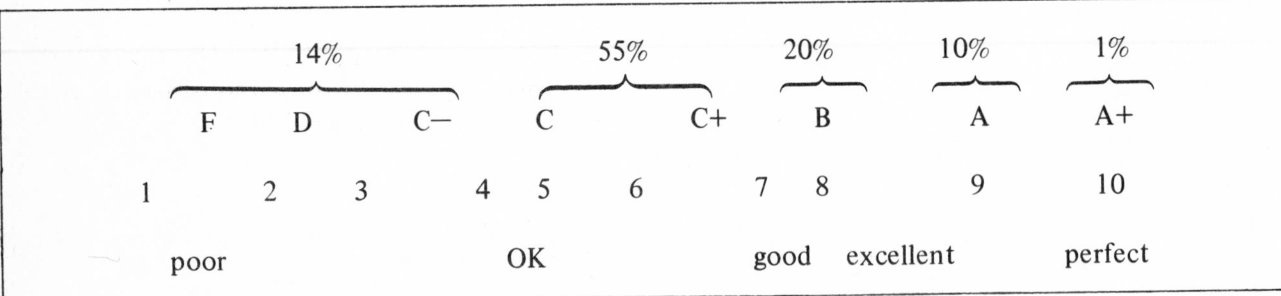

EXERCISE 4 CHECKLISTS

Checklist of Things to Do (before coming to class)

1. Prepare a 7- to 8-minute presentation in which you show a need to change and a plan by which that change can be brought about.
2. Read carefully all of the evaluation and grading forms to be used in this exercise.
3. Prepare a set of speaking notes (see page 148), and bring these notes to the in-class review session.
4. Practice your presentation using the Exercise 4 Feedback Form as a guide. Make sure your presentation contains all elements listed on that form.
5. Practice giving yourself feedback and then judge the quality of that feedback by using as a guide the Evaluator's Feedback From Speaker form (page 171).

Checklist for Conducting Workshop

1. The student in your workshop whose number is at the top of each column of the chart on page 150 is your group's coordinator. He or she is to do the following:
   a. Call the group to order and take attendance.
   b. Time the first speaker.
   c. Coordinate all activities of the workshop and make sure that the group complies with the instructions for the assignment.
   d. At the end of the workshop, fill out the Group Coordinator's Grade Summary Sheet and the Group Coordinator's Feedback Grade Summary Sheet.
2. The student whose number is at the bottom of each column of the chart on page 150 is the first speaker in the group and then becomes the timer for all following presentations.
3. The time limits are as follows:
   7 to 8 minutes for presentations
   2 minutes for filling out Feedback Forms
   12 to 15 minutes for feedback session
   2 to 4 minutes for filling out checklist on the Evaluators' Feedback From Speaker Form
4. All feedback is to be constructive and specific.

Your Name ________________________
No.________ Group ________ Sec.______

Exercise 4

FEEDBACK FORM

Feedback to Speaker ____________________ No. _______

Note: Become familiar with this checklist before you try to use it. (Check off each item as you hear it.)

Introduction:

_____ gained attention?
_____ focused attention?
_____ built positive rapport?
_____ stated topic clearly?
_____ defined terms?
_____ gave a forecast summary? (Included mention that there will be one part of the presentation showing why there is a need to change and a second part showing a proposal on how to bring about the change? A third optional part may be included showing the benefits of the proposed plan of change.)

Body:

SUBPOINT ONE: showing there is a need for change.

____stated subpoint clearly?
____gave forecast summary of subarguments?

Subargument 1 - forms of support used? (circle)

detailed example   specific instances   background data
analogy   statistics
explanation of logic   authority

____was documentation adequate?
____were summary and transitions used?

Subargument 2 - forms of support used? (circle)

detailed example   specific instances   background data
analogy   statistics
explanation of logic   authority

____was documentation adequate?
____was a running summary of subarguments 1 and 2 used?

Subargument 3 - forms of support used? (circle)

detailed example   specific instances   background data
analogy   statistics
explanation of logic   authority

____was documentation adequate?
____was the entire need argument summarized and concluded?
____was there a smooth transition from the need arguments to the plan?

SUBPOINT TWO: proposed plan of action designed to correct the problems.

____Would the proposal correct the problem mentioned in subargument 1?
____Would the proposal correct the problem mentioned in subargument 2?
____Would the proposal correct the problem mentioned in subargument 3?
____Does the proposal sound feasible?

Conclusion:

_____ summarized subpoints?
_____ restated topic?
_____ drew conclusion for listeners that proposal has been supported and should be adopted?
_____ concluding statement made you reflect over the topic?
_____ speaker used pointing?

From the over all atmosphere this speaker created, I felt that regarding this topic he was

inadequately prepared	1	2	3	4	5	very prepared
lacking in confidence	1	2	3	4	5	very confident
lacking in enthusiasm	1	2	3	4	5	very enthusiastic

Grades: (See criteria listed on page 152).

Note: If the speaker needs special help, do not give him a grade above 2 on the appropriate criterion. This lets the instructor know who needs special help.

(Circle one and record it as the raw score.)	Raw Score		Weight		Weighted Score
Criteria I 1 2 3 4 5 6 7 8 9 10 =	_____	X	3	=	_____
Criteria II 1 2 3 4 5 6 7 8 9 10 =	_____	X	5	=	_____
Criteria III 1 2 3 4 5 6 7 8 9 10 =	_____	X	1	=	_____
	Weighted Sum Grade				☐

Transfer this weighted sum grade to your Exercise 4 Grading Sheet.

Note: Three of these forms are to be used in the class review sessions and five to be used in the workshop sessions.

Your Name ____________________

No.________ Group________ Sec.______

Exercise 4

FEEDBACK FORM

Feedback to Speaker ____________________ No. _______

Note: Become familiar with this checklist before you try to use it. (Check off each item as you hear it.)

Introduction:

_____ gained attention?

_____ focused attention?

_____ built positive rapport?

_____ stated topic clearly?

_____ defined terms?

_____ gave a forecast summary? (Included mention that there will be one part of the presentation showing why there is a need to change and a second part showing a proposal on how to bring about the change? A third optional part may be included showing the benefits of the proposed plan of change.)

Body:

SUBPOINT ONE: showing there is a need for change.

____stated subpoint clearly?

____gave forecast summary of subarguments?

Subargument 1 - forms of support used? (circle)

detailed example	specific instances	background data
analogy	statistics	
explanation of logic	authority	

____was documentation adequate?

____were summary and transitions used?

Subargument 2 - forms of support used? (circle)

detailed example	specific instances	background data
analogy	statistics	
explanation of logic	authority	

____was documentation adequate?

____was a running summary of subarguments 1 and 2 used?

Subargument 3 - forms of support used? (circle)

detailed example	specific instances	background data
analogy	statistics	
explanation of logic	authority	

____was documentation adequate?

____was the entire need argument summarized and concluded?

____was there a smooth transition from the need arguments to the plan?

SUBPOINT TWO: proposed plan of action designed to correct the problems.

____Would the proposal correct the problem mentioned in subargument 1?

____Would the proposal correct the problem mentioned in subargument 2?

____Would the proposal correct the problem mentioned in subargument 3?

____Does the proposal sound feasible?

Conclusion:

_____ summarized subpoints?
_____ restated topic?
_____ drew conclusion for listeners that proposal has been supported and should be adopted?
_____ concluding statement made you reflect over the topic?
_____ speaker used pointing?

From the over all atmosphere this speaker created, I felt that regarding this topic he was

inadequately prepared	1	2	3	4	5	very prepared
lacking in confidence	1	2	3	4	5	very confident
lacking in enthusiasm	1	2	3	4	5	very enthusiastic

Grades: (See criteria listed on page 152).

Note: If the speaker needs special help, do not give him a grade above 2 on the appropriate criterion. This lets the instructor know who needs special help.

(Circle one and record it as the raw score.)		Raw Score		Weight		Weighted Score
Criteria I	1 2 3 4 5 6 7 8 9 10 =	____	X	3	=	____
Criteria II	1 2 3 4 5 6 7 8 9 10 =	____	X	5	=	____
Criteria III	1 2 3 4 5 6 7 8 9 10 =	____	X	1	=	____

Weighted Sum Grade ☐

Transfer this weighted sum grade to your Exercise 4 Grading Sheet.

Note: Three of these forms are to be used in the class review sessions and five to be used in the workshop sessions.

Your Name ____________________
No. ________ Group ________ Sec. ______

Exercise 4

FEEDBACK FORM

Feedback to Speaker ____________________ No. ______

Note: Become familiar with this checklist before you try to use it. (Check off each item as you hear it.)

Introduction:

_____ gained attention?
_____ focused attention?
_____ built positive rapport?
_____ stated topic clearly?
_____ defined terms?
_____ gave a forecast summary? (Included mention that there will be one part of the presentation showing why there is a need to change and a second part showing a proposal on how to bring about the change? A third optional part may be included showing the benefits of the proposed plan of change.)

Body:

SUBPOINT ONE: showing there is a need for change.

____stated subpoint clearly?
____gave forecast summary of subarguments?

Subargument 1 - forms of support used? (circle)

detailed example	specific instances	background data
analogy	statistics	
explanation of logic	authority	

____was documentation adequate?
____were summary and transitions used?

Subargument 2 - forms of support used? (circle)

detailed example	specific instances	background data
analogy	statistics	
explanation of logic	authority	

____was documentation adequate?
____was a running summary of subarguments 1 and 2 used?

Subargument 3 - forms of support used? (circle)

detailed example	specific instances	background data
analogy	statistics	
explanation of logic	authority	

____was documentation adequate?
____was the entire need argument summarized and concluded?
____was there a smooth transition from the need arguments to the plan?

SUBPOINT TWO: proposed plan of action designed to correct the problems.

____Would the proposal correct the problem mentioned in subargument 1?
____Would the proposal correct the problem mentioned in subargument 2?
____Would the proposal correct the problem mentioned in subargument 3?
____Does the proposal sound feasible?

Conclusion:

_____ summarized subpoints?
_____ restated topic?
_____ drew conclusion for listeners that proposal has been supported and should be adopted?
_____ concluding statement made you reflect over the topic?
_____ speaker used pointing?

From the over all atmosphere this speaker created, I felt that regarding this topic he was

inadequately prepared	1	2	3	4	5	very prepared
lacking in confidence	1	2	3	4	5	very confident
lacking in enthusiasm	1	2	3	4	5	very enthusiastic

Grades: (See criteria listed on page 152).

Note: If the speaker needs special help, do not give him a grade above 2 on the appropriate criterion. This lets the instructor know who needs special help.

(Circle one and record it as the raw score.)	Raw Score		Weight		Weighted Score
Criteria I 1 2 3 4 5 6 7 8 9 10 =	____	X	3	=	____
Criteria II 1 2 3 4 5 6 7 8 9 10 =	____	X	5	=	____
Criteria III 1 2 3 4 5 6 7 8 9 10 =	____	X	1	=	____
			Weighted Sum Grade		☐

Transfer this weighted sum grade to your Exercise 4 Grading Sheet.

Note: Three of these forms are to be used in the class review sessions and five to be used in the workshop sessions.

Your Name ______________________
No. _______ Group ________ Sec. _____

Exercise 4

FEEDBACK FORM

Feedback to Speaker ____________________ No. _______

Note: Become familiar with this checklist before you try to use it. (Check off each item as you hear it.)

Introduction:

_____ gained attention?
_____ focused attention?
_____ built positive rapport?
_____ stated topic clearly?
_____ defined terms?
_____ gave a forecast summary? (Included mention that there will be one part of the presentation showing why there is a need to change and a second part showing a proposal on how to bring about the change? A third optional part may be included showing the benefits of the proposed plan of change.)

Body:

SUBPOINT ONE: showing there is a need for change.

____stated subpoint clearly?
____gave forecast summary of subarguments?

Subargument 1 - forms of support used? (circle)

detailed example | specific instances | background data
analogy | statistics
explanation of logic | authority

____was documentation adequate?
____were summary and transitions used?

Subargument 2 - forms of support used? (circle)

detailed example | specific instances | background data
analogy | statistics
explanation of logic | authority

____was documentation adequate?
____was a running summary of subarguments 1 and 2 used?

Subargument 3 - forms of support used? (circle)

detailed example | specific instances | background data
analogy | statistics
explanation of logic | authority

____was documentation adequate?
____was the entire need argument summarized and concluded?
____was there a smooth transition from the need arguments to the plan?

SUBPOINT TWO: proposed plan of action designed to correct the problems.

____Would the proposal correct the problem mentioned in subargument 1?
____Would the proposal correct the problem mentioned in subargument 2?
____Would the proposal correct the problem mentioned in subargument 3?
____Does the proposal sound feasible?

Conclusion:

_____ summarized subpoints?
_____ restated topic?
_____ drew conclusion for listeners that proposal has been supported and should be adopted?
_____ concluding statement made you reflect over the topic?
_____ speaker used pointing?

From the over all atmosphere this speaker created, I felt that regarding this topic he was

inadequately prepared	1	2	3	4	5	very prepared
lacking in confidence	1	2	3	4	5	very confident
lacking in enthusiasm	1	2	3	4	5	very enthusiastic

Grades: (See criteria listed on page 152).

Note: If the speaker needs special help, do not give him a grade above 2 on the appropriate criterion. This lets the instructor know who needs special help.

(Circle one and record it as the raw score.)	Raw Score		Weight		Weighted Score
Criteria I 1 2 3 4 5 6 7 8 9 10 =	_____	X	3	=	_____
Criteria II 1 2 3 4 5 6 7 8 9 10 =	_____	X	5	=	_____
Criteria III 1 2 3 4 5 6 7 8 9 10 =	_____	X	1	=	_____
			Weighted Sum Grade		☐

Transfer this weighted sum grade to your Exercise 4 Grading Sheet.

Note: Three of these forms are to be used in the class review sessions and five to be used in the workshop sessions.

Your Name ____________________
No.________ Group ________ Sec. ________

Exercise 4

FEEDBACK FORM

Feedback to Speaker ____________________ No. ______

Note: Become familiar with this checklist before you try to use it. (Check off each item as you hear it.)

Introduction:

_____ gained attention?
_____ focused attention?
_____ built positive rapport?
_____ stated topic clearly?
_____ defined terms?
_____ gave a forecast summary? (Included mention that there will be one part of the presentation showing why there is a need to change and a second part showing a proposal on how to bring about the change? A third optional part may be included showing the benefits of the proposed plan of change.)

Body:

SUBPOINT ONE: showing there is a need for change.

____stated subpoint clearly?
____gave forecast summary of subarguments?

Subargument 1 - forms of support used? (circle)

detailed example	specific instances	background data
analogy	statistics	
explanation of logic	authority	

____was documentation adequate?
____were summary and transitions used?

Subargument 2 - forms of support used? (circle)

detailed example	specific instances	background data
analogy	statistics	
explanation of logic	authority	

____was documentation adequate?
____was a running summary of subarguments 1 and 2 used?

Subargument 3 - forms of support used? (circle)

detailed example	specific instances	background data
analogy	statistics	
explanation of logic	authority	

____was documentation adequate?
____was the entire need argument summarized and concluded?
____was there a smooth transition from the need arguments to the plan?

SUBPOINT TWO: proposed plan of action designed to correct the problems.

____Would the proposal correct the problem mentioned in subargument 1?
____Would the proposal correct the problem mentioned in subargument 2?
____Would the proposal correct the problem mentioned in subargument 3?
____Does the proposal sound feasible?

Conclusion:

_____ summarized subpoints?
_____ restated topic?
_____ drew conclusion for listeners that proposal has been supported and should be adopted?
_____ concluding statement made you reflect over the topic?
_____ speaker used pointing?

From the over all atmosphere this speaker created, I felt that regarding this topic he was

inadequately prepared	1	2	3	4	5	very prepared
lacking in confidence	1	2	3	4	5	very confident
lacking in enthusiasm	1	2	3	4	5	very enthusiastic

Grades: (See criteria listed on page 152).

Note: If the speaker needs special help, do not give him a grade above 2 on the appropriate criterion. This lets the instructor know who needs special help.

(Circle one and record it as the raw score.)

		Raw Score		Weight		Weighted Score
Criteria I	1 2 3 4 5 6 7 8 9 10 =	____	X	3	=	____
Criteria II	1 2 3 4 5 6 7 8 9 10 =	____	X	5	=	____
Criteria III	1 2 3 4 5 6 7 8 9 10 =	____	X	1	=	____
				Weighted Sum Grade		☐

Transfer this weighted sum grade to your Exercise 4 Grading Sheet.

Note: Three of these forms are to be used in the class review sessions and five to be used in the workshop sessions.

Your Name ____________________
No. ________ Group ________ Sec. ________

Exercise 4

FEEDBACK FORM

Feedback to Speaker ____________________ No. ______

Note: Become familiar with this checklist before you try to use it. (Check off each item as you hear it.)

Introduction:

_____ gained attention?
_____ focused attention?
_____ built positive rapport?
_____ stated topic clearly?
_____ defined terms?
_____ gave a forecast summary? (Included mention that there will be one part of the presentation showing why there is a need to change and a second part showing a proposal on how to bring about the change? A third optional part may be included showing the benefits of the proposed plan of change.)

Body:

SUBPOINT ONE: showing there is a need for change.

____stated subpoint clearly?
____gave forecast summary of subarguments?

Subargument 1 - forms of support used? (circle)

detailed example	specific instances	background data
analogy	statistics	
explanation of logic	authority	

____was documentation adequate?
____were summary and transitions used?

Subargument 2 - forms of support used? (circle)

detailed example	specific instances	background data
analogy	statistics	
explanation of logic	authority	

____was documentation adequate?
____was a running summary of subarguments 1 and 2 used?

Subargument 3 - forms of support used? (circle)

detailed example	specific instances	background data
analogy	statistics	
explanation of logic	authority	

____was documentation adequate?
____was the entire need argument summarized and concluded?
____was there a smooth transition from the need arguments to the plan?

SUBPOINT TWO: proposed plan of action designed to correct the problems.

____Would the proposal correct the problem mentioned in subargument 1?
____Would the proposal correct the problem mentioned in subargument 2?
____Would the proposal correct the problem mentioned in subargument 3?
____Does the proposal sound feasible?

Conclusion:

_____ summarized subpoints?
_____ restated topic?
_____ drew conclusion for listeners that proposal has been supported and should be adopted?
_____ concluding statement made you reflect over the topic?
_____ speaker used pointing?

From the over all atmosphere this speaker created, I felt that regarding this topic he was

inadequately prepared	1	2	3	4	5	very prepared
lacking in confidence	1	2	3	4	5	very confident
lacking in enthusiasm	1	2	3	4	5	very enthusiastic

Grades: (See criteria listed on page 152).

Note: If the speaker needs special help, do not give him a grade above 2 on the appropriate criterion. This lets the instructor know who needs special help.

(Circle one and record it as the raw score.)	Raw Score		Weight		Weighted Score
Criteria I 1 2 3 4 5 6 7 8 9 10 =	____	X	3	=	____
Criteria II 1 2 3 4 5 6 7 8 9 10 =	____	X	5	=	____
Criteria III 1 2 3 4 5 6 7 8 9 10 =	____	X	1	=	____
			Weighted Sum Grade		☐

Transfer this weighted sum grade to your Exercise 4 Grading Sheet.

Note: Three of these forms are to be used in the class review sessions and five to be used in the workshop sessions.

Your Name ____________________
No.________ Group________ Sec. ______

Exercise 4

FEEDBACK FORM

Feedback to Speaker ____________________ No. _______

Note: Become familiar with this checklist before you try to use it. (Check off each item as you hear it.)

Introduction:

_____ gained attention?
_____ focused attention?
_____ built positive rapport?
_____ stated topic clearly?
_____ defined terms?
_____ gave a forecast summary? (Included mention that there will be one part of the presentation showing why there is a need to change and a second part showing a proposal on how to bring about the change? A third optional part may be included showing the benefits of the proposed plan of change.)

Body:

SUBPOINT ONE: showing there is a need for change.

____stated subpoint clearly?
____gave forecast summary of subarguments?

Subargument 1 - forms of support used? (circle)

detailed example	specific instances	background data
analogy	statistics	
explanation of logic	authority	

____was documentation adequate?
____were summary and transitions used?

Subargument 2 - forms of support used? (circle)

detailed example	specific instances	background data
analogy	statistics	
explanation of logic	authority	

____was documentation adequate?
____was a running summary of subarguments 1 and 2 used?

Subargument 3 - forms of support used? (circle)

detailed example	specific instances	background data
analogy	statistics	
explanation of logic	authority	

____was documentation adequate?
____was the entire need argument summarized and concluded?
____was there a smooth transition from the need arguments to the plan?

SUBPOINT TWO: proposed plan of action designed to correct the problems.

____Would the proposal correct the problem mentioned in subargument 1?
____Would the proposal correct the problem mentioned in subargument 2?
____Would the proposal correct the problem mentioned in subargument 3?
____Does the proposal sound feasible?

Conclusion:

_____ summarized subpoints?
_____ restated topic?
_____ drew conclusion for listeners that proposal has been supported and should be adopted?
_____ concluding statement made you reflect over the topic?
_____ speaker used pointing?

From the over all atmosphere this speaker created, I felt that regarding this topic he was

inadequately prepared	1	2	3	4	5	very prepared
lacking in confidence	1	2	3	4	5	very confident
lacking in enthusiasm	1	2	3	4	5	very enthusiastic

Grades: (See criteria listed on page 152).

Note: If the speaker needs special help, do not give him a grade above 2 on the appropriate criterion. This lets the instructor know who needs special help.

(Circle one and record it as the raw score.)		Raw Score		Weight		Weighted Score
Criteria I	1 2 3 4 5 6 7 8 9 10 =	____	X	3	=	____
Criteria II	1 2 3 4 5 6 7 8 9 10 =	____	X	5	=	____
Criteria III	1 2 3 4 5 6 7 8 9 10 =	____	X	1	=	____

Weighted Sum Grade ☐

Transfer this weighted sum grade to your Exercise 4 Grading Sheet.

Note: Three of these forms are to be used in the class review sessions and five to be used in the workshop sessions.

Your Name ____________________________
No. ________ Group ________ Sec. ________

Exercise 4

FEEDBACK FORM

Feedback to Speaker ______________________ No. _______

Note: Become familiar with this checklist before you try to use it. (Check off each item as you hear it.)

Introduction:

_____ gained attention?
_____ focused attention?
_____ built positive rapport?
_____ stated topic clearly?
_____ defined terms?
_____ gave a forecast summary? (Included mention that there will be one part of the presentation showing why there is a need to change and a second part showing a proposal on how to bring about the change? A third optional part may be included showing the benefits of the proposed plan of change.)

Body:

SUBPOINT ONE: showing there is a need for change.

____stated subpoint clearly?
____gave forecast summary of subarguments?

Subargument 1 - forms of support used? (circle)

detailed example | specific instances | background data
analogy | statistics
explanation of logic | authority

____was documentation adequate?
____were summary and transitions used?

Subargument 2 - forms of support used? (circle)

detailed example | specific instances | background data
analogy | statistics
explanation of logic | authority

____was documentation adequate?
____was a running summary of subarguments 1 and 2 used?

Subargument 3 - forms of support used? (circle)

detailed example | specific instances | background data
analogy | statistics
explanation of logic | authority

____was documentation adequate?
____was the entire need argument summarized and concluded?
____was there a smooth transition from the need arguments to the plan?

SUBPOINT TWO: proposed plan of action designed to correct the problems.

____Would the proposal correct the problem mentioned in subargument 1?
____Would the proposal correct the problem mentioned in subargument 2?
____Would the proposal correct the problem mentioned in subargument 3?
____Does the proposal sound feasible?

Conclusion:

_____ summarized subpoints?
_____ restated topic?
_____ drew conclusion for listeners that proposal has been supported and should be adopted?
_____ concluding statement made you reflect over the topic?
_____ speaker used pointing?

From the over all atmosphere this speaker created, I felt that regarding this topic he was

inadequately prepared	1	2	3	4	5	very prepared
lacking in confidence	1	2	3	4	5	very confident
lacking in enthusiasm	1	2	3	4	5	very enthusiastic

Grades: (See criteria listed on page 152).

Note: If the speaker needs special help, do not give him a grade above 2 on the appropriate criterion. This lets the instructor know who needs special help.

(Circle one and record it as the raw score.)	Raw Score		Weight		Weighted Score
Criteria I 1 2 3 4 5 6 7 8 9 10 =	_____	X	3	=	_____
Criteria II 1 2 3 4 5 6 7 8 9 10 =	_____	X	5	=	_____
Criteria III 1 2 3 4 5 6 7 8 9 10 =	_____	X	1	=	_____

Weighted Sum Grade ☐

Transfer this weighted sum grade to your Exercise 4 Grading Sheet.

Note: Three of these forms are to be used in the class review sessions and five to be used in the workshop sessions.

Your Name ____________________
No.________ Group __________ Sec.______

Exercise 4

EVALUATOR'S FEEDBACK FROM SPEAKER

Feedback to Evaluator ______________________ No. _______

Instructions: On this form rate each evaluator regarding how much his or her feedback will help you improve your next presentation. Fill out the rating and ranking section of this form as soon as you finish receiving the feedback. Later you may add comments and transfer the ratings and rankings to your Exercise 4 Grading Sheet. Give that sheet to your group coordinator. Give this form to the student being rated.

	Circle One
The comments were specific rather than general.	+ √ −
The feedback was constructive and contained suggestions on how to improve.	+ √ −
He/she had a good feel of what creates a proper atmosphere.	+ √ −
He/she displayed a good understanding of how this presentation was to be organized.	+ √ −
He/she displayed familiarity with research on this topic.	+ √ −

(Circle One)

Rating: 1 = exceptional, 2 = excellent, 3 = good, 4 = fair, 5 = poor.

Ranking: 1st, 2nd, and 3rd, with no ties permitted. All others are ranked 4th.

Record the student rating and ranking on the Exercise 4 Grading Form.

If you feel a student's feedback was very poor, give him a total of 10. This will indicate to the instructor that this student needs special help.

Make comments on how the feedback could be improved:

____

____

____

____

____

____

Your Name ____________________
No.________ Group ________ Sec. ________

Exercise 4

EVALUATOR'S FEEDBACK FROM SPEAKER

Feedback to Evaluator ____________________ No. _______

Instructions: On this form rate each evaluator regarding how much his or her feedback will help you improve your next presentation. Fill out the rating and ranking section of this form as soon as you finish receiving the feedback. Later you may add comments and transfer the ratings and rankings to your Exercise 4 Grading Sheet. Give that sheet to your group coordinator. Give this form to the student being rated.

	Circle One
The comments were specific rather than general.	+ √ −
The feedback was constructive and contained suggestions on how to improve.	+ √ −
He/she had a good feel of what creates a proper atmosphere.	+ √ −
He/she displayed a good understanding of how this presentation was to be organized.	+ √ −
He/she displayed familiarity with research on this topic.	+ √ −

(Circle One)

Rating: 1 = exceptional, 2 = excellent, 3 = good, 4 = fair, 5 = poor.

Ranking: 1st, 2nd, and 3rd, with no ties permitted. All others are ranked 4th.

Record the student rating and ranking on the Exercise 4 Grading Form.

If you feel a student's feedback was very poor, give him a total of 10. This will indicate to the instructor that this student needs special help.

Make comments on how the feedback could be improved:

____

____

____

____

____

____

Your Name ______________________

No.________ Group________ Sec.________

Exercise 4

EVALUATOR'S FEEDBACK FROM SPEAKER

Feedback to Evaluator ______________________ No. ________

Instructions: On this form rate each evaluator regarding how much his or her feedback will help you improve your next presentation. Fill out the rating and ranking section of this form as soon as you finish receiving the feedback. Later you may add comments and transfer the ratings and rankings to your Exercise 4 Grading Sheet. Give that sheet to your group coordinator. Give this form to the student being rated.

	Circle One
The comments were specific rather than general.	+ √ –
The feedback was constructive and contained suggestions on how to improve.	+ √ –
He/she had a good feel of what creates a proper atmosphere.	+ √ –
He/she displayed a good understanding of how this presentation was to be organized.	+ √ –
He/she displayed familiarity with research on this topic.	+ √ –

(Circle One)

Rating: 1 = exceptional, 2 = excellent, 3 = good, 4 = fair, 5 = poor.

Ranking: 1st, 2nd, and 3rd, with no ties permitted. All others are ranked 4th.

Record the student rating and ranking on the Exercise 4 Grading Form.

If you feel a student's feedback was very poor, give him a total of 10. This will indicate to the instructor that this student needs special help.

Make comments on how the feedback could be improved:

____

____

____

____

____

____

Your Name ______________________
No.________ Group________ Sec.________

Exercise 4

EVALUATOR'S FEEDBACK FROM SPEAKER

Feedback to Evaluator ____________________ No. _______

Instructions: On this form rate each evaluator regarding how much his or her feedback will help you improve your next presentation. Fill out the rating and ranking section of this form as soon as you finish receiving the feedback. Later you may add comments and transfer the ratings and rankings to your Exercise 4 Grading Sheet. Give that sheet to your group coordinator. Give this form to the student being rated.

	Circle One
The comments were specific rather than general.	+ √ –
The feedback was constructive and contained suggestions on how to improve.	+ √ –
He/she had a good feel of what creates a proper atmosphere.	+ √ –
He/she displayed a good understanding of how this presentation was to be organized.	+ √ –
He/she displayed familiarity with research on this topic.	+ √ –

(Circle One)

Rating: 1 = exceptional, 2 = excellent, 3 = good, 4 = fair, 5 = poor.

Ranking: 1st, 2nd, and 3rd, with no ties permitted. All others are ranked 4th.

Record the student rating and ranking on the Exercise 4 Grading Form.

If you feel a student's feedback was very poor, give him a total of 10. This will indicate to the instructor that this student needs special help.

Make comments on how the feedback could be improved:

____

____

____

____

____

____

Your Name ____________________
No. ________ Group ________ Sec. ________

Exercise 4

EVALUATOR'S FEEDBACK FROM SPEAKER

Feedback to Evaluator ____________________ No. ________

Instructions: On this form rate each evaluator regarding how much his or her feedback will help you improve your next presentation. Fill out the rating and ranking section of this form as soon as you finish receiving the feedback. Later you may add comments and transfer the ratings and rankings to your Exercise 4 Grading Sheet. Give that sheet to your group coordinator. Give this form to the student being rated.

	Circle One
The comments were specific rather than general.	+ √ –
The feedback was constructive and contained suggestions on how to improve.	+ √ –
He/she had a good feel of what creates a proper atmosphere.	+ √ –
He/she displayed a good understanding of how this presentation was to be organized.	+ √ –
He/she displayed familiarity with research on this topic.	+ √ –

(Circle One)

Rating: 1 = exceptional, 2 = excellent, 3 = good, 4 = fair, 5 = poor.

Ranking: 1st, 2nd, and 3rd, with no ties permitted. All others are ranked 4th.

Record the student rating and ranking on the Exercise 4 Grading Form.

If you feel a student's feedback was very poor, give him a total of 10. This will indicate to the instructor that this student needs special help.

Make comments on how the feedback could be improved:

____

____

____

____

____

____

Your Name ______________________
No. ________ Group ________ Sec. ________

Exercise 4

GRADING SHEET

Grades you gave for presentations

Note: Weighted grade below 6 on Criterion I and below 10 on Criterion II are to be given to students whom you feel need special help.

No.	Speaker Name	Weighted Grades on Criteria				Weighted Sum Grade
____	____________	I ____	II ____	III ________	=	☐
____	____________	I ____	II ____	III ________	=	☐
____	____________	I ____	II ____	III ________	=	☐
____	____________	I ____	II ____	III ________	=	☐
____	____________	I ____	II ____	III ________	=	☐
____	____________	I ____	II ____	III ________	=	☐
	Total	____	____	________		____
	÷ by	____ number of speakers				
	= the average grade you gave	____	____	________		____

Grades you gave on feedback

Note: Give a total grade of 10 to students whom you feel need special help in their ability to give feedback. This lets the instructor know who needs help.

No.	Student Name	rating	+	ranking	=	Total
____	____________________	____	+	____	=	☐
____	____________________	____	+	____	=	☐
____	____________________	____	+	____	=	☐
____	____________________	____	+	____	=	☐
____	____________________	____	+	____	=	☐
____	____________________	____	+	____	=	☐
				Total		____

÷ by______ number of students
= the average grade
you gave ____

Complete this sheet and give it to your group coordinator. He will record these grades on the Group Coordinator's Grade Summary Sheets and return this form to you.

Coordinator's Name ____________________
No. ________ Group ________ Sec. ________

Exercise 4

GROUP COORDINATOR'S GRADE SUMMARY SHEET

	Student No.	____	____	____	____	____	____	____
Rater No.	Weighted sum grades.							
____		____	____	____	____	____	____	____
____		____	____	____	____	____	____	____
____		____	____	____	____	____	____	____
____		____	____	____	____	____	____	____
____		____	____	____	____	____	____	____
____		____	____	____	____	____	____	____
____		____	____	____	____	____	____	____
Sum		____	____	____	____	____	____	____
÷ by		____	____	____	____	____	____	____
= Average Grade		☐	☐	☐	☐	☐	☐	☐

Insert in the blanks the sum of the student's rating and ranking from the Grading Sheets filled out by each of the students in your group.

Fill out this Group Coordinator's Grade Summary Sheet. Then record each student's average grade on the Class Grade Summary Sheet. Use the column headed Exercise 4 Speaker Grade. Then give this sheet to your instructor. Return to the group members their Grading Sheets.

List below the names of any students who received two or more weighted grades of 6 or below on Criterion I, or who received two or more weighted grades of 10 or below on Criterion II, as recorded on the Grading Sheets.

Name ______________________________ No. ________

Name ______________________________ No. ________

Name ______________________________ No. ________

Coordinator's Name ____________________
No.________ Group________ Sec.________

Exercise 4

GROUP COORDINATOR'S FEEDBACK GRADE SUMMARY SHEET

	Student No.	____	____	____	____	____	____	____
Evaluation by: Number	Rating and Ranking Total Scores							
____		____	____	____	____	____	____	____
____		____	____	____	____	____	____	____
____		____	____	____	____	____	____	____
____		____	____	____	____	____	____	____
____		____	____	____	____	____	____	____
____		____	____	____	____	____	____	____
____		____	____	____	____	____	____	____
Sum		____	____	____	____	____	____	____
÷ by		____	____	____	____	____	____	____
= average grade		☐	☐	☐	☐	☐	☐	☐

Insert in the blanks the sum of the student's ratings and rankings. These grades are recorded on the bottom half of the Grading Sheet of each student.

After you fill out this Grade Summary Sheet, record the student's average grade on the Class Grade Summary Sheet. Use the column headed Exercise 4 Feedback Grade. Then give this form to your instructor. Return the Speaker's Feedback Grading Sheets to your group members.

List below the names of students who received 2 or more scores of 10.

Name ________________________________ No. ______

Name ________________________________ No. ______

List below the names of any students who were absent for all or part of any group session.

Name ________________________________ No. ______

Name ________________________________ No. ______

Your Name________________________
No.________ Group________ Sec.________

Exercise 4

STUDENT'S GRADE RECORD SHEET

Use this form to make a record of all of your Exercise 4 grades.

Grade received on speaking

From No.		Criteria Weighted Grade			Weighted Sum Grade
______	I ______	II ______	III _____	=	______
______	I ______	II ______	III _____	=	______
______	I ______	II ______	III _____	=	______
______	I ______	II ______	III _____	=	______
______	I ______	II ______	III _____	=	______
______	I ______	II ______	III _____	=	______
Total	______	______	_____		______
÷ by number of grade	______	______	_____		______
= your average grade	______	______	_____		☐ = Weighted Sum Grade Average

---

Grades received on feedback

From No.	rating	+	ranking	=	
______	______	+	______	=	______
______	______	+	______	=	______
______	______	+	______	=	______
______	______	+	______	=	______
______	______	+	______	=	______
______	______	+	______	=	______
Total	______		______		______
÷ by Number of grade	______		______		______
= your average grade	______		______		☐ = Sum Grade Average

EXERCISE 5

Studying Counter Proposals

PURPOSE OF ASSIGNMENT

The purpose of this exercise is to force you to challenge your reasoning and evidence before you present a proposal. Only after you are completely familiar with the counterarguments and evidence can you be confident that your own position is correct. As a secondary part of this exercise, the use of headings will be reviewed.

Introduction

For Exercise 5, you will reverse your point of reference regarding the class topic. In your earlier exercises, you have collected evidence to show why there is a need to change the present system and you have devised various plans by which such a change could be brought about. In Exercise 4, you included some discussion of the validity of arguments and plans, but even there the main point of reference was focused on finding materials, ideas, and plans to support the class proposal. For Exercise 5, you are going to completely reverse that point of reference. You are now going to attempt to find enough evidence, ideas, and documentation to completely refute everything that you have advocated in Exercises 2, 3, and 4.

For many students, this will be one of the most unusual and valuable exercises in the entire course. It is designed to create in you a healthy skepticism regarding the validity of your present beliefs. Very seldom are we asked to seek evidence to refute what we already believe and accept. Often, we must listen to others attack our beliefs, but the arguments of others are easily ignored or dismissed. When you collect the counter-evidence and construct the arguments refuting your own previously accepted beliefs, these arguments are not so easily dismissed. It is often disrupting for novices to discover how easy it is to find evidence contrary to their cherished beliefs. Perhaps it is so disrupting because we are not normally asked to refute our own biases. Scientists rarely actively seek evidence to disprove their own theories. Businessmen seeking financing do not usually seek evidence to present to the bank showing that they are a financial risk. Republicans tend to avoid reading pro-Democrat magazines, and vice versa. As is pointed out in Chapter Three, it is simply human nature to seek information that supports what we already believe. The universality of such behavior is described in numerous books and articles under such titles as prejudice, cognitive dissonance, congruity theory, and rationalization.

WHY STUDY COUNTERARGUMENTS

There are two dangers you face by avoiding or dismissing information contrary to your beliefs. First, you run the risk of holding false beliefs. If you avoid or refuse to evaluate new information, you are likely to maintain old beliefs even if they are not in your best interest. Such behavior is, in effect, a refusal to accept information that is in conflict with your current beliefs. It causes the freezing of beliefs and, thus, the freezing of behavior to patterns which were appropriate at some time in the past. Once they are frozen you cannot tell whether those behaviors are still appropriate or not because you will avoid receiving or considering any new negative information. Such freezing of beliefs is potentially harmful, because it does not permit you to adapt to changes in your environment or culture. On the assumption that it is stupid to do things that we know are potentially harmful to us, this behavior can be considered a sign of stupidity. (This definition of stupidity is discussed in more detail in Chapter Two of Part II in this book.)

There is a second danger of not examining counterevidence and arguments. Our old beliefs or behaviors may be correct, but because we do not fully understand the arguments against them, we are not capable of properly defending our beliefs. If you refuse to study these counterarguments, you cannot hope to understand why people object to your arguments or beliefs. This is the point with which we are most concerned in this exercise. To fully refute another person's arguments, you must fully understand why they believe as they do and what evidence is available to support their beliefs. If you are proposing that a bank lend you money, you had better know what possible objections they might have to financing your business. Only when you know what their objections are and what evidence they are basing them on are you in a position to prepare to overcome those objections.

Researching Counterarguments

The research for this paper is probably already half done. Think back over the material you read in search of evidence to support arguments favoring the topic. It is likely that you dismissed some good counterarguments because they did not support what you were trying to prove at that time. Often, one can find material opposing an argument in the same article that was used to document the case supporting it. You must be careful not to reject arguments and evidence simply because you do not agree with them. At this point, you are not asked to believe or disbelieve the arguments. Your task is simply to gather counterevidence. Until all of that evidence has been collected and analyzed, it would be premature for you to make any *final decision* to believe or disbelieve any of the arguments pro or con.

To do research on controversial issues often requires that you close your minds, temporarily, so that you can focus your attention on a single task and avoid distraction. For example, if you are to find evidence to refute a no-fault auto insurance proposal, you may wish to first forget about no-fault. You should just study all of the positive aspects of the present insurance system. After all of that knowledge has been analyzed and digested, you will be in a much better position to see the strengths and weaknesses of no-fault than you would have been if you had first cluttered your mind with all sorts of proposals. You must understand the thing you wish to change before you can intelligently propose how to change it.

Positive Approach

Your paper should be written from a positive point of view. It should stress the positive characteristics of the present system. It should not be a defensive paper. To illustrate this, let us again use the no-fault auto insurance example from Exercise 3. The topic is, "The state should adopt a no-fault auto insurance program." You may wish to state the topic in similar form and then say you oppose it. Or you may reword it to state, "The state should *not* adopt a no-fault auto insurance policy." Regardless of how you state the proposition, your arguments should be designed primarily to support the present system rather than to defend it from attack.

There are several positive ways of developing arguments. For example, let us look at how we could reword the first subargument that was used in the example in Exercise 3 (see page 86). Its original wording was, "It (no-fault) would enable accident victims to receive compensation more rapidly." To take a positive approach, we could point out how rapidly most claims are now paid. We might add that only a small percentage are ever delayed and those are delayed for good reason. That reason might be that it is often important to find out who was at fault in the accident so that the guilty, rather than the innocent victim or the public, must pay. We could also point out the danger of a change. We could show that abolishing the fault system would make some people less concerned about their driving record and thus more danger-our to all of us. Positive arguments such as these are much more likely to impress the audience than are defensive statements. You need to offer positive reasons for keeping the present system.

There is another important reason for preparing positive arguments. What if the opponents' arguments are superficial? If you are prepared only to contradict what the opponents say and their presentation is ill-prepared and deals only with superficial issues, then your counterarguments will of necessity also be superficial. Those hearing the presentation are likely to lower their opinion of both the opposition and you. It is important in business meetings that you be prepared to support your position with strong positive arguments if only to maintain your good reputation. If you prepare your arguments with a positive approach, you do not have to worry about the other person's poor performance making you look bad. If you write your Exercise 5 papers with a positive approach, the paper will be convincing and impressive even to a person who has never read any pro arguments on the subject.

PREASSIGNMENT INSTRUCTIONS

Step 1. Read your Exercise 3 paper. Examine each argument advocating a need for a change from the present system to a new system. Check each argument to make sure it shows an inherent need for making the change advocated in the class topic. If the basic argument is good, then outline the evidence you used to support it.

Step 2. Make a list of all of the acceptable arguments you used in Exercises 3 and 4. If all of your arguments in Exercises 3 and 4 are acceptable, these are the arguments you are to refute in the Exercise 5 paper. However, if one of your arguments is superficial or off target, use a substitute argument to refute in your Exercise 5 paper. The simplest way to find a substitute argument is to borrow one from a friend's paper. If you need to use a substitute argument, select it at this time so you will have it available as you begin researching counterevidence. Add the substitute argument to your list of arguments and outline the evidence used to support it.

Step 3. Look up every source used as evidence to support each Exercise 3 and 4 argument. Examine these sources carefully for evidence of weakness. Some of the main things to check for are the following:

1. Who wrote the material? What are his or her qualifications and/or biases?
2. When was the material written? Is it current or out of date?
3. If a research study is referred to, who did the research, who paid for the research, when was the research actually done, and how valid was the research study?
4. Could other conclusions be drawn from the same evidence?
5. Is the quoted material used out of context?

Step 4. Carefully review the proposed plan of change that you used in Exercise 4. Check the plan to determine the following:

1. Does it eliminate or significantly reduce the problems mentioned in the need for change arguments? If it does not, either the arguments or the plan can be attacked as irrelevant.
2. Does it cause any additional undesirable side effects such as an increased tax burden or violations of constitutional rights? If so, the plan can be rejected.

Step 5. Seek other sources of counterevidence and counterarguments until all of the arguments you used in Exercises 3 and 4 can be refuted or at least neutralized.

Step 6. Now temporarily forget about the Exercise 3 and 4 arguments, and start gathering material to show the benefits of the present system. This preassignment analysis should reveal weaknesses in your Exercise 3 and 4 arguments and should greatly simplify the task of refuting them.

SOME MORE BASICS

As written manuscripts become longer, there is an increasing need that the parts of the manuscript be separated and identified by headings. In Exercise 5, headings are required to guide our reading. Since this paper is refuting an earlier paper, the readers are going to have to keep referring back and forth from one paper to the other. Headings will enable all of us, in the role of readers, to do this more rapidly.

How to Use Headings

There are no set rules for using headings. The style used varies from journal to journal and book to book. Printed material has many more heading options available to use than does a typed manuscript. Printers can use various styles and sizes of type to set things off.

The most important rule you should follow in using headings is to be consistent throughout your paper. The rest is mostly common sense. More important sections should have bigger and bolder headings than are used for the subsections.

The devices that make a heading stand out are the following:

1. Blank lines above and below
2. Centering on an otherwise blank line
3. Use of capital letters
4. Use of an underline
5. Beginning to the left or right of the normal margin

Any combination of these might be used for a system of headings. Figure 5-1 illustrates headings of decreasing boldness. There are no set rules on how to use headings for Exercise 5. Each of you must design your own system of headings to suit your own needs. For example, refer to the textbooks, journals, and typed manuscripts such as dissertations.

FIGURE 5-1 Sample Headings

MAIN HEADING
(start on new page)

LEVEL I HEADING
(leave at least 4* spaces above and several below)

LEVEL II HEADING
(leave at least 3* spaces above and one below)

Level III Heading
(leave at least 3* spaces above and one below)

Level IV Heading
(leave at least 3* spaces above. Start paragraph on same line.)

Another type of heading that will be useful in your Exercise 5 papers is a number followed by a period: "1". Numbers may be used in your paper to identify the various subarguments. For example, you might write, There are three major arguments showing why we must change. They are as follows:

1.
2.
3.

Such headings help the reader to find various parts of a paper.

*This assumes that a paper is typed double-spaced. For single-spaced papers, reduce these values by half.

ASSIGNMENT INSTRUCTIONS

Write a paper showing the strengths of the system that was challenged by the class proposal. In this paper, refute all of the need for change arguments you used in Exercises 3 and 4, and refute the plan you used in Exercise 4. Make an original and 12* copies of the Exercise 5 paper.

Attach to the back of each copy of your Exercise 5 paper a copy of your Exercise 3 paper. Either paper clip or staple the two papers together. You may use substitute arguments to replace weak or inappropriate arguments from your Exercise 3 paper. If you do so, be sure to include in your Exercise 5 paper a note stating which subargument from Exercise 3 you are omitting, and give the exact wording of the substitute argument.

Paper Size

The paper for Exercise 5, including references, is to be no longer than 4½ nor shorter than 3½ pages in length. It is to be typed single-spaced on 8½″ X 11″ paper. All pages are to have 1¼″ margins at the top and 1″ margins on the sides and bottom.

Paper Heading

In the upper right-hand corner of the margin of the first page, type your name and class number. Directly below, type "Evaluator No._______." Below that, type "Copy No.______." Then number the copies from 1 to 12*.

In the center of the paper, 1¼″ below the top, write "Exercise 5" and then the semester and year, skip two spaces, and type your paper title (see Figure 5-2). Your paper is also to contain headings identifying the various subsections of the paper. No specific format for headings is required.

FIGURE 5-2 Exercise 5 Paper Heading Sample

John Doe No. 25
Evaluator No. ______
Copy No. ______

Exercise 5, Fall 19--

(Title)

Paper References and Bibliography

This exercise requires a minimum of eight references to be footnoted in the paper. The style for references is to be the same as that described for Exercise 3 (see page 97).

Forms of Support

Each counterargument must contain at least one form of support designed primarily to inform or arouse and one form of support designed primarily to convince. If more information regarding forms of support is needed, refer to the descriptions in Exercise 3.

*This number may be modified by your instructor.

Passing Out Papers

On the day Exercise 5 is due, bring to class the original and 12* copies of your paper. If for some reason you cannot make it to class on that day, please arrange for someone else to pass out your papers and collect the papers you are to grade.

Use the Exercise 5 Paper Number Record Form (page 199) to list the numbers of the persons who are to receive each of the copies of your paper and also to list the numbers of all of the papers you are to receive for grading.

The "0" copy of your paper will be collected for the instructor's records. Copies 1-12 will be passed out to classmates for them to study, evaluate, and grade. A copy of your Exercise 3 paper must be attached to the back of copies 1-12 of your Exercise 5 papers.

Evaluation and Grading of Papers

You will receive 12 of your classmates' papers. These are excellent sources of ideas and references on the class topic. Read these papers to learn as well as to evaluate. For the first six papers (copies 1-6), completely fill out the Feedback Form (page 201) with written evaluations and suggestions. For papers 7-12*, fill out only the checklist and grading section of the Feedback Form.

For papers numbered 1-6, it is important that you write very detailed analytical comments to the authors. These comments are to be an analysis of the paper, not judgmental statements. Judgmental statements are comments such as "very good" or "you did an excellent job of developing this issue." This type of comment should be avoided. It tells the author only that you have favorably judged his work; it does not tell him why you judged it that way.

The type of analytical comments we are seeking are those that give the author specific information about how adequately he dealt with the counterarguments and issues. An appropriate comment might be as follows:

> The date of the statistics in your counterargument on page 3, line 10, was 1971. That is five years earlier than the statistics in your Exercise 3 paper. You cannot refute 1976 data with 1971 data. However, even 1976 data may be too old since in 1978 our state did adopt a type of no-fault insurance. There is an excellent article on this new law in the *Herald Examiner* of Feb. 3, 1978.

Such a comment not only tells the author what is wrong with his argument, but it also tells him where he might go to get information to correct the shortcoming. Remember, when you are an evaluator, the authors will be giving you feedback and a grade on how helpful your feedback was to them. Keep in mind that the reason we give feedback is to help each other improve, not to judge each other.

---

*This number may be modified by your instructor.

*Grading of papers 7-12 may be omitted at the option of the instructor. This reduction is recommended for less advanced or short courses.

There are three general criteria to use in grading these papers:

Criterion I. Presentation of paper. Consider under Criterion I neatness, spelling, grammar, layout on page, readability of sentences, or any other factors which affect your response to a paper apart from the organization or content of the message.

Criterion II. Organization of paper. Consider under Criterion II how accurately the author conformed to the exact layout specified for this paper. Use the checklists on the Feedback Form as a guide to show whether or not the author included all that he was supposed to in the layout of this paper. Be careful to check that each argument in the Exercise 3 paper (or its substitute) was refuted in this paper.

Criterion III. Content of paper. Consider under Criterion III the logic of the author's counterarguments and the adequacy of the material used to support them. Note that this criterion is weighted heavier now than it was for earlier assignments. This is the most important criterion to consider while grading Exercise 5 papers.

Some Grading Guides. In Exercise 1, the writers could use any form of organization they desired. The main concern in grading these papers was to see if the students could, in an unstructured situation, turn in a paper of acceptable quality. In grading the Exercise 5 papers, it should be assumed that the students, as a minimum, will have presentable papers. That is, they will be neat, the spelling will be correct, the punctuation and grammar will be acceptable, and the correct size paper will be used. These are all technical skills that the authors should correct or at least, have someone else correct. If any of these mechanical problems are noticed on a paper, be sure to call them to the author's attention on the Feedback Form.

Exercises 3 and 4 focused on organization of material. This is also important to Exercise 5, even though it is not the primary focus of this exercise. It is assumed that all Exercise 5 papers will be properly organized and will use adequate and appropriate forms of support. If the organization is faulty, call this to the author's attention.

The main focus for grading Exercise 5 is to be on the content of the paper. For a paper to be effective, it must be presentable and well organized. These qualities make it readable, but a readable paper must also have some content worth reading. For Exercise 5, pay special attention to the logic of the arguments and to the adequacy of the forms of support used. Be especially careful to watch for unsupported assumptions. Note that Criterion III has a weight of 6 for this paper. The meaning of number grades is shown in Figure 5-3 by comparing them to letter grades and percentile ranks.

FIGURE 5-3 Meaning of Number Grades

	14%			55%		20%	10%	1%
	F	D	C–	C	C+	B	A	A+
1	2	3	4	5	6	7 8	9	10
poor				OK		good	excellent	perfect

Recording of Grades

1. When all papers have been graded, record the grades on the Exercise 5 Grading Form (page 227). This form is to be given to the instructor on the day the graded papers are returned to the authors.
2. When your Exercise 5 papers are returned to you, record your grades on your Exercise 5 Author's Grade Record Form (page 229). Use this form to compute your Exercise 5 Sum Grade Average.

3. Your Author's Grade Record Form is to be completed and given to the instructor no later than one class period after you have received your graded papers. Before turning in your Author's Grade Record Form, record your Sum Grade Average on the Class Grade Summary Sheet.

4. If you have two or more unweighted ratings of 2 or below on any one of the three criteria, take your Author's Grade Record Form and your set of Exercise 5 papers to the instructor no later than one class period after you have received your graded papers. The instructor will determine what you must do before you will be permitted to go on to Exercise 7. Until you receive clearance from the instructor, you will not be permitted to do Exercise 7.

Grading of the Feedback

The second-level feedback for Exercise 5 will be written on the Grader Quality Report (page 231). It is similar to the one used for Exercise 3. As soon as your graded papers are returned, read the comments on copies 1-6. Then grade the evaluators on the helpfulness and quality of the comments written to you on the Feedback Forms and on your papers. Grade each of the six evaluators using Categories A, B, and C of the Grader Quality Report. Evaluators who grade papers 7-12 are only to fill out the checklist on the Feedback Form; therefore, you are to grade those students only on Category A of the Grader Quality Report. The form for grading feedback, Grader Quality Report, is the same as that used in Exercise 3. You may refer to page 100 for more detailed instructions on how to use the form.

EXERCISE 5 CHECKLISTS

Check Your Own Paper First

Before duplicating the Exercise 5 paper, you should check your own work first for the following:

1. Spelling
2. Punctuation
3. Grammar
4. Neatness
5. Margins

If you are not sure of any of these items, ask a friend to proof your paper.

6. Read the three yes-no questions at the top of the Feedback Form. They are as follows: Remember, just one "no" means your paper must be redone.
   (a) Does this paper contain at least eight references?
   (b) Is this paper between 3½ and 4½ pages in length?
   (c) Is each section of this paper identified by a heading?
7. Check each item on the Feedback Form and grade your own paper. If you would give the paper any minuses, redo that part of the paper.
8. Check your paper for readability. Have you used complete sentences that are not too long? Is the meaning clear? Are any sentences awkward?

FINAL CHECKLIST

Checklist of things to do for Exercise 5.

1. Make a list of the arguments and the plan used in Exercise 3 and 4.
2. Write your paper countering these arguments.
3. Use the checklist on this page to check your own work before turning it in.
4. Papers are due for in-class review (date) _____/_____/_____

   Bring to class one copy of your paper.
5. Papers are due for distribution (date) _____/_____/_____

   Bring to class copies 0-12* of your paper.

   Bring to class your Paper Number Record Form (page 199).
6. Graded papers are to be returned (date)

   Bring to class the graded papers.

   Bring to class to turn in your Exercise 5 Grading Form (page 227).
7. Record all grades you received on your Author's Grade Record Form (page 229) and compute your Sum Grade Average.
8. Complete the Grader Quality Report (page 231).
9. Record by (date)________________.

   Your Sum Grade Average on the Class Grade Summary Sheet.

   The Grader Quality scores on the Grader Quality Master Chart.**

---

*This number may be modified by your instructor.

**Your class may or may not be using the Grader Quality Master Chart.

Your Name ____________________
No. ______ Group ______ Sec. ______

Exercise 5

PAPER NUMBER RECORD FORM

My papers are to be passed out to:

Paper No.	Student No.	Check When Returned Graded
1	______	______
2	______	______
3	______	______
4	______	______
5	______	______
6	______	______
7	______	______
8	______	______
9	______	______
10	______	______
11	______	______
12	______	______
	______	______
	______	______
	______	______

I am to receive papers from:

Paper No.	Student No.
______	______
______	______
______	______
______	______
______	______
______	______
______	______
______	______
______	______
______	______
______	______
______	______
______	______
______	______
______	______

Papers from the following students were not returned graded:

Copy No.	Student No.
______	______
______	______
______	______

Check with these students. If you still do not find your paper, report the loss to the instructor.

I should have but did not receive papers from:

Copy No.	Student No.
______	______
______	______
______	______

Please report to your instructor if any papers are not received in time to be graded.

Before distributing your paper, record on each the class number of the student who is to receive and evaluate that paper. For example, if student 25 is to receive your copy No. 2 paper, write:

Evaluator No. __25__
Copy No. __2__

Your Name ____________________
No. ________ Group ________ Sec. ________

EXERCISE 5: Feedback Form to Author

Yes No Does this paper contain at least 3 references?
Yes No Is this paper between 3½ and 4½ pages in length?
Yes No Is each section of this paper identified by a heading?

If the answer to any of the above questions is no, the paper is unacceptable, and must be redone. Give the paper a grade of 1 on Criterion II. However, finish evaluating this paper and give it a grade.

\+ √ – Does the introduction gain and focus your attention?
\+ √ – Is there anything in this paper to build rapport?
\+ √ – Is this paper organized so that it is easy to follow–to identify the subsections?
If √ or - is circled above, explain how to correct the shortcoming.

____
____
____
____
(Write additional comments on paper)

Arguments showing a need for change.

Subargument one: Read the Assignment 3 paper. Write the first subargument in that paper on the line below: (*If a substitute argument is used to replace this argument, write the substitute argument here.*) ____________________

____
____
____

Read the first counterargument. Write it down: ____________________

____
____

Do these two arguments match? Yes ______ No ______

Which of the following forms of support are used to back the counter argument?

detailed examples background data specific instances analogies
statistics explanations of logic testimonies of authorities

Yes No Does this argument contain positive information supporting the present system as well as information refuting the Exercise 3 argument?
\+ √ – Is this argument adequately documented and supported?
\+ √ – Does this argument refute its counterpart in Assignment 3?
Explain why this counterargument is or is not effective and how to improve it.

____
____
____
(Write additional comments on paper)

Subargument two: Read the Assignment 3 paper. Write the second subargument in that paper on the line below: (*If a substitute argument is used to replace this argument, write the substitute argument here.*) ____________________

____
____

Read the second counterargument. Write it down: ____________________

____
____

Do these two arguments match? Yes ______ No ______

Which of the following forms of support are used to back the counter argument?

detailed examples background data specific instances analogies
statistics explanations of logic testimonies of authorities

Yes No — Does this argument contain positive information supporting the present system as as well as information refuting the Exercise 3 arguments?

\+ √ − Is this argument adequately documented and supported?

\+ √ − Does this argument refute its counterpart in Assignment 3?

Explain why this counterargument is or is not effective and how to improve it.

____

____

____

(Write additional comments on paper)

Subargument three: Read the Assignment 3 paper. Write the third subargument in that paper on the line below: (*If a substitute argument is used to replace this argument, write the substitute argument here.*) ______________________________

____

____

Read the third counterargument. Write it down: ______________________________

____

____

____

Do these two arguments match? Yes_____ No _____

Which of the following forms of support are used to back the counterargument?

detailed examples background data specific instances analogies

statistics explanations of logic testimonies of authorities

Yes No — Does this argument contain positive information supporting the present system as well as information refuting the Exercise 3 arguments?

\+ √ − Is this argument adequately documented and supported?

\+ √ − Does this argument refute its counterpart in Assignment 3?

Explain why this counterargument is or is not effective and how to improve it.

____

____

____

(Write additional comments on paper)

\+ √ − Are possible negative side effects of the Exercise 4 plan exposed?

\+ √ − Does the refutation of the plan identify all possible discrepancies between what the need argument calls for and what the plan actually does? Explain below how to improve the refutation of the plan.

____

____

____

(Write additional comments on paper)

Did the conclusion:

\+ √ − 1. Summarize the counterarguments effectively?

\+ √ − 2. Restate the topic proposal?

\+ √ − 3. Draw a conclusion for the reader that the proposal had been refuted and should be rejected?

\+ √ − 4. Do something to make you reflect back over the topic?

See explanation of grading criteria on page 100.

											Raw Score		Weight		Weighted Grades
Criteria I	1	2	3	4	5	6	7	8	9	10	= _____	X	1	=	_____
Criteria II	1	2	3	4	5	6	7	8	9	10	= _____	X	3	=	_____
Criteria III	1	2	3	4	5	6	7	8	9	10	= _____	X	6	=	_____
														Sum Grade	_____

Transfer the weighted grades to the Exercise 5 Grading Form (page 227).

Note: This Feedback Form is to be attached (staple or paper clip) to the front of the student's paper and returned to him with the graded paper.

Your Name ______________________
No. ________ Group ________ Sec. ________

EXERCISE 5: Feedback Form to Author

Yes No Does this paper contain at least 3 references?
Yes No Is this paper between 3½ and 4½ pages in length?
Yes No Is each section of this paper identified by a heading?

If the answer to any of the above questions is no, the paper is unacceptable, and must be redone. Give the paper a grade of 1 on Criterion II. However, finish evaluating this paper and give it a grade.

\+ √ – Does the introduction gain and focus your attention?
\+ √ – Is there anything in this paper to build rapport?
\+ √ – Is this paper organized so that it is easy to follow—to identify the subsections?
If √ or - is circled above, explain how to correct the shortcoming.

____
____
____
____
(Write additional comments on paper)

Arguments showing a need for change.

Subargument one: Read the Assignment 3 paper. Write the first subargument in that paper on the line below: (*If a substitute argument is used to replace this argument, write the substitute argument here.*) ______________________

____
____
____

Read the first counterargument. Write it down: ______________________

____
____

Do these two arguments match? Yes ______ No ______
Which of the following forms of support are used to back the counter argument?
detailed examples background data specific instances analogies
statistics explanations of logic testimonies of authorities

Yes No Does this argument contain positive information supporting the present system as well as information refuting the Exercise 3 argument?
\+ √ – Is this argument adequately documented and supported?
\+ √ – Does this argument refute its counterpart in Assignment 3?
Explain why this counterargument is or is not effective and how to improve it.

____
____
____
(Write additional comments on paper)

Subargument two: Read the Assignment 3 paper. Write the second subargument in that paper on the line below: (*If a substitute argument is used to replace this argument, write the substitute argument here.*) ______________________

____
____

Read the second counterargument. Write it down: ______________________

____
____

Do these two arguments match? Yes _____ No ______
Which of the following forms of support are used to back the counter argument?
detailed examples background data specific instances analogies
statistics explanations of logic testimonies of authorities

Yes No Does this argument contain positive information supporting the present system as as well as information refuting the Exercise 3 arguments?

\+ √ − Is this argument adequately documented and supported?

\+ √ − Does this argument refute its counterpart in Assignment 3?

Explain why this counterargument is or is not effective and how to improve it.

____

____

____

(Write additional comments on paper)

Subargument three: Read the Assignment 3 paper. Write the third subargument in that paper on the line below: (*If a substitute argument is used to replace this argument, write the substitute argument here.*)______________________

____

____

Read the third counterargument. Write it down:______________________

____

____

____

Do these two arguments match? Yes_____ No _____

Which of the following forms of support are used to back the counterargument?

detailed examples background data specific instances analogies
statistics explanations of logic testimonies of authorities

Yes No Does this argument contain positive information supporting the present system as well as information refuting the Exercise 3 arguments?

\+ √ − Is this argument adequately documented and supported?

\+ √ − Does this argument refute its counterpart in Assignment 3?

Explain why this counterargument is or is not effective and how to improve it.

____

____

____

(Write additional comments on paper)

\+ √ − Are possible negative side effects of the Exercise 4 plan exposed?

\+ √ − Does the refutation of the plan identify all possible discrepancies between what the need argument calls for and what the plan actually does? Explain below how to improve the refutation of the plan.

____

____

____

(Write additional comments on paper)

Did the conclusion:

\+ √ − 1. Summarize the counterarguments effectively?

\+ √ − 2. Restate the topic proposal?

\+ √ − 3. Draw a conclusion for the reader that the proposal had been refuted and should be rejected?

\+ √ − 4. Do something to make you reflect back over the topic?

See explanation of grading criteria on page 100.

												Raw Score		Weight		Weighted Grades
Criteria I	1	2	3	4	5	6	7	8	9	10	=	_____	X	1	=	_____
Criteria II	1	2	3	4	5	6	7	8	9	10	=	_____	X	3	=	_____
Criteria III	1	2	3	4	5	6	7	8	9	10	=	_____	X	6	=	_____

Sum Grade _____

Transfer the weighted grades to the Exercise 5 Grading Form (page 227).

Note: This Feedback Form is to be attached (staple or paper clip) to the front of the student's paper and returned to him with the graded paper.

Your Name ______________________________
No.________ Group __________ Sec. __________

EXERCISE 5: Feedback Form to Author

Yes No Does this paper contain at least 3 references?
Yes No Is this paper between 3½ and 4½ pages in length?
Yes No Is each section of this paper identified by a heading?

If the answer to any of the above questions is no, the paper is unacceptable, and must be redone. Give the paper a grade of 1 on Criterion II. However, finish evaluating this paper and give it a grade.

\+ √ – Does the introduction gain and focus your attention?
\+ √ – Is there anything in this paper to build rapport?
\+ √ – Is this paper organized so that it is easy to follow—to identify the subsections?
If √ or - is circled above, explain how to correct the shortcoming.

____
____
____
____
(Write additional comments on paper)

Arguments showing a need for change.

Subargument one: Read the Assignment 3 paper. Write the first subargument in that paper on the line below: (*If a substitute argument is used to replace this argument, write the substitute argument here.*)______________________________

____
____
____

Read the first counterargument. Write it down: ______________________

____
____

Do these two arguments match? Yes_______ No_______
Which of the following forms of support are used to back the counter argument?
detailed examples background data specific instances analogies
statistics explanations of logic testimonies of authorities

Yes No Does this argument contain positive information supporting the present system as well as information refuting the Exercise 3 argument?
\+ √ – Is this argument adequately documented and supported?
\+ √ – Does this argument refute its counterpart in Assignment 3?
Explain why this counterargument is or is not effective and how to improve it.

____
____
____
(Write additional comments on paper)

Subargument two: Read the Assignment 3 paper. Write the second subargument in that paper on the line below: (*If a substitute argument is used to replace this argument, write the substitute argument here.*)______________________________

____
____

Read the second counterargument. Write it down: ______________________

____
____

Do these two arguments match? Yes_____No______
Which of the following forms of support are used to back the counter argument?
detailed examples background data specific instances analogies
statistics explanations of logic testimonies of authorities

Yes No Does this argument contain positive information supporting the present system as as well as information refuting the Exercise 3 arguments?

\+ √ − Is this argument adequately documented and supported?

\+ √ − Does this argument refute its counterpart in Assignment 3?

Explain why this counterargument is or is not effective and how to improve it.

____

____

____

(Write additional comments on paper)

Subargument three: Read the Assignment 3 paper. Write the third subargument in that paper on the line below: (*If a substitute argument is used to replace this argument, write the substitute argument here.*)______________________

____

____

Read the third counterargument. Write it down:______________________

____

____

____

Do these two arguments match? Yes_____ No _____

Which of the following forms of support are used to back the counterargument?

detailed examples background data specific instances analogies statistics explanations of logic testimonies of authorities

Yes No Does this argument contain positive information supporting the present system as well as information refuting the Exercise 3 arguments?

\+ √ − Is this argument adequately documented and supported?

\+ √ − Does this argument refute its counterpart in Assignment 3?

Explain why this counterargument is or is not effective and how to improve it.

____

____

____

(Write additional comments on paper)

\+ √ − Are possible negative side effects of the Exercise 4 plan exposed?

\+ √ − Does the refutation of the plan identify all possible discrepancies between what the need argument calls for and what the plan actually does? Explain below how to improve the refutation of the plan.

____

____

____

(Write additional comments on paper)

Did the conclusion:

\+ √ − 1. Summarize the counterarguments effectively?

\+ √ − 2. Restate the topic proposal?

\+ √ − 3. Draw a conclusion for the reader that the proposal had been refuted and should be rejected?

\+ √ − 4. Do something to make you reflect back over the topic?

See explanation of grading criteria on page 100.

												Raw Score		Weight		Weighted Grades
Criteria I	1	2	3	4	5	6	7	8	9	10	=	_____	X	1	=	_____
Criteria II	1	2	3	4	5	6	7	8	9	10	=	_____	X	3	=	_____
Criteria III	1	2	3	4	5	6	7	8	9	10	=	_____	X	6	=	_____

Sum Grade _____

Transfer the weighted grades to the Exercise 5 Grading Form (page 227).

Note: This Feedback Form is to be attached (staple or paper clip) to the front of the student's paper and returned to him with the graded paper.

Your Name ______________________
No. ________ Group ________ Sec. ________

EXERCISE 5: Feedback Form to Author

Yes No Does this paper contain at least 3 references?
Yes No Is this paper between 3½ and 4½ pages in length?
Yes No Is each section of this paper identified by a heading?

If the answer to any of the above questions is no, the paper is unacceptable, and must be redone. Give the paper a grade of 1 on Criterion II. However, finish evaluating this paper and give it a grade.

+ √ – Does the introduction gain and focus your attention?
+ √ – Is there anything in this paper to build rapport?
+ √ – Is this paper organized so that it is easy to follow—to identify the subsections?

If √ or - is circled above, explain how to correct the shortcoming.

____

____

____

____

(Write additional comments on paper)

Arguments showing a need for change.

Subargument one: Read the Assignment 3 paper. Write the first subargument in that paper on the line below: (*If a substitute argument is used to replace this argument, write the substitute argument here.*) ______________________

____

____

____

Read the first counterargument. Write it down: ______________________

____

____

Do these two arguments match? Yes ______ No ______
Which of the following forms of support are used to back the counter argument?
detailed examples background data specific instances analogies
statistics explanations of logic testimonies of authorities

Yes No Does this argument contain positive information supporting the present system as well as information refuting the Exercise 3 argument?
+ √ – Is this argument adequately documented and supported?
+ √ – Does this argument refute its counterpart in Assignment 3?

Explain why this counterargument is or is not effective and how to improve it.

____

____

____

(Write additional comments on paper)

Subargument two: Read the Assignment 3 paper. Write the second subargument in that paper on the line below: (*If a substitute argument is used to replace this argument, write the substitute argument here.*) ______________________

____

____

Read the second counterargument. Write it down: ______________________

____

____

Do these two arguments match? Yes ______ No ______
Which of the following forms of support are used to back the counter argument?
detailed examples background data specific instances analogies
statistics explanations of logic testimonies of authorities

Yes No — Does this argument contain positive information supporting the present system as as well as information refuting the Exercise 3 arguments?

+ √ − Is this argument adequately documented and supported?

+ √ − Does this argument refute its counterpart in Assignment 3?

Explain why this counterargument is or is not effective and how to improve it.

____

____

____

(Write additional comments on paper)

Subargument three: Read the Assignment 3 paper. Write the third subargument in that paper on the line below: (*If a substitute argument is used to replace this argument, write the substitute argument here.*)______________________

____

____

Read the third counterargument. Write it down:______________________

____

____

____

Do these two arguments match? Yes_____ No _____

Which of the following forms of support are used to back the counterargument?

detailed examples background data specific instances analogies
statistics explanations of logic testimonies of authorities

Yes No — Does this argument contain positive information supporting the present system as well as information refuting the Exercise 3 arguments?

+ √ − Is this argument adequately documented and supported?

+ √ − Does this argument refute its counterpart in Assignment 3?

Explain why this counterargument is or is not effective and how to improve it.

____

____

____

(Write additional comments on paper)

+ √ − Are possible negative side effects of the Exercise 4 plan exposed?

+ √ − Does the refutation of the plan identify all possible discrepancies between what the need argument calls for and what the plan actually does? Explain below how to improve the refutation of the plan.

____

____

____

(Write additional comments on paper)

Did the conclusion:

+ √ − 1. Summarize the counterarguments effectively?

+ √ − 2. Restate the topic proposal?

+ √ − 3. Draw a conclusion for the reader that the proposal had been refuted and should be rejected?

+ √ − 4. Do something to make you reflect back over the topic?

See explanation of grading criteria on page 100.

												Raw Score		Weight		Weighted Grades
Criteria I	1	2	3	4	5	6	7	8	9	10	=	_____	X	1	=	_____
Criteria II	1	2	3	4	5	6	7	8	9	10	=	_____	X	3	=	_____
Criteria III	1	2	3	4	5	6	7	8	9	10	=	_____	X	6	=	_____

Sum Grade _____

Transfer the weighted grades to the Exercise 5 Grading Form (page 227).

Note: This Feedback Form is to be attached (staple or paper clip) to the front of the student's paper and returned to him with the graded paper.

Your Name ____________________

No. ________ Group ________ Sec. ________

EXERCISE 5: Feedback Form to Author

Yes No Does this paper contain at least 3 references?
Yes No Is this paper between 3½ and 4½ pages in length?
Yes No Is each section of this paper identified by a heading?

If the answer to any of the above questions is no, the paper is unacceptable, and must be redone. Give the paper a grade of 1 on Criterion II. However, finish evaluating this paper and give it a grade.

+ √ − Does the introduction gain and focus your attention?
+ √ − Is there anything in this paper to build rapport?
+ √ − Is this paper organized so that it is easy to follow—to identify the subsections?

If √ or - is circled above, explain how to correct the shortcoming.

____

____

____

____

(Write additional comments on paper)

Arguments showing a need for change.

Subargument one: Read the Assignment 3 paper. Write the first subargument in that paper on the line below: (*If a substitute argument is used to replace this argument, write the substitute argument here.*) ____________________

____

____

____

Read the first counterargument. Write it down: ____________________

____

____

Do these two arguments match? Yes ______ No ______

Which of the following forms of support are used to back the counter argument?

detailed examples background data specific instances analogies
statistics explanations of logic testimonies of authorities

Yes No Does this argument contain positive information supporting the present system as well as information refuting the Exercise 3 argument?
+ √ − Is this argument adequately documented and supported?
+ √ − Does this argument refute its counterpart in Assignment 3?

Explain why this counterargument is or is not effective and how to improve it.

____

____

____

(Write additional comments on paper)

Subargument two: Read the Assignment 3 paper. Write the second subargument in that paper on the line below: (*If a substitute argument is used to replace this argument, write the substitute argument here.*) ____________________

____

____

Read the second counterargument. Write it down: ____________________

____

____

Do these two arguments match? Yes _____ No _____

Which of the following forms of support are used to back the counter argument?

detailed examples background data specific instances analogies
statistics explanations of logic testimonies of authorities

Yes	No	
		Does this argument contain positive information supporting the present system as as well as information refuting the Exercise 3 arguments?
+ √ −		Is this argument adequately documented and supported?
+ √ −		Does this argument refute its counterpart in Assignment 3?
		Explain why this counterargument is or is not effective and how to improve it.

____

____

____

(Write additional comments on paper)

Subargument three: Read the Assignment 3 paper. Write the third subargument in that paper on the line below: (*If a substitute argument is used to replace this argument, write the substitute argument here.*) ______________________________

____

____

Read the third counterargument. Write it down: ______________________________

____

____

____

Do these two arguments match? Yes_____ No _____

Which of the following forms of support are used to back the counterargument?

detailed examples   background data   specific instances   analogies
statistics   explanations of logic   testimonies of authorities

Yes	No	
		Does this argument contain positive information supporting the present system as well as information refuting the Exercise 3 arguments?
+ √ −		Is this argument adequately documented and supported?
+ √ −		Does this argument refute its counterpart in Assignment 3?
		Explain why this counterargument is or is not effective and how to improve it.

____

____

____

(Write additional comments on paper)

+ √ −	Are possible negative side effects of the Exercise 4 plan exposed?
+ √ −	Does the refutation of the plan identify all possible discrepancies between what the need argument calls for and what the plan actually does? Explain below how to improve the refutation of the plan.

____

____

____

(Write additional comments on paper)

Did the conclusion:

+ √ −	1. Summarize the counterarguments effectively?
+ √ −	2. Restate the topic proposal?
+ √ −	3. Draw a conclusion for the reader that the proposal had been refuted and should be rejected?
+ √ −	4. Do something to make you reflect back over the topic?

See explanation of grading criteria on page 100.

												Raw Score		Weight		Weighted Grades
Criteria I	1	2	3	4	5	6	7	8	9	10	=	_____	X	1	=	_____
Criteria II	1	2	3	4	5	6	7	8	9	10	=	_____	X	3	=	_____
Criteria III	1	2	3	4	5	6	7	8	9	10	=	_____	X	6	=	_____

Sum Grade _____

Transfer the weighted grades to the Exercise 5 Grading Form (page 227).

Note: This Feedback Form is to be attached (staple or paper clip) to the front of the student's paper and returned to him with the graded paper.

Your Name ______________________
No. ________ Group __________ Sec. ________

EXERCISE 5: Feedback Form to Author

Yes No Does this paper contain at least 3 references?
Yes No Is this paper between 3½ and 4½ pages in length?
Yes No Is each section of this paper identified by a heading?

If the answer to any of the above questions is no, the paper is unacceptable, and must be redone. Give the paper a grade of 1 on Criterion II. However, finish evaluating this paper and give it a grade.

+ √ – Does the introduction gain and focus your attention?
+ √ – Is there anything in this paper to build rapport?
+ √ – Is this paper organized so that it is easy to follow—to identify the subsections?

If √ or - is circled above, explain how to correct the shortcoming.

____

____

____

____

(Write additional comments on paper)

Arguments showing a need for change.

Subargument one: Read the Assignment 3 paper. Write the first subargument in that paper on the line below: (*If a substitute argument is used to replace this argument, write the substitute argument here.*) ______________________

____

____

____

Read the first counterargument. Write it down: ______________________

____

____

Do these two arguments match? Yes ______ No ______

Which of the following forms of support are used to back the counter argument?
detailed examples background data specific instances analogies
statistics explanations of logic testimonies of authorities

Yes No Does this argument contain positive information supporting the present system as well as information refuting the Exercise 3 argument?
+ √ – Is this argument adequately documented and supported?
+ √ – Does this argument refute its counterpart in Assignment 3?

Explain why this counterargument is or is not effective and how to improve it.

____

____

____

(Write additional comments on paper)

Subargument two: Read the Assignment 3 paper. Write the second subargument in that paper on the line below: (*If a substitute argument is used to replace this argument, write the substitute argument here.*) ______________________

____

____

Read the second counterargument. Write it down: ______________________

____

____

Do these two arguments match? Yes _____ No _____

Which of the following forms of support are used to back the counter argument?
detailed examples background data specific instances analogies
statistics explanations of logic testimonies of authorities

Yes No — Does this argument contain positive information supporting the present system as as well as information refuting the Exercise 3 arguments?

+ √ − Is this argument adequately documented and supported?

+ √ − Does this argument refute its counterpart in Assignment 3?

Explain why this counterargument is or is not effective and how to improve it.

____

(Write additional comments on paper)

Subargument three: Read the Assignment 3 paper. Write the third subargument in that paper on the line below: (*If a substitute argument is used to replace this argument, write the substitute argument here.*) ____________________

Read the third counterargument. Write it down: ____________________

Do these two arguments match? Yes_____ No _____

Which of the following forms of support are used to back the counterargument?

detailed examples   background data   specific instances   analogies

statistics   explanations of logic   testimonies of authorities

Yes No — Does this argument contain positive information supporting the present system as well as information refuting the Exercise 3 arguments?

+ √ − Is this argument adequately documented and supported?

+ √ − Does this argument refute its counterpart in Assignment 3?

Explain why this counterargument is or is not effective and how to improve it.

____

(Write additional comments on paper)

+ √ − Are possible negative side effects of the Exercise 4 plan exposed?

+ √ − Does the refutation of the plan identify all possible discrepancies between what the need argument calls for and what the plan actually does? Explain below how to improve the refutation of the plan.

____

(Write additional comments on paper)

Did the conclusion:

+ √ − 1. Summarize the counterarguments effectively?

+ √ − 2. Restate the topic proposal?

+ √ − 3. Draw a conclusion for the reader that the proposal had been refuted and should be rejected?

+ √ − 4. Do something to make you reflect back over the topic?

See explanation of grading criteria on page 100.

												Raw Score		Weight		Weighted Grades
Criteria I	1	2	3	4	5	6	7	8	9	10	=	_____	X	1	=	_____
Criteria II	1	2	3	4	5	6	7	8	9	10	=	_____	X	3	=	_____
Criteria III	1	2	3	4	5	6	7	8	9	10	=	_____	X	6	=	_____
														Sum Grade		_____

Transfer the weighted grades to the Exercise 5 Grading Form (page 227).

Note: This Feedback Form is to be attached (staple or paper clip) to the front of the student's paper and returned to him with the graded paper.

Your Name ____________________
No. ________ Group ________ Sec. ________

EXERCISE 5: Feedback Form to Author

Yes	No	Does this paper contain at least 3 references?
Yes	No	Is this paper between 3½ and 4½ pages in length?
Yes	No	Is each section of this paper identified by a heading?

If the answer to any of the above questions is no, the paper is unacceptable, and must be redone. Give the paper a grade of 1 on Criterion II. However, finish evaluating this paper and give it a grade.

+ √ −	Does the introduction gain and focus your attention?
+ √ −	Is there anything in this paper to build rapport?
+ √ −	Is this paper organized so that it is easy to follow—to identify the subsections?

If √ or - is circled above, explain how to correct the shortcoming.

____

____

____

____

(Write additional comments on paper)

Arguments showing a need for change.

Subargument one: Read the Assignment 3 paper. Write the first subargument in that paper on the line below: (*If a substitute argument is used to replace this argument, write the substitute argument here.*) ____________________

____

____

____

Read the first counterargument. Write it down: ____________________

____

____

Do these two arguments match? Yes ______ No ______

Which of the following forms of support are used to back the counter argument?

detailed examples   background data   specific instances   analogies
statistics   explanations of logic   testimonies of authorities

Yes No	Does this argument contain positive information supporting the present system as well as information refuting the Exercise 3 argument?
+ √ −	Is this argument adequately documented and supported?
+ √ −	Does this argument refute its counterpart in Assignment 3?

Explain why this counterargument is or is not effective and how to improve it.

____

____

____

(Write additional comments on paper)

Subargument two: Read the Assignment 3 paper. Write the second subargument in that paper on the line below: (*If a substitute argument is used to replace this argument, write the substitute argument here.*) ____________________

____

____

Read the second counterargument. Write it down: ____________________

____

____

Do these two arguments match? Yes _____ No _____

Which of the following forms of support are used to back the counter argument?

detailed examples   background data   specific instances   analogies
statistics   explanations of logic   testimonies of authorities

Yes No — Does this argument contain positive information supporting the present system as as well as information refuting the Exercise 3 arguments?

+ √ − Is this argument adequately documented and supported?

+ √ − Does this argument refute its counterpart in Assignment 3?

Explain why this counterargument is or is not effective and how to improve it.

___

___

___

(Write additional comments on paper)

Subargument three: Read the Assignment 3 paper. Write the third subargument in that paper on the line below: (*If a substitute argument is used to replace this argument, write the substitute argument here.*) ___

___

___

Read the third counterargument. Write it down: ___

___

___

___

Do these two arguments match? Yes___ No ___

Which of the following forms of support are used to back the counterargument?

detailed examples   background data   specific instances   analogies
statistics   explanations of logic   testimonies of authorities

Yes No — Does this argument contain positive information supporting the present system as well as information refuting the Exercise 3 arguments?

+ √ − Is this argument adequately documented and supported?

+ √ − Does this argument refute its counterpart in Assignment 3?

Explain why this counterargument is or is not effective and how to improve it.

___

___

___

(Write additional comments on paper)

+ √ − Are possible negative side effects of the Exercise 4 plan exposed?

+ √ − Does the refutation of the plan identify all possible discrepancies between what the need argument calls for and what the plan actually does? Explain below how to improve the refutation of the plan.

___

___

___

(Write additional comments on paper)

Did the conclusion:

+ √ − 1. Summarize the counterarguments effectively?

+ √ − 2. Restate the topic proposal?

+ √ − 3. Draw a conclusion for the reader that the proposal had been refuted and should be rejected?

+ √ − 4. Do something to make you reflect back over the topic?

See explanation of grading criteria on page 100.

												Raw Score		Weight		Weighted Grades
Criteria I	1	2	3	4	5	6	7	8	9	10	=	___	X	1	=	___
Criteria II	1	2	3	4	5	6	7	8	9	10	=	___	X	3	=	___
Criteria III	1	2	3	4	5	6	7	8	9	10	=	___	X	6	=	___

Sum Grade ___

Transfer the weighted grades to the Exercise 5 Grading Form (page 227).

Note: This Feedback Form is to be attached (staple or paper clip) to the front of the student's paper and returned to him with the graded paper.

Your Name ____________________
No. ________ Group ________ Sec. ________

EXERCISE 5: Feedback Form to Author

Yes No — Does this paper contain at least 3 references?
Yes No — Is this paper between 3½ and 4½ pages in length?
Yes No — Is each section of this paper identified by a heading?

If the answer to any of the above questions is no, the paper is unacceptable, and must be redone. Give the paper a grade of 1 on Criterion II. However, finish evaluating this paper and give it a grade.

+ √ − Does the introduction gain and focus your attention?
+ √ − Is there anything in this paper to build rapport?
+ √ − Is this paper organized so that it is easy to follow—to identify the subsections?

If √ or - is circled above, explain how to correct the shortcoming.

____

____

____

____

(Write additional comments on paper)

Arguments showing a need for change.

Subargument one: Read the Assignment 3 paper. Write the first subargument in that paper on the line below: (*If a substitute argument is used to replace this argument, write the substitute argument here.*) ______________________

____

____

____

Read the first counterargument. Write it down: ______________________

____

____

Do these two arguments match? Yes ______ No ______

Which of the following forms of support are used to back the counter argument?

detailed examples background data specific instances analogies
statistics explanations of logic testimonies of authorities

Yes No — Does this argument contain positive information supporting the present system as well as information refuting the Exercise 3 argument?
+ √ − Is this argument adequately documented and supported?
+ √ − Does this argument refute its counterpart in Assignment 3?

Explain why this counterargument is or is not effective and how to improve it.

____

____

____

(Write additional comments on paper)

Subargument two: Read the Assignment 3 paper. Write the second subargument in that paper on the line below: (*If a substitute argument is used to replace this argument, write the substitute argument here.*) ______________________

____

____

Read the second counterargument. Write it down: ______________________

____

____

Do these two arguments match? Yes ______ No ______

Which of the following forms of support are used to back the counter argument?

detailed examples background data specific instances analogies
statistics explanations of logic testimonies of authorities

Yes No	Does this argument contain positive information supporting the present system as as well as information refuting the Exercise 3 arguments?
+ √ –	Is this argument adequately documented and supported?
+ √ –	Does this argument refute its counterpart in Assignment 3?
	Explain why this counterargument is or is not effective and how to improve it.

____

____

____

(Write additional comments on paper)

Subargument three: Read the Assignment 3 paper. Write the third subargument in that paper on the line below: (*If a substitute argument is used to replace this argument, write the substitute argument here.*)____________________

____

____

Read the third counterargument. Write it down:____________________

____

____

____

Do these two arguments match? Yes_____ No _____

Which of the following forms of support are used to back the counterargument?

detailed examples background data specific instances analogies
statistics explanations of logic testimonies of authorities

Yes No	Does this argument contain positive information supporting the present system as well as information refuting the Exercise 3 arguments?
+ √ –	Is this argument adequately documented and supported?
+ √ –	Does this argument refute its counterpart in Assignment 3?
	Explain why this counterargument is or is not effective and how to improve it.

____

____

____

(Write additional comments on paper)

+ √ –	Are possible negative side effects of the Exercise 4 plan exposed?
+ √ –	Does the refutation of the plan identify all possible discrepancies between what the need argument calls for and what the plan actually does? Explain below how to improve the refutation of the plan.

____

____

____

(Write additional comments on paper)

Did the conclusion:

+ √ –	1. Summarize the counterarguments effectively?
+ √ –	2. Restate the topic proposal?
+ √ –	3. Draw a conclusion for the reader that the proposal had been refuted and should be rejected?
+ √ –	4. Do something to make you reflect back over the topic?

See explanation of grading criteria on page 100.

												Raw Score		Weight		Weighted Grades
Criteria I	1	2	3	4	5	6	7	8	9	10	=	_____	X	1	=	_____
Criteria II	1	2	3	4	5	6	7	8	9	10	=	_____	X	3	=	_____
Criteria III	1	2	3	4	5	6	7	8	9	10	=	_____	X	6	=	_____

Sum Grade _____

Transfer the weighted grades to the Exercise 5 Grading Form (page 227).

Note: This Feedback Form is to be attached (staple or paper clip) to the front of the student's paper and returned to him with the graded paper.

Your Name ______________________
No.________ Group________ Sec.________

EXERCISE 5: Feedback Form to Author

Yes No — Does this paper contain at least 3 references?
Yes No — Is this paper between 3½ and 4½ pages in length?
Yes No — Is each section of this paper identified by a heading?

If the answer to any of the above questions is no, the paper is unacceptable, and must be redone. Give the paper a grade of 1 on Criterion II. However, finish evaluating this paper and give it a grade.

+ √ − Does the introduction gain and focus your attention?
+ √ − Is there anything in this paper to build rapport?
+ √ − Is this paper organized so that it is easy to follow—to identify the subsections?

If √ or - is circled above, explain how to correct the shortcoming.

____
____
____
____
(Write additional comments on paper)

Arguments showing a need for change.

Subargument one: Read the Assignment 3 paper. Write the first subargument in that paper on the line below: (*If a substitute argument is used to replace this argument, write the substitute argument here.*) ____

____
____
____

Read the first counterargument. Write it down: ____

____
____

Do these two arguments match? Yes_______ No_______
Which of the following forms of support are used to back the counter argument?
detailed examples   background data   specific instances   analogies
statistics   explanations of logic   testimonies of authorities

Yes No — Does this argument contain positive information supporting the present system as well as information refuting the Exercise 3 argument?
+ √ − Is this argument adequately documented and supported?
+ √ − Does this argument refute its counterpart in Assignment 3?

Explain why this counterargument is or is not effective and how to improve it.

____
____
____
(Write additional comments on paper)

Subargument two: Read the Assignment 3 paper. Write the second subargument in that paper on the line below: (*If a substitute argument is used to replace this argument, write the substitute argument here.*) ____

____
____

Read the second counterargument. Write it down: ____

____
____

Do these two arguments match? Yes_____No______
Which of the following forms of support are used to back the counter argument?
detailed examples   background data   specific instances   analogies
statistics   explanations of logic   testimonies of authorities

Yes No — Does this argument contain positive information supporting the present system as as well as information refuting the Exercise 3 arguments?

+ √ − Is this argument adequately documented and supported?

+ √ − Does this argument refute its counterpart in Assignment 3?

Explain why this counterargument is or is not effective and how to improve it.

____

____

____

(Write additional comments on paper)

Subargument three: Read the Assignment 3 paper. Write the third subargument in that paper on the line below: (*If a substitute argument is used to replace this argument, write the substitute argument here.*) ____________________

____

____

Read the third counterargument. Write it down: ____________________

____

____

____

Do these two arguments match? Yes_____ No _____

Which of the following forms of support are used to back the counterargument?

detailed examples background data specific instances analogies

statistics explanations of logic testimonies of authorities

Yes No — Does this argument contain positive information supporting the present system as well as information refuting the Exercise 3 arguments?

+ √ − Is this argument adequately documented and supported?

+ √ − Does this argument refute its counterpart in Assignment 3?

Explain why this counterargument is or is not effective and how to improve it.

____

____

____

(Write additional comments on paper)

+ √ − Are possible negative side effects of the Exercise 4 plan exposed?

+ √ − Does the refutation of the plan identify all possible discrepancies between what the need argument calls for and what the plan actually does? Explain below how to improve the refutation of the plan.

____

____

____

(Write additional comments on paper)

Did the conclusion:

+ √ − 1. Summarize the counterarguments effectively?

+ √ − 2. Restate the topic proposal?

+ √ − 3. Draw a conclusion for the reader that the proposal had been refuted and should be rejected?

+ √ − 4. Do something to make you reflect back over the topic?

See explanation of grading criteria on page 100.

												Raw Score		Weight		Weighted Grades
Criteria I	1	2	3	4	5	6	7	8	9	10	=	_____	X	1	=	_____
Criteria II	1	2	3	4	5	6	7	8	9	10	=	_____	X	3	=	_____
Criteria III	1	2	3	4	5	6	7	8	9	10	=	_____	X	6	=	_____

Sum Grade _____

Transfer the weighted grades to the Exerçise 5 Grading Form (page 227).

Note: This Feedback Form is to be attached (staple or paper clip) to the front of the student's paper and returned to him with the graded paper.

Your Name ______________________________

No. ________ Group __________ Sec. ________

EXERCISE 5: Feedback Form to Author

Yes No — Does this paper contain at least 3 references?

Yes No — Is this paper between 3½ and 4½ pages in length?

Yes No — Is each section of this paper identified by a heading?

If the answer to any of the above questions is no, the paper is unacceptable, and must be redone. Give the paper a grade of 1 on Criterion II. However, finish evaluating this paper and give it a grade.

+ √ − Does the introduction gain and focus your attention?

+ √ − Is there anything in this paper to build rapport?

+ √ − Is this paper organized so that it is easy to follow—to identify the subsections?

If √ or - is circled above, explain how to correct the shortcoming.

____

____

____

____

(Write additional comments on paper)

Arguments showing a need for change.

Subargument one: Read the Assignment 3 paper. Write the first subargument in that paper on the line below: (*If a substitute argument is used to replace this argument, write the substitute argument here.*) ______________________________

____

____

____

Read the first counterargument. Write it down: ______________________

____

____

Do these two arguments match? Yes _______ No _______

Which of the following forms of support are used to back the counter argument?

detailed examples background data specific instances analogies

statistics explanations of logic testimonies of authorities

Yes No — Does this argument contain positive information supporting the present system as well as information refuting the Exercise 3 argument?

+ √ − Is this argument adequately documented and supported?

+ √ − Does this argument refute its counterpart in Assignment 3?

Explain why this counterargument is or is not effective and how to improve it.

____

____

____

(Write additional comments on paper)

Subargument two: Read the Assignment 3 paper. Write the second subargument in that paper on the line below: (*If a substitute argument is used to replace this argument, write the substitute argument here.*) ______________________________

____

____

Read the second counterargument. Write it down: ______________________

____

____

Do these two arguments match? Yes _____ No ______

Which of the following forms of support are used to back the counter argument?

detailed examples background data specific instances analogies

statistics explanations of logic testimonies of authorities

Yes No — Does this argument contain positive information supporting the present system as as well as information refuting the Exercise 3 arguments?

+ √ − Is this argument adequately documented and supported?

+ √ − Does this argument refute its counterpart in Assignment 3?

Explain why this counterargument is or is not effective and how to improve it.

____

____

____

(Write additional comments on paper)

Subargument three: Read the Assignment 3 paper. Write the third subargument in that paper on the line below: (*If a substitute argument is used to replace this argument, write the substitute argument here.*) ____________________

____

____

Read the third counterargument. Write it down: ____________________

____

____

____

Do these two arguments match? Yes_____ No _____

Which of the following forms of support are used to back the counterargument?

detailed examples   background data   specific instances   analogies

statistics   explanations of logic   testimonies of authorities

Yes No — Does this argument contain positive information supporting the present system as well as information refuting the Exercise 3 arguments?

+ √ − Is this argument adequately documented and supported?

+ √ − Does this argument refute its counterpart in Assignment 3?

Explain why this counterargument is or is not effective and how to improve it.

____

____

____

(Write additional comments on paper)

+ √ − Are possible negative side effects of the Exercise 4 plan exposed?

+ √ − Does the refutation of the plan identify all possible discrepancies between what the need argument calls for and what the plan actually does? Explain below how to improve the refutation of the plan.

____

____

____

(Write additional comments on paper)

Did the conclusion:

+ √ − 1. Summarize the counterarguments effectively?

+ √ − 2. Restate the topic proposal?

+ √ − 3. Draw a conclusion for the reader that the proposal had been refuted and should be rejected?

+ √ − 4. Do something to make you reflect back over the topic?

See explanation of grading criteria on page 100.

												Raw Score		Weight		Weighted Grades
Criteria I	1	2	3	4	5	6	7	8	9	10	=	_____	X	1	=	_____
Criteria II	1	2	3	4	5	6	7	8	9	10	=	_____	X	3	=	_____
Criteria III	1	2	3	4	5	6	7	8	9	10	=	_____	X	6	=	_____

Sum Grade _____

Transfer the weighted grades to the Exerçise 5 Grading Form (page 227).

Note: This Feedback Form is to be attached (staple or paper clip) to the front of the student's paper and returned to him with the graded paper.

Your Name ____________________

No. ________ Group ________ Sec. ________

EXERCISE 5: Feedback Form to Author

Yes No — Does this paper contain at least 3 references?

Yes No — Is this paper between 3½ and 4½ pages in length?

Yes No — Is each section of this paper identified by a heading?

If the answer to any of the above questions is no, the paper is unacceptable, and must be redone. Give the paper a grade of 1 on Criterion II. However, finish evaluating this paper and give it a grade.

+ √ − Does the introduction gain and focus your attention?

+ √ − Is there anything in this paper to build rapport?

+ √ − Is this paper organized so that it is easy to follow—to identify the subsections?

If √ or - is circled above, explain how to correct the shortcoming.

____

____

____

____

(Write additional comments on paper)

Arguments showing a need for change.

Subargument one: Read the Assignment 3 paper. Write the first subargument in that paper on the line below: (*If a substitute argument is used to replace this argument, write the substitute argument here.*) ____________________

____

____

____

Read the first counterargument. Write it down: ____________________

____

____

Do these two arguments match? Yes ______ No ______

Which of the following forms of support are used to back the counter argument?

detailed examples   background data   specific instances   analogies

statistics   explanations of logic   testimonies of authorities

Yes No — Does this argument contain positive information supporting the present system as well as information refuting the Exercise 3 argument?

+ √ − Is this argument adequately documented and supported?

+ √ − Does this argument refute its counterpart in Assignment 3?

Explain why this counterargument is or is not effective and how to improve it.

____

____

____

(Write additional comments on paper)

Subargument two: Read the Assignment 3 paper. Write the second subargument in that paper on the line below: (*If a substitute argument is used to replace this argument, write the substitute argument here.*) ____________________

____

____

Read the second counterargument. Write it down: ____________________

____

____

Do these two arguments match? Yes _____ No _____

Which of the following forms of support are used to back the counter argument?

detailed examples   background data   specific instances   analogies

statistics   explanations of logic   testimonies of authorities

Yes No	Does this argument contain positive information supporting the present system as as well as information refuting the Exercise 3 arguments?
+ √ −	Is this argument adequately documented and supported?
+ √ −	Does this argument refute its counterpart in Assignment 3?
	Explain why this counterargument is or is not effective and how to improve it.

____

____

____

(Write additional comments on paper)

Subargument three: Read the Assignment 3 paper. Write the third subargument in that paper on the line below: (*If a substitute argument is used to replace this argument, write the substitute argument here.*)______________

____

____

Read the third counterargument. Write it down:______________

____

____

____

Do these two arguments match? Yes_____ No _____

Which of the following forms of support are used to back the counterargument?

detailed examples background data specific instances analogies
statistics explanations of logic testimonies of authorities

Yes No	Does this argument contain positive information supporting the present system as well as information refuting the Exercise 3 arguments?
+ √ −	Is this argument adequately documented and supported?
+ √ −	Does this argument refute its counterpart in Assignment 3?
	Explain why this counterargument is or is not effective and how to improve it.

____

____

____

(Write additional comments on paper)

+ √ −	Are possible negative side effects of the Exercise 4 plan exposed?
+ √ −	Does the refutation of the plan identify all possible discrepancies between what the need argument calls for and what the plan actually does? Explain below how to improve the refutation of the plan.

____

____

____

(Write additional comments on paper)

Did the conclusion:

+ √ −	1. Summarize the counterarguments effectively?
+ √ −	2. Restate the topic proposal?
+ √ −	3. Draw a conclusion for the reader that the proposal had been refuted and should be rejected?
+ √ −	4. Do something to make you reflect back over the topic?

See explanation of grading criteria on page 100.

												Raw Score		Weight		Weighted Grades
Criteria I	1	2	3	4	5	6	7	8	9	10	=	_____	X	1	=	_____
Criteria II	1	2	3	4	5	6	7	8	9	10	=	_____	X	3	=	_____
Criteria III	1	2	3	4	5	6	7	8	9	10	=	_____	X	6	=	_____

Sum Grade _____

Transfer the weighted grades to the Exercise 5 Grading Form (page 227).

Note: This Feedback Form is to be attached (staple or paper clip) to the front of the student's paper and returned to him with the graded paper.

Your Name ______________________
No.________ Group ________ Sec.________

EXERCISE 5: Feedback Form to Author

Yes No — Does this paper contain at least 3 references?
Yes No — Is this paper between 3½ and 4½ pages in length?
Yes No — Is each section of this paper identified by a heading?

If the answer to any of the above questions is no, the paper is unacceptable, and must be redone. Give the paper a grade of 1 on Criterion II. However, finish evaluating this paper and give it a grade.

+ √ – Does the introduction gain and focus your attention?
+ √ – Is there anything in this paper to build rapport?
+ √ – Is this paper organized so that it is easy to follow—to identify the subsections?

If √ or - is circled above, explain how to correct the shortcoming.

____

____

____

____

(Write additional comments on paper)

Arguments showing a need for change.

Subargument one: Read the Assignment 3 paper. Write the first subargument in that paper on the line below: *(If a substitute argument is used to replace this argument, write the substitute argument here.)* ______________________

____

____

____

Read the first counterargument. Write it down: ______________________

____

____

Do these two arguments match? Yes ______ No ______

Which of the following forms of support are used to back the counter argument?

detailed examples background data specific instances analogies
statistics explanations of logic testimonies of authorities

Yes No — Does this argument contain positive information supporting the present system as well as information refuting the Exercise 3 argument?
+ √ – Is this argument adequately documented and supported?
+ √ – Does this argument refute its counterpart in Assignment 3?

Explain why this counterargument is or is not effective and how to improve it.

____

____

____

(Write additional comments on paper)

Subargument two: Read the Assignment 3 paper. Write the second subargument in that paper on the line below: *(If a substitute argument is used to replace this argument, write the substitute argument here.)* ______________________

____

____

Read the second counterargument. Write it down: ______________________

____

____

Do these two arguments match? Yes ______ No ______

Which of the following forms of support are used to back the counter argument?

detailed examples background data specific instances analogies
statistics explanations of logic testimonies of authorities

Yes	No	
		Does this argument contain positive information supporting the present system as as well as information refuting the Exercise 3 arguments?
+ √ −		Is this argument adequately documented and supported?
+ √ −		Does this argument refute its counterpart in Assignment 3?
		Explain why this counterargument is or is not effective and how to improve it.

____

____

____

(Write additional comments on paper)

Subargument three: Read the Assignment 3 paper. Write the third subargument in that paper on the line below: (*If a substitute argument is used to replace this argument, write the substitute argument here.*)____________________________________

____

____

Read the third counterargument. Write it down:____________________________________

____

____

____

Do these two arguments match? Yes_____ No _____

Which of the following forms of support are used to back the counterargument?

detailed examples   background data   specific instances   analogies
statistics   explanations of logic   testimonies of authorities

Yes	No	
		Does this argument contain positive information supporting the present system as well as information refuting the Exercise 3 arguments?
+ √ −		Is this argument adequately documented and supported?
+ √ −		Does this argument refute its counterpart in Assignment 3?
		Explain why this counterargument is or is not effective and how to improve it.

____

____

____

(Write additional comments on paper)

+ √ −	Are possible negative side effects of the Exercise 4 plan exposed?
+ √ −	Does the refutation of the plan identify all possible discrepancies between what the need argument calls for and what the plan actually does? Explain below how to improve the refutation of the plan.

____

____

____

(Write additional comments on paper)

Did the conclusion:

+ √ −	1. Summarize the counterarguments effectively?
+ √ −	2. Restate the topic proposal?
+ √ −	3. Draw a conclusion for the reader that the proposal had been refuted and should be rejected?
+ √ −	4. Do something to make you reflect back over the topic?

See explanation of grading criteria on page 100.

												Raw Score		Weight		Weighted Grades
Criteria I	1	2	3	4	5	6	7	8	9	10	=	_____	X	1	=	_____
Criteria II	1	2	3	4	5	6	7	8	9	10	=	_____	X	3	=	_____
Criteria III	1	2	3	4	5	6	7	8	9	10	=	_____	X	6	=	_____

Sum Grade _____

Transfer the weighted grades to the Exercise 5 Grading Form (page 227).

Note: This Feedback Form is to be attached (staple or paper clip) to the front of the student's paper and returned to him with the graded paper.

Your Name ____________________
No.________ Group________ Sec.________

EXERCISE 5: Feedback Form to Author

Yes No Does this paper contain at least 3 references?
Yes No Is this paper between 3½ and 4½ pages in length?
Yes No Is each section of this paper identified by a heading?

If the answer to any of the above questions is no, the paper is unacceptable, and must be redone. Give the paper a grade of 1 on Criterion II. However, finish evaluating this paper and give it a grade.

+ √ − Does the introduction gain and focus your attention?
+ √ − Is there anything in this paper to build rapport?
+ √ − Is this paper organized so that it is easy to follow—to identify the subsections?
If √ or - is circled above, explain how to correct the shortcoming.

____

____

____

____

(Write additional comments on paper)

Arguments showing a need for change.

Subargument one: Read the Assignment 3 paper. Write the first subargument in that paper on the line below: (*If a substitute argument is used to replace this argument, write the substitute argument here.*)____________________

____

____

____

Read the first counterargument. Write it down: ____________________

____

____

Do these two arguments match? Yes_______ No_______
Which of the following forms of support are used to back the counter argument?
detailed examples background data specific instances analogies
statistics explanations of logic testimonies of authorities

Yes No Does this argument contain positive information supporting the present system as well as information refuting the Exercise 3 argument?
+ √ − Is this argument adequately documented and supported?
+ √ − Does this argument refute its counterpart in Assignment 3?
Explain why this counterargument is or is not effective and how to improve it.

____

____

____

(Write additional comments on paper)

Subargument two: Read the Assignment 3 paper. Write the second subargument in that paper on the line below: (*If a substitute argument is used to replace this argument, write the substitute argument here.*)____________________

____

____

Read the second counterargument. Write it down: ____________________

____

____

Do these two arguments match? Yes_____No______
Which of the following forms of support are used to back the counter argument?
detailed examples background data specific instances analogies
statistics explanations of logic testimonies of authorities

Yes No — Does this argument contain positive information supporting the present system as as well as information refuting the Exercise 3 arguments?

+ √ − Is this argument adequately documented and supported?

+ √ − Does this argument refute its counterpart in Assignment 3?

Explain why this counterargument is or is not effective and how to improve it.

____

____

____

(Write additional comments on paper)

Subargument three: Read the Assignment 3 paper. Write the third subargument in that paper on the line below: (*If a substitute argument is used to replace this argument, write the substitute argument here.*) ____________________

____

____

Read the third counterargument. Write it down: ____________________

____

____

____

Do these two arguments match? Yes_____ No _____

Which of the following forms of support are used to back the counterargument?

detailed examples background data specific instances analogies

statistics explanations of logic testimonies of authorities

Yes No — Does this argument contain positive information supporting the present system as well as information refuting the Exercise 3 arguments?

+ √ − Is this argument adequately documented and supported?

+ √ − Does this argument refute its counterpart in Assignment 3?

Explain why this counterargument is or is not effective and how to improve it.

____

____

____

(Write additional comments on paper)

+ √ − Are possible negative side effects of the Exercise 4 plan exposed?

+ √ − Does the refutation of the plan identify all possible discrepancies between what the need argument calls for and what the plan actually does? Explain below how to improve the refutation of the plan.

____

____

____

(Write additional comments on paper)

Did the conclusion:

+ √ − 1. Summarize the counterarguments effectively?

+ √ − 2. Restate the topic proposal?

+ √ − 3. Draw a conclusion for the reader that the proposal had been refuted and should be rejected?

+ √ − 4. Do something to make you reflect back over the topic?

See explanation of grading criteria on page 100.

												Raw Score		Weight		Weighted Grades
Criteria I	1	2	3	4	5	6	7	8	9	10	=	_____	X	1	=	_____
Criteria II	1	2	3	4	5	6	7	8	9	10	=	_____	X	3	=	_____
Criteria III	1	2	3	4	5	6	7	8	9	10	=	_____	X	6	=	_____

Sum Grade _____

Transfer the weighted grades to the Exercise 5 Grading Form (page 227).

Note: This Feedback Form is to be attached (staple or paper clip) to the front of the student's paper and returned to him with the graded paper.

Your Name ______________________
No. ________ Group ________ Sec. ________

Exercise 5

GRADING FORM

Paper Copy No.	Author's Name and	No.		Weighted Grade on Criteria			Sum Grade
1	________	No. ____	I ____	II ____	III ____	=	☐
2	________	No. ____	I ____	II ____	III ____	=	☐
3	________	No. ____	I ____	II ____	III ____	=	☐
4	________	No. ____	I ____	II ____	III ____	=	☐
5	________	No. ____	I ____	II ____	III ____	=	☐
6	________	No. ____	I ____	II ____	III ____	=	☐
7	________	No. ____	I ____	II ____	III ____	=	☐
8	________	No. ____	I ____	II ____	III ____	=	☐
9	________	No. ____	I ____	II ____	III ____	=	☐
10	________	No. ____	I ____	II ____	III ____	=	☐
11	________	No. ____	I ____	II ____	III ____	=	☐
12	________	No. ____	I ____	II ____	III ____	=	☐
	________	No. ____	I ____	II ____	III ____	=	☐
	________	No. ____	I ____	II ____	III ____	=	☐

	I	II	III	=	
Totals	I ____	II ____	III ____	=	____
divided by number graded	____	____	____	=	____
equals the average grade given by you	I ____	II ____	III ____	=	____

Give this form to your instructor on the day the graded papers are returned to the authors. That due date is ______________________

Your Name ______________________

No. ________ Group ________ Sec. ________

Exercise 5

AUTHOR'S GRADE RECORD FORM

Record the grades you received on this form.

Your Copy No.	Evaluator No.	Weighted Grade on Criteria:				Sum Grade
1.	________	I ______	II ______	III ______	=	______
2.	________	I ______	II ______	III ______	=	______
3.	________	I ______	II ______	III ______	=	______
4.	________	I ______	II ______	III ______	=	______
5.	________	I ______	II ______	III ______	=	______
6.	________	I ______	II ______	III ______	=	______
7.	________	I ______	II ______	III ______	=	______
8.	________	I ______	II ______	III ______	=	______
9.	________	I ______	II ______	III ______	=	______
10.	________	I ______	II ______	III ______	=	______
11.	________	I ______	II ______	III ______	=	______
12.	________	I ______	II ______	III ______	=	______
	________	I ______	II ______	III ______	=	______
	________	I ______	II ______	III ______	=	______

Sum of Grades	I ______	II ______	III ______	=	______
divided by number of graders	______	______	______		______
equals the average grade you received	I ______	II ______	III ______	=	[ ] This is your *Sum Grade Average*

When this form is completed, record your Sum Grade Average on the Class Grade Summary Sheet. Use the column headed Exercise 5 Paper Grade. This form is to be given to the instructor no later than one class period after you have received your graded papers.

This form is due on ______________________.

Note: If you have any grades of 1 (weighted grades of 3) for Criteria II, bring the grading sheets and your papers to the instructor, who will decide what you need to do to make your paper acceptable. Until your paper is acceptable, you cannot do the next written assignment.

Your Name ____________________
No.________ Group__________ Sec.______

Exercise 5

GRADER QUALITY REPORT

This written assignment requires a great deal of effort on the part of the graders. If they do not carefully read and evaluate your paper, they cannot give you proper feedback on how to improve. Some graders may not be aware that their feedback is either incomplete or superficial. This form is designed to provide such information to each grader. Go over each feedback sheet before filling out this form. Then use this form to grade the quality of the feedback to you.

Rate each category 1 = very superior 2 = excellent 3 = O.K. 4 = below average X = very poor

Paper Copy No.	Grader No.	Category A Checklists on feed-back form were filled out completely	Category B Suggestions on how to improve were written out	Category C The quality of suggestions on how to improve were
1	______	______	______	______
2	______	______	______	______
3	______	______	______	______
4	______	______	______	______
5	______	______	______	______
6	______	______	______	______
7	______	______	(Do not rate 7-12 on Categories B or C)	
8	______	______		
9	______	______		
10	______	______		
11	______	______		
12	______	______		

Note: The X rating is designed to identify students who need special help. It is not a punishment. If you give an evaluator an "X" rating, take your paper which he graded and his Feedback Form to the instructor. The instructor will return these to the evaluator and will show him how to improve the quality of his feedback. When the re-evaluation is done, the paper is to be returned to the instructor so the X can be removed. All X's must be removed before a student can grade the next written assignment.

A master chart containing each student's number will be posted in the room. Record ratings on that chart in *pen*. The column on the left of the chart will contain the number of the student evaluator you are rating. The top of the chart lists your number as the rater.

	1	2	3	4
1				
2		223		
3		334		
4		32X		

If you are student No. 2 and you gave evaluator No. 4 an O.K. (3) in category A, an excellent (2) in category B, and a very poor (X) in category C, his grade would be recorded as shown in the sample chart as 32X. Put only one number in the square of evaluators who had your paper copies 7-12.

EXERCISE 6

Teamwork

PURPOSE OF ASSIGNMENT

In this exercise you will practice working in teams. The research and preparation of proposals will be done by teams of two. The evaluation of the proposals and the counterarguments will be done by teams of four. The main focus of this exercise is on learning to listen to and share ideas with others.

Introduction

In a school setting, normally individual work is stressed. This is basically because of the need to measure and grade individual progress. In the business world, group work is much more common because there is less need to identify individual contribution. There is more concern with how much is produced and with the quality of the work produced than with who produced it. This will also be the concern of Exercise 6. We will focus on teamwork. By working with others, you have a chance to learn from their ideas, mistakes, and suggestions. You also learn to help each other. Helping others is one of the most important tasks of any good manager. In Exercise 6 you will also pull together all of the material you have prepared for Exercises 3, 4, and 5. Working with your partner, you are to prepare a complete proposal supporting the class topic. In this proposal, you are to show that there is a need to change, to present a plan of how to bring about the needed change, and to show the benefits of the proposed change over the current system.

The feedback sessions will be the most important part of this exercise. After each person presents his or her material, each workshop group will spend 20 to 25 minutes going over the logic and the adequacy of the documentation used to support the presentation. Each workshop member is also to present counterarguments and evidence so that the group can have an in-depth discussion-debate of the pros and cons of the resolution.

PREASSIGNMENT INSTRUCTIONS

Selection of Partners

Before you begin working on this presentation, you must have a partner. You will be allowed to choose your own partner. Those who have no preference of partners will be assigned one by the instructor. The partner you choose will also be your partner for Exercise 8.

SOME MORE BASICS: PART I

Internal consistency is one of the most important aspects of any presentation. In this exercise there are three primary aspects of the proposal that you must convey to the audience. You must show that there is a need to change from the present system; you must show how that change can be brought about; and you must show the advantage of the proposed new system as compared to the old. These three aspects of the proposal must be consistent with each other. If the need argument states that the present system is too slow, you must offer a plan that would create a faster system. This new system must not only be faster, but it must also have minimal negative side effects. For example, democracy is a slow way of making laws. We could replace it with a dictatorship. Dictatorships can enact laws rapidly—if we are willing to give up our freedom. The need for and the plan of a dictatorship might be consistent, but the side effects are so great that the proposal is not likely to be accepted.

The need for change arguments must show a need for the specific changes called for by the topic. We will once again use the no-fault auto insurance topic as an example.

The need arguments must show that there is a need for a no-fault auto insurance system. As was pointed out in Exercise 3 under the heading "Inherency," there is no value in just showing the need for mass marketing auto insurance. There are many auto insurance plans other than no-fault that can be mass marketed. It is not enough that the need arguments show a need for mass marketing, nor is it enough for the plan to show how mass marketing would work. Neither argument supports the proposal to adopt a no-fault auto insurance plan. The arguments showing a need for a change and for the proposed plan of change are not inherently related to the topic proposal. We could adopt mass marketing without adopting no-fault.

Another common inconsistency is when the need for change arguments point out a problem that the proposed plan of change will not correct. An example would be when a person argues that the present system is too expensive and then includes nothing in his proposed plan to save money. Such proposals are easily rejected. Opponents can accept the argument that there is a need to save money. Then, they simply reject the proposal because the plan does not offer a money-saving solution.

The benefits of the proposed change must also be consistent with need to change arguments and with the proposed plan. Usually the arguments showing the benefits of the plan are the arguments that tie the whole presentation together. For example, we might point out that one benefit of the proposed no-fault insurance plan would be that it saves money. We might then point out that one of our arguments for changing from the present system is that current insurance rates are unreasonably high. Then we would point out as a benefit argument how our proposed no-fault insurance plan would cause premiums to be lowered. We could go even further and present evidence to show that in states having no-fault insurance plans premiums actually have been lowered. We could use statistics and analogies to show how much lower premiums would be in our state if our plan were adopted. In this example, the arguments for change, the proposed plan, and the benefits of that plan all tie together to make a consistent total case. If our arguments and ideas are internally consistent with each other, then our proposal is much more likely to be accepted.

ASSIGNMENT INSTRUCTIONS

Each team is to carefully review the material both members used for Exercises 3, 4, and 5. Each team should also review the ideas picked up from reading or listening to presentations of others in the class. The two members of one team may even want to get together with other teams and exchange ideas and sources.

With the research material fresh in your minds, prepare, as a team, a single 10-minute presentation supporting the class topic. Although you will prepare this presentation jointly, you will present it separately for Exercise 6. This presentation must show there is a need to change from the present system, a plan by which this change could be brought about, and advantages of the proposed change over the current system.

Pointing, running summaries, and adequate forms of support should be used in this presentation. No specific requirements are made regarding the use of any of these. Beginning with this presentation, you are freer to start developing your own style.

Defense

After your team's presentation favoring the topic is prepared, list all of the possible counterarguments.

As you think of each counterargument or objection that might be made, try to think of how you could refute that argument or objection. Write down these counterarguments and identify what pieces of documentation the two of you have or need to get to support the counterarguments.

Next, go one step further. List how you could counter these counter-counterarguments if you were opposing the topic. Again, write down the counter-counterarguments you would use, and identify the documentation you have or need to have available to support those arguments. You will need these counter and counter-counterarguments for the workshop sessions in this exercise. This counter material should be as carefully prepared as are the presentations.

Write Out Counter Arguments

Each team must write out at least four counterarguments and at least two counter-counterarguments with a brief explanation of the logic and documentation to support each. These arguments are to be typed. The typed copy is to be no more than 3 nor less than 2 pages in length, single-spaced. Each team is to give the instructor one copy of its counterarguments on the day of the class review session. Make sure that both team members have a copy to use in the Exercise 6 feedback, discussion-debate sessions.

Speaking Notes

The presentation of the Exercise 6 assignment is to be given from notes. It is *not* to be written, read, or memorized. The speaking notes should be similar to those used for Exercise 4 (see Exercise 4, page 171).

Organization of Groups

Each team will be divided for the workshops. To set up the workshops, one member of each team will go to the right side of the room and one will go to the left. Those on the left will count off by 4's, as will those on the right. Each set of four persons will form a workshop group. This system assures that the two team members will be in different groups, so they will each be exposed to different ideas and plans.

Group Coordinator and Timer

The person who was "number one" in the count off that formed each group will be the Group Coordinator. He or she will keep a record of attendance and tardiness and will give that report to the instructor. He or she will also time the first speaker. The first speaker will be the "number four" person in the count off. That person is to be the timer for all remaining speakers and for the feedback sessions.

Presentations and Time Limits

Each presentation should last 10 minutes. The presentations should be followed by a 20- to 25-minute feedback, discussion-debate session, in which the other three members in the group present counterarguments and evidence. These discussion-debate sessions are to be at least 20 minutes long; do not cut them short.

Goal of the Feedback. The goal in presenting the counterarguments is *not* to knock down the speakers' arguments and plans; rather, it is to show their weaknesses and *how they can overcome them.* You can expose weaknesses in the speakers' arguments but you must be sure to help them build up the arguments again with new arguments or ideas. It is most important to remember that when you are an evaluator, you are to be a helper, not a critic. Your role is that of a friend helping the speaker to prepare to face real opposition later. These sessions should be very informal. The main purpose is to share ideas. If one person has a good quote or idea, he or she should share it with all in the group.

Taking Notes in Workshop. At the end of the workshop meetings, each person will have heard the complete proposals of three other teams and the counterarguments opposing each case. Since partners are not in the same workshops, each team of two will have heard six other teams cases.

You should take notes on these other proposals so that you can add these ideas to your own before beginning the two most important exercises, Exercises 7 and 8.

At the end of the discussion-debate session, the speaker should review with his group the counterarguments to the case which he and his partner wrote out for the in-class review.

SOME MORE BASICS: PART II

How to Take Listening Notes

We have already discussed how to make research and speaking notes. Now we are going to focus on how to take notes as a listener. Almost any time a group of businessmen attend a meeting, each will have a pad for taking notes. The purpose of taking notes is to aid our recall later so we can remember the points made in the meeting.

Taking notes can be greatly simplified if you have already learned to listen carefully and to organize your notes. Since you are already familiar with the type of organization the speakers are going to use, your listening and your note-taking will be greatly simplified. To refresh your memory on this organization, you may wish to look over the Exercise 6 Feedback Form. It outlines the organization the speakers are to follow. Taking notes also will help during the discussion-debate sessions and will provide a record to use later when you discuss the proposals with your partner.

While taking notes for Exercise 6, use the note sheet provided (page 259) to outline each speaker's presentation as he or she gives it. The following is a description of the main items to outline a proposal.

1. Before the presentation begins, write the topic statement at the top of your sheet. As the presentation begins, listen for the operational definitions of the terms used in the topic statement. If the definitions sound questionable, make a brief note to that effect. Do not write an explanation of why they are questionable or you might miss what comes next. To provide an example of how to write brief notes, let's assume that a speaker defined "nuclear weapons" to include nuclear-powered submarines. We might conclude from such a definition that an unarmed nuclear-powered research submarine would be a nuclear weapon. Such a definition would be questionable. On the note sheet you might write:

Topic Statement:	Counterarguments:
All aboveground nuclear testing should be halted. Definition? Unarmed vessel weapon?	

These notes are enough to remind you that you wanted to question that definition.

2. Write the speaker's first argument. We will assume that his argument is: "Testing of nuclear weapons must be outlawed because the radioactive fallout is contaminating the air we breathe." On the note sheet, you should write:

Topic Statement:	Counterarguments
All aboveground nuclear testing should be halted. Definition? Unarmed vessel weapon? Need for change: 1. Fallout contaminates air.	

Note that there is no need to write out each argument, word for word.

3. Write what material the speaker uses to support the argument. For example, a quote may have been given by Dr. Linus Pauling, stating that the radioactivity in the air has increased following nuclear testing to a level that is causing birth defects. On the note sheet, you might write only:

Topic Statement:	Counterarguments
All aboveground nuclear testing should be halted. Definition: Unarmed vessel weapon? Need for change: 1. Fallout contaminates air. A. Linus Pauling: caused birth defects, (statistics) 1962 study.	

You need write only a brief note on each argument and each piece of support offered. In parentheses, write what form of support was used. Make brief notes so you do not fail to listen to the second argument while trying to write notes on the first. During the discussion period, you can ask the speaker to give you the exact source if you wish to look it up.

4. When the speaker begins to present the proposal on how to change, write on the note sheet the heading, "Proposal" or "Plan of Change."

3. Cause accidental war

    A. Radical dictator might develop weapons.
        1. Spain situation (detailed example)

        2. Argentina

    B. Have started wars for frivolous reasons in past. (historical data, specific instances)

Plan of Change:

1. Have the U.N. draft a treaty that all members might sign.

2. Appoint international inspection team.

5. When the speaker begins listing the advantage of his proposed change over the present system, write on the note sheet "Advantages."

2. Appoint international inspection team.

Advantages:

1. The amount of radioactivity in air would be reduced.
    "British Med J." report,
    Pauling (testimony)

The notes should be written briefly during a presentation. You can use the speakers' running summaries as a means of checking your notes. For this reason, it is important that as a speaker you use clear running and final summaries in your presentation.

Counterargument Notes

Following each presentation, take 3 or 4 minutes to write on your note sheet, opposite each argument, key counterarguments you might use against the proposal. Document these counterarguments when possible from the research files you generated for Exercise 5. Do not forget to take notes on the counter and counter-counterarguments offered by others in the discussion period.

PROCEDURES FOR PRESENTATIONS

Practice

For Exercise 6 you each have the advantage of having a partner to work with. Use your partner as an audience while practicing. This will give each of you a chance to sit back and listen to your team's entire presentation. It will also give each of you a chance to practice taking notes. Use the Exercise 6 Feedback Form as a checklist to make sure you have included all necessary parts in your presentation. Also be sure to practice giving and discussing counterarguments after the presentation. This discussion part of Exercise 6 is even more important than the presentation part. Note that while each person gives only a 10-minute presentation, you each participate in 80 to 100 minutes of feedback and discussion of counter and counter-counterarguments.

Class Review

You will spend one or two days in class reviewing this assignment before you form small workshop groups. In the review session, you will first give the instructor a copy of each team's list of counter and counter-counterarguments. Then, you will review these arguments.

One or two workshop groups will appear before the class to go through a complete presentation and review. During the presentation, you will all participate by filling out a Note Sheet and a Feedback Form. Following the discussion part of the session, you will each rate and rank the three persons giving the feedback. The key elements that you will be listening for are (1) Were their comments specific and constructive? (2) Did they present good counterarguments? (3) Did they figure out a way to counter the counterarguments. By observing one group and discussing each member's behavior, you can get ideas on what to do and what to avoid doing in your own workshops.

Grading Criteria

Fill out a Feedback Form (page 243) for each speaker. Then, transfer the grades on the Feedback Form to the Exercise 6 Grading Form. Give this Grading Form to your Group Coordinator.

There are three general criteria to use in grading the Exercise 6 presentation.

Criterion I. Presentation. Consider under Criterion I eye contact, vocal quality, stance, dress, volume, and any other factor affecting your response to the speaker apart from the organization or content of his message. Also consider whether or not the speaker created an air of preparedness, confidence, and enthusiasm.

Criterion II. Organization of presentation. Consider under Criterion II how accurately the author conformed to the exact layout specified for this presentation. Use the checklists on the Feedback Form as a guide to show whether or not the author included all that he was supposed to in the organization of this presentation. Remember, Exercise 6 permits us freedom of how to organize our material as long as the presentation achieves its purpose. No set organizational format is required.

Criterion III. Content of presentation. Consider under Criterion III the logic of the author's arguments and the adequacy of the material used to support them. Check the inherency of each subargument and the appropriateness and adequacy of the forms of support used to substantiate them. Be careful to note whether or not there is consistency in the argument for change, the proposed plan, and the advantages attributed to the change. These arguments should all support each other.

Some Grading Guides. In grading this presentation, it should be assumed that the student, as a minimum, will have acceptable delivery. That is, his stance, eye contact, and vocal quality will be acceptable. If any of these delivery problems are noticed, be sure to call them to the speaker's attention during the feedback.

Exercises 3 and 4 focused on organization of material. Organization is important in Exercise 6 even though it is no longer the primary focus. It is assumed that presentations for Exercise 6 will be well organized and use adequate and appropriate forms of support.

The main focus for grading Exercise 6 is on content. In this assignment, you will give each member of your workshop group two grades. The first grade is to be based on the student's presentation. The second grade is to be based on each student's performance during the feedback, discussion-debate sessions. *Grade the students on how they performed in ALL of the feedback sessions*, not just on the feedback they gave you. The purpose of the feedback, discussion-debate session is that the group helps each other develop stronger arguments, both supporting and opposing the topic. Each of you as group members is expected to offer documented counterarguments.

FIGURE 3-4 Meaning of Number Grades

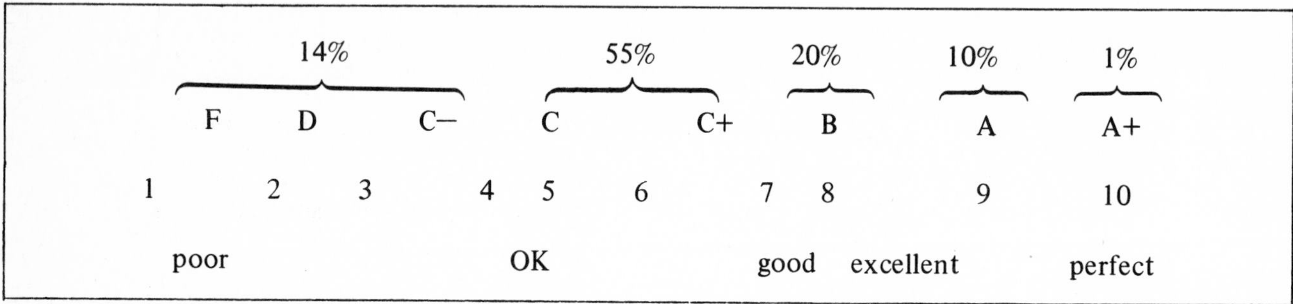

EXERCISE 6 CHECKLISTS

Checklist of Things to Do (before coming to class)

1. Together with your teammate, review the arguments, ideas, documentation, and plans that you have used or heard others use in Exercises 2, 3, 4, and 5.
2. Together with your teammate, prepare a 10-minute presentation supporting the class topic. The presentation must show a need for change, a plan by which the change can be brought about, and a comparison of the benefits of that plan to the present system.
3. Prepare a set of speaking notes similar to those used in Exercise 4. Bring these notes to the in-class review session.
4. Together with your teammate, write at least four counterarguments and two counter-counterarguments and document them. (Length limit is 2 to 3 pages.) Bring these typed sheets of counterarguments to the in-class review session.
5. Practice giving your presentation to your partner.
6. Practice taking listening notes while your partner practices his presentation. Then present counterarguments and counter those counterarguments.

Checklist for Conducting Workshops

1. The student in your workshop who was number one in the count off that formed your group is to be the group coordinator. (If he or she has been a group coordinator previously, then go to the person with the next highest number.) The group coordinator is to do the following:
   a. Call the group together and take attendance.
   b. Time the first speaker.
   c. Coordinate all activities of the workshop and make sure that the group complies with the instructions for the assignment.
   d. At the end of the workshop, fill out the Group Coordinator's Grade Summary Sheet and the Group Coordinator's Feedback Grade Summary Sheet.

2. The student in your group who was four in the count off that formed your group is to be the first speaker and then the timer for all presentations that follow.

3. The time limits are as follows:
   10 minutes for presentations.
   3 minutes for filling out Feedback Forms.
   20 to 25 minutes for discussion-debate session; do not cut these sessions short.
   2 to 4 minutes for filling out checklists on the Discussion-Debate Session Evaluation and Feedback Form.

4. As a listener, you must fill out listening Note Sheets. Show these to the speakers for their comments on whether or not your notes adequately reflect what they said.

Your Name ______________________
No. ________ Group ________ Sec. ________

Exercise 6

FEEDBACK FORM
Feedback to Author ______________________ **No.** ________

Instructions: Use this Feedback Form as a guide of what to include on your Note Sheet. *Do not* attempt to fill out this form while listening to a speaker. Fill it out after the speaker is finished. You have your Note Sheet to help you remember what was discussed. Filling out this form from your Note Sheet is a good test of your listening and note-taking ability. If you did a good job of listening and note-taking, this form should be simple to complete.

Introduction:

+ √ – Introduction gained and focused attention?
+ √ – Topic was clearly stated and defined?
+ √ – Forecast summary was clear and complete? It outlined: (1) a need for a change, (2) a proposed plan of change, and (3) the benefits of the change?

I. *Subpart One*: Need for change arguments:

+ √ – Arguments showing needs for a change were clearly introduced.
+ √ – Forecast summary of need for change subarguments was clear.

1. First argument showing a need for change was supported using which of the following forms of support?

____ detailed example ____ specific instances ____ background data
____ analogy ____ statistics
____ explanation of logic ____ authority

+ √ – Was this a good subargument to support this case?
+ √ – Was this argument supported adequately with information and documentation?
+ √ – Is this argument inherently related to the topic?

2. Second argument showing a need for change was supported using which of the following forms of support?

____ detailed example ____ specific instances ____ background data
____ analogy ____ statistics
____ explanation of logic ____ authority

+ √ – Was this a good subargument to support this case?
+ √ – Did this speaker do a good job of developing this argument to inform and persuade you?
+ √ – Is this argument inherently related to the topic?

3. Third argument showing a need for change was supported using which of the following forms of support?

____ detailed example ____ specific instances ____ background data
____ analogy ____ statistics
____ explanation of logic ____ authority

+ √ – Was this a good subargument to support this case?
+ √ – Did this speaker do a good job of developing this argument to inform you and persuade you?
+ √ – Is this argument inherently related to the topic?

II. *Subpart Two*: Proposed plan of change:

+ √ — will remove or greatly reduce the problem described in 1.
+ √ — will remove or greatly reduce the problem described in 2.
+ √ — will remove or greatly reduce the problem described in 3.
+ √ — This proposed plan of change seems practical and workable.
+ √ — This proposed plan of change was clearly explained.

III. *Subpart Three*: Advantages of the change:

+ √ — Arguments showing advantages of the proposed change were introduced?
+ √ — A forecast summary of subarguments relating to the advantages was clear? (This forecast summary may be omitted if not needed for clarity.)
+ √ — The first advantage argument was adequately explained and documented?
+ √ — The second advantage argument was adequately explained and documented?
+ √ — The third advantage argument was adequately explained and documented?

Conclusion:

+ √ — The conclusion contained a summary?
+ √ — The conclusion tied together (1) the argument for a change, (2) the proposed plan of change and, (3) the advantages of the change?
+ √ — The logic of the presentation held together so that it could be easily followed.

Grades (See criteria explanation on page 239.)

	(Circle one and record it as the raw score)	Raw Score	X	Weight	=	Weighted Score
Criteria I	1 2 3 4 5 6 7 8 9 10=	____	X	1	=	____
Criteria II	1 2 3 4 5 6 7 8 9 10=	____	X	3	=	____
Criteria III	1 2 3 4 5 6 7 8 9 10=	____	X	6	=	____
		Weighted Sum Grade				____

Transfer weighted grades to the Exercise 6 Grading Form.

Your Name ____________________
No.________ Group________ Sec.________

Exercise 6

FEEDBACK FORM
Feedback to Author ____________________ **No.**________

Instructions: Use this Feedback Form as a guide of what to include on your Note Sheet. *Do not* attempt to fill out this form while listening to a speaker. Fill it out after the speaker is finished. You have your Note Sheet to help you remember what was discussed. Filling out this form from your Note Sheet is a good test of your listening and note-taking ability. If you did a good job of listening and note-taking, this form should be simple to complete.

Introduction:

+ √ – Introduction gained and focused attention?
+ √ – Topic was clearly stated and defined?
+ √ – Forecast summary was clear and complete? It outlined: (1) a need for a change, (2) a proposed plan of change, and (3) the benefits of the change?

I. *Subpart One*: Need for change arguments:

+ √ – Arguments showing needs for a change were clearly introduced.
+ √ – Forecast summary of need for change subarguments was clear.

1. First argument showing a need for change was supported using which of the following forms of support?

____ detailed example ____ specific instances ____ background data
____ analogy ____ statistics
____ explanation of logic ____ authority

+ √ – Was this a good subargument to support this case?
+ √ – Was this argument supported adequately with information and documentation?
+ √ – Is this argument inherently related to the topic?

2. Second argument showing a need for change was supported using which of the following forms of support?

____ detailed example ____ specific instances ____ background data
____ analogy ____ statistics
____ explanation of logic ____ authority

+ √ – Was this a good subargument to support this case?
+ √ – Did this speaker do a good job of developing this argument to inform and persuade you?
+ √ – Is this argument inherently related to the topic?

3. Third argument showing a need for change was supported using which of the following forms of support?

____ detailed example ____ specific instances ____ background data
____ analogy ____ statistics
____ explanation of logic ____ authority

+ √ – Was this a good subargument to support this case?
+ √ – Did this speaker do a good job of developing this argument to inform you and persuade you?
+ √ – Is this argument inherently related to the topic?

II. *Subpart Two*: Proposed plan of change:

+ √ − will remove or greatly reduce the problem described in 1.
+ √ − will remove or greatly reduce the problem described in 2.
+ √ − will remove or greatly reduce the problem described in 3.
+ √ − This proposed plan of change seems practical and workable.
+ √ − This proposed plan of change was clearly explained.

III. *Subpart Three*: Advantages of the change:

+ √ − Arguments showing advantages of the proposed change were introduced?
+ √ − A forecast summary of subarguments relating to the advantages was clear? (This forecast summary may be omitted if not needed for clarity.)
+ √ − The first advantage argument was adequately explained and documented?
+ √ − The second advantage argument was adequately explained and documented?
+ √ − The third advantage argument was adequately explained and documented?

Conclusion:

+ √ − The conclusion contained a summary?
+ √ − The conclusion tied together (1) the argument for a change, (2) the proposed plan of change and, (3) the advantages of the change?
+ √ − The logic of the presentation held together so that it could be easily followed.

Grades (See criteria explanation on page 239.)

	(Circle one and record it as the raw score)	Raw Score	X	Weight	=	Weighted Score
Criteria I	1 2 3 4 5 6 7 8 9 10=	____	X	1	=	____
Criteria II	1 2 3 4 5 6 7 8 9 10=	____	X	3	=	____
Criteria III	1 2 3 4 5 6 7 8 9 10=	____	X	6	=	____
		Weighted Sum Grade				____

Transfer weighted grades to the Exercise 6 Grading Form.

Your Name ____________________
No. ______ Group ______ Sec. ______

Exercise 6

FEEDBACK FORM
Feedback to Author ____________________ No. ______

Instructions: Use this Feedback Form as a guide of what to include on your Note Sheet. *Do not* attempt to fill out this form while listening to a speaker. Fill it out after the speaker is finished. You have your Note Sheet to help you remember what was discussed. Filling out this form from your Note Sheet is a good test of your listening and note-taking ability. If you did a good job of listening and note-taking, this form should be simple to complete.

Introduction:

+ √ − Introduction gained and focused attention?
+ √ − Topic was clearly stated and defined?
+ √ − Forecast summary was clear and complete? It outlined: (1) a need for a change, (2) a proposed plan of change, and (3) the benefits of the change?

I. *Subpart One*: Need for change arguments:

+ √ − Arguments showing needs for a change were clearly introduced.
+ √ − Forecast summary of need for change subarguments was clear.

1. First argument showing a need for change was supported using which of the following forms of support?

____ detailed example ____ specific instances ____ background data
____ analogy ____ statistics
____ explanation of logic ____ authority

+ √ − Was this a good subargument to support this case?
+ √ − Was this argument supported adequately with information and documentation?
+ √ − Is this argument inherently related to the topic?

2. Second argument showing a need for change was supported using which of the following forms of support?

____ detailed example ____ specific instances ____ background data
____ analogy ____ statistics
____ explanation of logic ____ authority

+ √ − Was this a good subargument to support this case?
+ √ − Did this speaker do a good job of developing this argument to inform and persuade you?
+ √ − Is this argument inherently related to the topic?

3. Third argument showing a need for change was supported using which of the following forms of support?

____ detailed example ____ specific instances ____ background data
____ analogy ____ statistics
____ explanation of logic ____ authority

+ √ − Was this a good subargument to support this case?
+ √ − Did this speaker do a good job of developing this argument to inform you and persuade you?
+ √ − Is this argument inherently related to the topic?

II. *Subpart Two*: Proposed plan of change:

+ √ – will remove or greatly reduce the problem described in 1.
+ √ – will remove or greatly reduce the problem described in 2.
+ √ – will remove or greatly reduce the problem described in 3.
+ √ – This proposed plan of change seems practical and workable.
+ √ – This proposed plan of change was clearly explained.

III. *Subpart Three*: Advantages of the change:

+ √ – Arguments showing advantages of the proposed change were introduced?
+ √ – A forecast summary of subarguments relating to the advantages was clear? (This forecast summary may be omitted if not needed for clarity.)
+ √ – The first advantage argument was adequately explained and documented?
+ √ – The second advantage argument was adequately explained and documented?
+ √ – The third advantage argument was adequately explained and documented?

Conclusion:

+ √ – The conclusion contained a summary?
+ √ – The conclusion tied together (1) the argument for a change, (2) the proposed plan of change and, (3) the advantages of the change?
+ √ – The logic of the presentation held together so that it could be easily followed.

Grades (See criteria explanation on page 239.)

	(Circle one and record it as the raw score)										Raw Score	X	Weight	=	Weighted Score
Criteria I	1	2	3	4	5	6	7	8	9	10=	____	X	1	=	____
Criteria II	1	2	3	4	5	6	7	8	9	10=	____	X	3	=	____
Criteria III	1	2	3	4	5	6	7	8	9	10=	____	X	6	=	____
											Weighted Sum Grade				____

Transfer weighted grades to the Exercise 6 Grading Form.

Your Name ______________________________

No.________ Group ________ Sec.__________

Exercise 6

FEEDBACK FORM

Feedback to Author______________________________ No. ________

Instructions: Use this Feedback Form as a guide of what to include on your Note Sheet. *Do not* attempt to fill out this form while listening to a speaker. Fill it out after the speaker is finished. You have your Note Sheet to help you remember what was discussed. Filling out this form from your Note Sheet is a good test of your listening and note-taking ability. If you did a good job of listening and note-taking, this form should be simple to complete.

Introduction:

+ √ — Introduction gained and focused attention?

+ √ — Topic was clearly stated and defined?

+ √ — Forecast summary was clear and complete? It outlined: (1) a need for a change, (2) a proposed plan of change, and (3) the benefits of the change?

I. *Subpart One*: Need for change arguments:

+ √ — Arguments showing needs for a change were clearly introduced.

+ √ — Forecast summary of need for change subarguments was clear.

1. First argument showing a need for change was supported using which of the following forms of support?

____ detailed example ____ specific instances ____ background data

____ analogy ____ statistics

____ explanation of logic ____ authority

+ √ — Was this a good subargument to support this case?

+ √ — Was this argument supported adequately with information and documentation?

+ √ — Is this argument inherently related to the topic?

2. Second argument showing a need for change was supported using which of the following forms of support?

____ detailed example ____ specific instances ____ background data

____ analogy ____ statistics

____ explanation of logic ____ authority

+ √ — Was this a good subargument to support this case?

+ √ — Did this speaker do a good job of developing this argument to inform and persuade you?

+ √ — Is this argument inherently related to the topic?

3. Third argument showing a need for change was supported using which of the following forms of support?

____ detailed example ____ specific instances ____ background data

____ analogy ____ statistics

____ explanation of logic ____ authority

+ √ — Was this a good subargument to support this case?

+ √ — Did this speaker do a good job of developing this argument to inform you and persuade you?

+ √ — Is this argument inherently related to the topic?

II. *Subpart Two*: Proposed plan of change:

+ √ − will remove or greatly reduce the problem described in 1.
+ √ − will remove or greatly reduce the problem described in 2.
+ √ − will remove or greatly reduce the problem described in 3.
+ √ − This proposed plan of change seems practical and workable.
+ √ − This proposed plan of change was clearly explained.

III. *Subpart Three*: Advantages of the change:

+ √ − Arguments showing advantages of the proposed change were introduced?
+ √ − A forecast summary of subarguments relating to the advantages was clear? (This forecast summary may be omitted if not needed for clarity.)
+ √ − The first advantage argument was adequately explained and documented?
+ √ − The second advantage argument was adequately explained and documented?
+ √ − The third advantage argument was adequately explained and documented?

Conclusion:

+ √ − The conclusion contained a summary?
+ √ − The conclusion tied together (1) the argument for a change, (2) the proposed plan of change and, (3) the advantages of the change?
+ √ − The logic of the presentation held together so that it could be easily followed.

Grades (See criteria explanation on page 239.)

	(Circle one and record it as the raw score)	Raw Score	X	Weight	=	Weighted Score
Criteria I	1 2 3 4 5 6 7 8 9 10=	____	X	1	=	____
Criteria II	1 2 3 4 5 6 7 8 9 10=	____	X	3	=	____
Criteria III	1 2 3 4 5 6 7 8 9 10=	____	X	6	=	____
				Weighted Sum Grade		____

Transfer weighted grades to the Exercise 6 Grading Form.

Your Name ______________________________
No. ________ Group ________ Sec. ________

Exercise 6

FEEDBACK FORM
Feedback to Author ____________________________ **No.** ________

Instructions: Use this Feedback Form as a guide of what to include on your Note Sheet. *Do not* attempt to fill out this form while listening to a speaker. Fill it out after the speaker is finished. You have your Note Sheet to help you remember what was discussed. Filling out this form from your Note Sheet is a good test of your listening and note-taking ability. If you did a good job of listening and note-taking, this form should be simple to complete.

Introduction:

+ √ — Introduction gained and focused attention?
+ √ — Topic was clearly stated and defined?
+ √ — Forecast summary was clear and complete? It outlined: (1) a need for a change, (2) a proposed plan of change, and (3) the benefits of the change?

I. *Subpart One*: Need for change arguments:

+ √ — Arguments showing needs for a change were clearly introduced.
+ √ — Forecast summary of need for change subarguments was clear.

1. First argument showing a need for change was supported using which of the following forms of support?

____ detailed example ____ specific instances ____ background data
____ analogy ____ statistics
____ explanation of logic ____ authority

+ √ — Was this a good subargument to support this case?
+ √ — Was this argument supported adequately with information and documentation?
+ √ — Is this argument inherently related to the topic?

2. Second argument showing a need for change was supported using which of the following forms of support?

____ detailed example ____ specific instances ____ background data
____ analogy ____ statistics
____ explanation of logic ____ authority

+ √ — Was this a good subargument to support this case?
+ √ — Did this speaker do a good job of developing this argument to inform and persuade you?
+ √ — Is this argument inherently related to the topic?

3. Third argument showing a need for change was supported using which of the following forms of support?

____ detailed example ____ specific instances ____ background data
____ analogy ____ statistics
____ explanation of logic ____ authority

+ √ — Was this a good subargument to support this case?
+ √ — Did this speaker do a good job of developing this argument to inform you and persuade you?
+ √ — Is this argument inherently related to the topic?

II. *Subpart Two*: Proposed plan of change:

+ √ – will remove or greatly reduce the problem described in 1.
+ √ – will remove or greatly reduce the problem described in 2.
+ √ – will remove or greatly reduce the problem described in 3.
+ √ – This proposed plan of change seems practical and workable.
+ √ – This proposed plan of change was clearly explained.

III. *Subpart Three*: Advantages of the change:

+ √ – Arguments showing advantages of the proposed change were introduced?
+ √ – A forecast summary of subarguments relating to the advantages was clear? (This forecast summary may be omitted if not needed for clarity.)
+ √ – The first advantage argument was adequately explained and documented?
+ √ – The second advantage argument was adequately explained and documented?
+ √ – The third advantage argument was adequately explained and documented?

Conclusion:

+ √ – The conclusion contained a summary?
+ √ – The conclusion tied together (1) the argument for a change, (2) the proposed plan of change and, (3) the advantages of the change?
+ √ – The logic of the presentation held together so that it could be easily followed.

Grades (See criteria explanation on page 239.)

	(Circle one and record it as the raw score)										Raw Score	X	Weight	=	Weighted Score
Criteria I	1	2	3	4	5	6	7	8	9	10=	____	X	1	=	____
Criteria II	1	2	3	4	5	6	7	8	9	10=	____	X	3	=	____
Criteria III	1	2	3	4	5	6	7	8	9	10=	____	X	6	=	____
											Weighted Sum Grade				____

Transfer weighted grades to the Exercise 6 Grading Form.

Your Name ______________________
No. ________ Group ________ Sec. ________

Exercise 6

DISCUSSION-DEBATE SESSION EVALUATION AND FEEDBACK FORM

To Speaker ____________________________ No. _______

Instructions: Fill out this form after all four presentations and discussions are completed.

Yes
No
1. Did the student offer constructive suggestions to you on how you could improve your case? If yes, how valuable would you rate the suggestions:

little value 1 2 3 4 5 6 much value

Yes
No
2. Did the student offer constructive suggestions to others in your group? If yes, how valuable over-all would you rate the suggestions:

little value 1 2 3 4 5 6 much value

Yes
No
3. Did the student offer any counterarguments during the four feedback, discussion-debate sessions? If yes, were these well-developed, documented counterarguments:

poorly developed 1 2 3 4 5 6 well developed

Yes
No
4. Did the student offer any counter-counterarguments during the four feedback, discussion-debate sessions? If yes, were these well developed and documented:

poorly developed 1 2 3 4 5 6 well developed

5. How much did this student participate in the discussion:

little participation 1 2 3 4 5 6 much participation

6. How valuable to you were this student's contributions to the discussion—suggestions, ideas, evidence, and so on:

little value 1 2 3 4 5 6 much value

If any "no's" are circled, record them on your Grading Form.

To determine this student's grade, add up the numbers circled on each of the six scales listed. The highest possible score is 36.

This student's score is [ ]. Record this score on your Grading Form. Then give this sheet to the student being evaluated.

Your Name ______________________
No. ________ Group ________ Sec. ________

Exercise 6

DISCUSSION-DEBATE SESSION
EVALUATION AND FEEDBACK FORM

To Speaker ____________________________ No. ________

Instructions: Fill out this form after all four presentations and discussions are completed.

Yes
No
1. Did the student offer constructive suggestions to you on how you could improve your case? If yes, how valuable would you rate the suggestions:

little value 1 2 3 4 5 6 much value

Yes
No
2. Did the student offer constructive suggestions to others in your group? If yes, how valuable over-all would you rate the suggestions:

little value 1 2 3 4 5 6 much value

Yes
No
3. Did the student offer any counterarguments during the four feedback, discussion-debate sessions? If yes, were these well-developed, documented counterarguments:

poorly developed 1 2 3 4 5 6 well developed

Yes
No
4. Did the student offer any counter-counterarguments during the four feedback, discussion-debate sessions? If yes, were these well developed and documented:

poorly developed 1 2 3 4 5 6 well developed

5. How much did this student participate in the discussion:

little participation 1 2 3 4 5 6 much participation

6. How valuable to you were this student's contributions to the discussion—suggestions, ideas, evidence, and so on:

little value 1 2 3 4 5 6 much value

If any "no's" are circled, record them on your Grading Form.

To determine this student's grade, add up the numbers circled on each of the six scales listed. The highest possible score is 36.

This student's score is [ ]. Record this score on your Grading Form. Then give this sheet to the student being evaluated.

Your Name ______________________
No. ________ Group ________ Sec. ________

Exercise 6

DISCUSSION-DEBATE SESSION
EVALUATION AND FEEDBACK FORM

To Speaker ______________________ No. ________

Instructions: Fill out this form after all four presentations and discussions are completed.

Yes
No
1. Did the student offer constructive suggestions to you on how you could improve your case? If yes, how valuable would you rate the suggestions:

little value 1 2 3 4 5 6 much value

Yes
No
2. Did the student offer constructive suggestions to others in your group? If yes, how valuable over-all would you rate the suggestions:

little value 1 2 3 4 5 6 much value

Yes
No
3. Did the student offer any counterarguments during the four feedback, discussion-debate sessions? If yes, were these well-developed, documented counterarguments:

poorly developed 1 2 3 4 5 6 well developed

Yes
No
4. Did the student offer any counter-counterarguments during the four feedback, discussion-debate sessions? If yes, were these well developed and documented:

poorly developed 1 2 3 4 5 6 well developed

5. How much did this student participate in the discussion:

little participation 1 2 3 4 5 6 much participation

6. How valuable to you were this student's contributions to the discussion–suggestions, ideas, evidence, and so on:

little value 1 2 3 4 5 6 much value

If any "no's" are circled, record them on your Grading Form.

To determine this student's grade, add up the numbers circled on each of the six scales listed. The highest possible score is 36.

This student's score is [ ]. Record this score on your Grading Form. Then give this sheet to the student being evaluated.

NOTE SHEET

Topic Statement:	Counterarguments:

NOTE SHEET

Topic Statement:	Counterarguments:

NOTE SHEET

Topic Statement:	Counterarguments:

Your Name ______________________
No. ________ Group ________ Sec. ________

Exercise 6

GRADING FORM

Grades you gave on speeches

No.	Speaker's Name	Weighted Grades Criteria				Weighted Sum Grade
		I	II	III		
____	______________	I ____	II ____	III ____	=	____
____	______________	I ____	II ____	III ____	=	____
____	______________	I ____	II ____	III ____	=	____
____	______________	I ____	II ____	III ____	=	____
	Total	____	____	____		____
	÷ by	____ number of speakers				
	= the average grade you gave	____	____	____		____

Grades you gave for Feedback, Discussion-Debate Session

No.	Name	Circle the number of any item with "no's" circled	Grade
____	______________	1 2 3 4	☐
____	______________	1 2 3 4	☐
____	______________	1 2 3 4	☐
____	______________	1 2 3 4	☐
		Total	____

÷ by ______ number of students
= the average grade you gave ____

Complete this sheet and give it to your group coordinator. He or she will record these grades on a master sheet and return this form to you.

Your Name ______________________
No. ________ Group ________ Sec. ________

Exercise 6

STUDENT GRADE RECORD SHEET

Grades received on speaking

From	Weighted Grades Criteria					Weighted Sum Grade
No. ____	I ____	II ____	III	____	=	____
No. ____	I ____	II ____	III	____	=	____
No. ____	I ____	II ____	III	____	=	____
No. ____	I ____	II ____	III	____	=	____
Total	____	____		____		____
÷ by number of grades	____	____		____		____
= your average grade	____	____		____		☐

Grades received for feedback, discussion-debate sessions

From	Grade
No. ____	☐
No. ____	☐
No. ____	☐
No. ____	☐
Total	____
÷ by number of grades	____
= your average grade	☐

Number of "No's" received on each item

1. ____ 2. ____ 3. ____ 4. ____

If you received more than two "no's" on any item or a total score below 20, you are to see the instructor for special help before you go on to Exercise 8.

Coordinator's Name ____________________
No. ________ Group ________ Sec. ________

Exercise 6

GROUP COORDINATOR'S GRADE SUMMARY SHEET

Insert on the blanks the students' weighted sum grades from the Speaker's Grading Forms.

	Student No.	____	____	____	____	____
Rater No.	____	____	____	____	____	____
	____	____	____	____	____	____
	____	____	____	____	____	____
	____	____	____	____	____	____
	____	____	____	____	____	____
Sum		____	____	____	____	____
÷ by number of raters		____	____	____	____	____
= Average grade		☐	☐	☐	☐	☐

After completing this form, show it to each person in your group so they can fill out their Grade Record Sheets. Then record each student's average grade on the Class Grade Summary Sheet. Use the column headed "Exercise 6 Speaker Grade." Give this sheet to the instructor. Return to your group members their Grading Forms.

Note: List at the bottom of this form the names of the members of the group who believe they are not fully prepared to go on to the final assignments. These students should contact the instructor for special help rather than risk failing this course. Any student with an average grade below 50 should consider asking for help.

Name ________________________________ No. ________

Name ________________________________ No. ________

Coordinator's Name____________________
No. ________ Group________ Sec. ________

Exercise 6

GROUP COORDINATOR'S FEEDBACK GRADE SUMMARY SHEET

Insert in the blanks the students' feedback, discussion-debate session grade. Show this form to each person in the group so they can fill out their Student Grade Record Sheets. Then, record each student's average grade on the class Grade Summary Sheet. Use the column headed "Exercise 6 Feedback Grade." Give this sheet to the instructor and return the Grading Forms to the group members.

	Student No. ____	____	____	____	____
Rater No. ____	____	____	____	____	____
____	____	____	____	____	____
____	____	____	____	____	____
____	____	____	____	____	____
____	____	____	____	____	____
Sum	____	____	____	____	____
÷ by number of raters	____	____	____	____	____
= Average grade	☐	☐	☐	☐	☐

List the number of "No's" each student received; if zero, put an "x."

Student	Item: 1.	2.	3.	4.
No. ____	____	____	____	____
No. ____	____	____	____	____
No. ____	____	____	____	____
No. ____	____	____	____	____

Students who have more than two "No's" on any item or a grade below 20 are to see the instructor so they can receive special help before going on to Exercise 8.

List at the bottom of this form the names of students who were absent from or tardy for any group session.

Name ____________________________ No. ____ Excuse ________________________

Name ____________________________ No. ____ Excuse ________________________

EXERCISE 7

Displaying Your Writing Ability

PURPOSE OF ASSIGNMENT

The earlier assignments in this course have all been practice and learning exercises. This is the final written assignment. This is not a learning exercise: it is rather an assignment in which you display what you have learned. Your grades on this assignment will account for 50% of your course grade. As with all of your previous exercises, this one has two major parts: the presentation of material and the constructive evaluation of those presentations. The grades on this assignment will account for a major part of your final course grade.

Introduction

Grading Safeguards. The grading of this final paper must be taken very seriously. In earlier assignments, the grades were merely feedback. This let the other students know how the papers would be evaluated in a real situation. This is the real situation. This is the grade that goes on your permanent college records.

There are many safeguards built into this grading system. First, names are omitted so the graders are not influenced by reason of sex, race, age, or familiarity with the author. Second, each paper is graded by 16 different peers, who grade independently. Even if one person knows another student's number and distorts the grade too high or too low, that one grade counts so little that it is not likely to affect anyone's final grade. The key here is independence of grading. *Do NOT compare grades with any other student at any time before all grades are turned in. To do so is cheating, and the penalty is the same as that for cheating on exams.* If you know of any such cheating, report it to the instructor for your own protection.

Third, no one knows in advance which 16 students are going to grade his paper or whose papers they are going to grade. In most cases, you will not grade the paper of anyone who is grading your paper. This makes any type of collusion virtually impossible.

Fourth, the grades given a paper are not revealed to the author until after he has graded the evaluators on the quality of their feedback to him. This removes any possible temptation to grade down the feedback of students who might have given a low grade on a paper. However, all grades and the identity of graders will be made known at the end of the course. So do not feel that you can secretly give a friend an unduly high grade or an enemy an unduly low grade without your actions being exposed.

Fifth, the students have a right to challenge any grade that deviates greatly from the mean grade they receive. If someone makes such a challenge, the total grading of the student whose grades were challenged will be reviewed. If any irregularities or biases are found, the student's grading will be deleted from all records.

There is one final protection to keep the grades fair. The instructor will grade the class. If all students happen to grade each other too low or too high, that will not affect the final grading, because the instructor must grade the over-all quality of the class and set the cutoff scores for A's, B's, and so on. The instructor's grading is used to maintain a consistency in the grading of the course from year to year and to protect you from overly conservative or unfair grading.

All of these safeguards may seem like overkill. That is exactly what is intended. These grades may very likely be among the most accurate and fair grades you will ever receive in college.

ASSIGNMENT INSTRUCTIONS

The paper for Exercise 7 is to contain a complete presentation supporting the proposal selected by the class. In this paper, you are to show why there is a need to change from the present system, present a plan of action by which that change can be brought about, and show the advantage of the proposed change as compared to the present system.

Explanation of Weakness

At the end of this paper, add a one-half page (maximum length) explanation of any weak areas in your arguments or plan. Describe each weakness and explain why you were not able to strengthen it. For example, there may be no documentation supporting one of your subarguments. The explanation might be that you could not find any material dealing with that issue and thus had to rely upon logic to support it. The evaluators can then take this into consideration when grading your paper.

Format

This paper need not follow the rigid format required for earlier exercises. Those exercises were like basketball drills. Their purpose was to familiarize you with various types of structure and support material and to force you to raise your standards. This assignment is like the basketball game rather than the drill. Now the goal is to show your very best performance. And this may require that you modify the rigid structure which you practiced in earlier assignments. *If you choose to modify the structure, be careful to remember that these structures were designed to help achieve certain objectives; you will still be graded on how well the paper achieves those objectives.* The introduction must still gain and focus attention and build rapport. The topic still needs to be clearly stated and the terms need to be operationally defined. The forecast summary is optional for this paper, but some techniques such as forecast summaries, headings, and spaces between key sections should be used to help the reader perceive and follow the organization of the paper.

Support Material

For this presentation, there is *no* requirement that each subargument contain certain amounts or types of support material. There is only the requirement that each subargument be adequately supported. You have the option of omitting the arousing, informing, or convincing forms of support if you believe that the readers are already adequately aroused, informed, or convinced. However, there is still the requirement that the reader be aroused, informed, and convinced after he has read the paper, regardless of how this was accomplished.

No In-Class Review

There will be no in-class review of this final paper. It is your responsibility to review your own paper and, if necessary, to have others review it before you bring it to class.

Length

This paper is not to exceed 6 pages in total length. The main text is to be not less than 3½ or more than 4½ pages in length. It is to be typed single-spaced, on 8½ x 11″ sheets of paper. The explanation of weaknesses is to be at the end of the paper and is to be not more than one-half page in length. Only references are to appear on the sixth page. Use the same system of references as described for Exercises 3 and 5. It is not necessary to have a sixth page if the references can fit on the fifth page. All pages are to be stapled together.

Layout of Paper

The margins are to be 1¼″ at the top and 1″ at the sides and bottom. In the upper right-hand corner of the top margin on the first page, type your section number and class number. *Do not write your name on these papers* except on the instructor's copy. Directly below your number write "Evaluator No.____." Below that write "Copy No.____," and then number the copies from 0 to 16.* In the center of the page 1¼″ below the top, type "Exercise 7," and then the semester and year. Below that, type the title.

FIGURE 7-1 Exercise 7 Paper Heading Format

Section No._____ Author No. __25__
Evaluator No. ______
Copy No. __6__

Exercise 7, Fall 19--

(TITLE)

Distribution of Papers

On the day Exercise 7 is due, bring to class an original and 16*copies of your paper. The "0" copy is for the instructor. Copies 1-16* will be distributed to classmates for evaluation and grading. If for some reason you cannot attend class on that day, you must arrange for someone else to pass out your papers and to collect the papers you are to grade.

Use the Exercise 7 Paper Number Record Form (page 279) to list the numbers of the persons who are to receive copies of your paper for evaluation and grading. Also use this form to list the numbers of all of the papers you are to receive for evaluation and grading.

Evaluation and Grading of Papers

You will receive 16* of your classmates' papers. For those numbered 1-8, completely fill out the Feedback Form (page 281) with written evaluations and constructive suggestions. For papers numbered 9-16,** fill out only the checklist part of the Feedback Form; you do not need to write any comments. Grade all 16 papers, using the Exercise 7 Grade Computation Form (page 313). Do *not* write a grade on any Exercise 7 papers or Feedback Forms.

---

*This number may be modified by your instructor.

**Grading of papers 9-16 may be omitted at the option of your instructor.

Grading Criteria

There are three general criteria to use in grading these papers.

Criterion I. Presentation of paper. Consider under Criterion I neatness, spelling, grammar, layout on page, readability of sentences, or any other factor which affects your response to the paper apart from its organization or content. This criterion is weighted 10%.

Criterion II. Organization of paper. Consider under Criterion II how effectively the author laid out the sections of his paper. Was it easy to follow? Were there enough headings, transitions, and summaries to keep you from getting lost? Did the paper contain adequate documentation and a good balance between informative and persuasive forms of support? This criterion is weighted 30%.

Criterion III. Content of paper. Consider under Criterion III the logic of the author's arguments and the adequacy of the material used to support them. Check the inherency of each subargument and the appropriateness and adequacy of the forms of support used to substantiate each. Compare the arguments for change, the planned change, and the purported advantage. Make sure all of these are consistent with the topic and with each other. This criterion is weighted 60%.

This is the final paper for this course. It should be far better than the earlier papers in presentation, organization, and content. As graders, you also should be more competent to grade on all three criteria. Grade fairly and completely. You are not likely to know whose papers you are grading unless you look up the number. It is suggested that you will do a better and fairer job if you do not know who wrote the paper. Remember, all grading is to be done *independently*. Be careful to write clear, constructive feedback on the first eight papers, because that feedback will in turn be graded.

FIGURE 7-2 Meaning of Number Grades

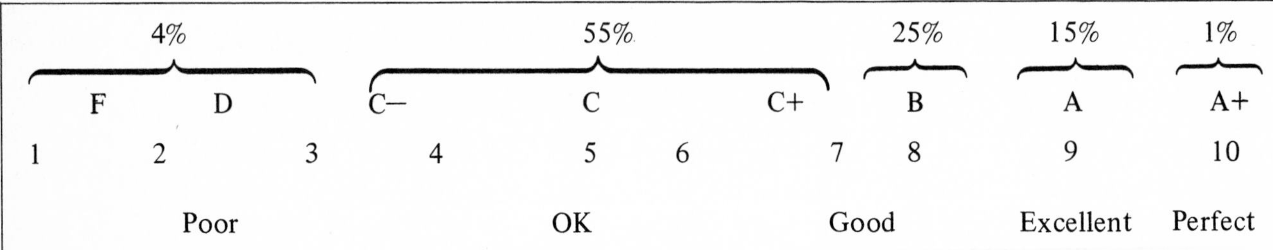

Note: The percentages shown for the grades have been shifted upwards for Exercises 7 and 8. That is because many of the poor students will already have dropped. Many others will have significantly improved. Therefore, there will be a larger percentage of high grades.

These grading percentages should be followed rather closely. *Students who give a disproportionate number of high or low grades may be asked to justify their grading standards.*

Grader Quality Reports

Learning to evaluate a proposal is as important as learning to write and to present it. If one cannot evaluate a report, then he cannot even tell whether or not his own work is good, because that requires evaluation. A major goal of this course has been to teach you to be able to evaluate your own work as well as that of your peers. When you can effectively evaluate your own work, you are no longer a dependent child who must always ask someone else, "Is this long enough?" "Is this O.K.?" "What should I say?" If you become a manager, you will be expected to be able to work independently. You will become the ones who must evaluate the work of those below you and advise them on how to improve. You should all have achieved this ability to evaluate your own work and the work of others now that you have progressed to Exercise 7.

In earlier assignments, you devoted much time to studying and evaluating the work of your fellow students. You have given feedback to them on the quality of their work and they have in turn given feedback to you on the value of your feedback to them. Now it is time to receive one final grade on the quality of the written feedback you give to others.

How to Grade the Feedback

The Grader Quality Report (page 317) for this exercise is similar to those used for Exercises 3 and 5, except on this one you must compute a total score. The first two categories are fairly objective. Category A asks if the checklist on the feedback form was filled out completely. Category B asks if the written comments on the feedback form contain specific detailed comments, as opposed to general statements such as, "Your paper was good." Specific comments should refer to specific statements or sources and should say why the grader feels they are good or bad. Categories A and B should be simple to grade.

Category C is more subjective to grade. You must carefully read each comment on the paper and the Feedback Form and then evaluate how helpful the comment is and how accurate the perception is on which it is based. You must be careful not to grade flattering comments high because they are flattering. Flattery often only deceives us and keeps us from learning how to improve. The highest grades should go to those who give you the best analysis of what problems you need to correct and the best ideas on how you can correct them. The total grade should be the sum of the grades on categories A + B + (2 X C). The C category is weighted double.

See pages 320 and 329 of Exercise 8 and the course syllabus for an explanation of how final grades in this course will be computed.

EXERCISE 7 CHECKLIST

Check Your Own Paper First

This is your final paper. It accounts for a large percentage of your grade in this course. Check it carefully before it is duplicated. There will be no in-class review before this final paper is distributed. It is now totally up to you to check your own work. Check for the following:

1. Spelling
2. Punctuation
3. Grammar
4. Neatness
5. Margins
6. Go over each item in the Feedback Form and grade your own paper. If you would give your paper any minuses, redo that section of the paper.
7. Go over each argument once again for logic, appropriateness, and adequacy of support.
8. Give your paper a final check for readability. Have you used complete sentences? Are sentences too long or awkward?

Your Name ____________________
No. ________ Group ________ Sec. ________

Exercise 7

PAPER NUMBER RECORD FORM

My papers are to be passed out to:

Paper No.	Student No.	Check When Returned Graded
1	______	______
2	______	______
3	______	______
4	______	______
5	______	______
6	______	______
7	______	______
8	______	______
9	______	______
10	______	______
11	______	______
12	______	______
13	______	______
14	______	______
15	______	______
16	______	______

I am to receive papers from:

Paper No.	Student No.
______	______
______	______
______	______
______	______
______	______
______	______
______	______
______	______
______	______
______	______
______	______
______	______
______	______
______	______
______	______
______	______

Papers from the following students were not returned graded:

Copy No.	Student No.
______	______
______	______
______	______

Check with these students. If you still do not find your paper, report the loss to the instructor.

I should have but did not receive papers from:

Copy No.	Student No.
______	______
______	______
______	______

Please report to your instructor if any papers are not received in time to be graded.

Before distributing your paper, record on each copy the class number of the student who is to receive and evaluate that paper. For example, if student 25 is to receive your copy No. 2 paper, write as follows:

Evaluator No. __25__

Copy No. __2__

Your Name ______________________

No. ________ Group ________ Sec. ________

Exercise 7: Feedback Form to Author ______________________ **No.** ________

Yes No Is this paper of proper length and does it have proper margins?

Does the introduction do the following:

+ √ − introduce the topic and gain and focus attention on it?
+ √ − clearly define the terms?
+ √ − build rapport—did its appearance and style make you feel this paper would be worth reading?

Write what specific things are effective or need improving in the introduction.

____

____

____

____

____

(Write additional comments on student's paper)

I. *Arguments showing need for change*:

+ √ − Are each of the subarguments clearly identified by headings, a forecast summary, or both?

Is subargument one

+ √ − clearly identified and explained?
+ √ − inherently related to the main argument?
+ √ − backed with enough convincing support?
+ √ − backed with enough informing and arousing support?

Which forms of support are used? (Circle)

detailed examples — background data — specific instances
analogies — statistics
explanations of logic — testimonies of authorities

Explain what is needed to improve this subargument.

____

____

____

____

____

(Write additional comments on student's paper)

Is subargument two

+ √ − clearly identified and explained?
+ √ − inherently related to the main argument?
+ √ − backed with enough convincing support?
+ √ − backed with enough informing and arousing support?

Which forms of support are used? (Circle)

detailed examples — background data — specific instances
analogies — statistics
explanations of logic — testimonies of authorities

Explain what is needed to improve this subargument.

____

____

____

____

____

(Write additional comments on student's paper)

Is subargument three

+ √ − clearly identified and explained?
+ √ − inherently related to the main argument?
+ √ − backed with enough convincing support?
+ √ − backed with enough informing and arousing support?

Which forms of support are used? (Circle)

detailed examples — background data — specific instances
analogies — statistics
explanations of logic — testimonies of authorities

Explain what is needed to improve this subargument.

(Write additional comments on student's paper)

+ √ − Is this section of the paper clearly summarized?
+ √ − Are the subarguments shown to clearly support the main argument?

II. *Proposed plan of how to change*:

+ √ − Is the plan easy to understand?
+ √ − Would the plan remove the problems described in subargument one?
+ √ − Would the plan remove the problems described in subargument two?
+ √ − Would the plan remove the problems described in subargument three?
+ √ − Does the plan sound practical and feasible?

Write your evaluation of this plan.

(Write additional comments on student's paper)

III. *Advantages of the new proposal*:

+ √ − Are each of the subarguments in this section clearly identified by a forecast summary, headings, or both?

Is advantage one

+ √ − clearly identified and explained?
+ √ − inherently related to this proposal rather than an advantage that could be obtained as easily in other ways?
+ √ − backed with enough convincing support?
+ √ − backed with enough arousing and informing support?

Write a short evaluation of this advantage.

(Write additional comments on student's paper)

Is advantage two

+ √ − clearly identified and explained?
+ √ − inherently related to this proposal rather than an advantage that could be obtained as easily in other ways?
+ √ − backed with enough convincing support?
+ √ − backed with enough arousing and informing support?

Write a short evaluation of this advantage.

(Write additional comments on student's paper)

Does the conclusion

+ √ − summarize the paper effectively?
+ √ − bring the original statement of the topic back to your attention?
+ √ − draw the conclusion for the reader that the proposal has been supported, that the plan of change is a good one, that there are clear advantages to adopting the proposal, and that we therefore should adopt it?

Do Not Put a Grade on This Form. Record the Author's Grade Only on the Exercise 7 Grade Computation Form (page 313) and Grading Form (page 315).

Your Name ______________________
No. ________ Group ________ Sec. ________

Exercise 7: Feedback Form to Author ________________________ **No.** ________

Yes No Is this paper of proper length and does it have proper margins?

Does the introduction do the following:
+ √ − introduce the topic and gain and focus attention on it?
+ √ − clearly define the terms?
+ √ − build rapport—did its appearance and style make you feel this paper would be worth reading?
Write what specific things are effective or need improving in the introduction.

____
____
____
____
____
(Write additional comments on student's paper)

I. *Arguments showing need for change*:
+ √ − Are each of the subarguments clearly identified by headings, a forecast summary, or both?

Is subargument one
+ √ − clearly identified and explained?
+ √ − inherently related to the main argument?
+ √ − backed with enough convincing support?
+ √ − backed with enough informing and arousing support?

Which forms of support are used? (Circle)

detailed examples · background data · specific instances
analogies · statistics
explanations of logic · testimonies of authorities

Explain what is needed to improve this subargument.

____
____
____
____
____
(Write additional comments on student's paper)

Is subargument two
+ √ − clearly identified and explained?
+ √ − inherently related to the main argument?
+ √ − backed with enough convincing support?
+ √ − backed with enough informing and arousing support?

Which forms of support are used? (Circle)

detailed examples · background data · specific instances
analogies · statistics
explanations of logic · testimonies of authorities

Explain what is needed to improve this subargument.

____
____
____
____
____
(Write additional comments on student's paper)

Is subargument three
+ √ − clearly identified and explained?
+ √ − inherently related to the main argument?
+ √ − backed with enough convincing support?
+ √ − backed with enough informing and arousing support?

Which forms of support are used? (Circle)

detailed examples · background data · specific instances
analogies · statistics
explanations of logic · testimonies of authorities

Explain what is needed to improve this subargument.

(Write additional comments on student's paper)

+ √ − Is this section of the paper clearly summarized?
+ √ − Are the subarguments shown to clearly support the main argument?

II. *Proposed plan of how to change*:

+ √ − Is the plan easy to understand?
+ √ − Would the plan remove the problems described in subargument one?
+ √ − Would the plan remove the problems described in subargument two?
+ √ − Would the plan remove the problems described in subargument three?
+ √ − Does the plan sound practical and feasible?

Write your evaluation of this plan.

(Write additional comments on student's paper)

III. *Advantages of the new proposal*:

+ √ − Are each of the subarguments in this section clearly identified by a forecast summary, headings, or both?

Is advantage one

+ √ − clearly identified and explained?
+ √ − inherently related to this proposal rather than an advantage that could be obtained as easily in other ways?
+ √ − backed with enough convincing support?
+ √ − backed with enough arousing and informing support?

Write a short evaluation of this advantage.

(Write additional comments on student's paper)

Is advantage two

+ √ − clearly identified and explained?
+ √ − inherently related to this proposal rather than an advantage that could be obtained as easily in other ways?
+ √ − backed with enough convincing support?
+ √ − backed with enough arousing and informing support?

Write a short evaluation of this advantage.

(Write additional comments on student's paper)

Does the conclusion

+ √ − summarize the paper effectively?
+ √ − bring the original statement of the topic back to your attention?
+ √ − draw the conclusion for the reader that the proposal has been supported, that the plan of change is a good one, that there are clear advantages to adopting the proposal, and that we therefore should adopt it?

Do Not Put a Grade on This Form. Record the Author's Grade Only on the Exercise 7 Grade Computation Form (page 313) and Grading Form (page 315).

Your Name ______________________

No. ________ Group ________ Sec. ________

Exercise 7: Feedback Form to Author ______________________ No. ________

Yes No Is this paper of proper length and does it have proper margins?

Does the introduction do the following:

+ √ − introduce the topic and gain and focus attention on it?
+ √ − clearly define the terms?
+ √ − build rapport—did its appearance and style make you feel this paper would be worth reading?

Write what specific things are effective or need improving in the introduction.

____

____

____

____

____

(Write additional comments on student's paper)

I. *Argument showing need for change*:

+ √ − Are each of the subarguments clearly identified by headings, a forecast summary, or both?

Is subargument one

+ √ − clearly identified and explained?
+ √ − inherently related to the main argument?
+ √ − backed with enough convincing support?
+ √ − backed with enough informing and arousing support?

Which forms of support are used? (Circle)

detailed examples | background data | specific instances
analogies | | statistics
explanations of logic | | testimonies of authorities

Explain what is needed to improve this subargument.

____

____

____

____

____

(Write additional comments on student's paper)

Is subargument two

+ √ − clearly identified and explained?
+ √ − inherently related to the main argument?
+ √ − backed with enough convincing support?
+ √ − backed with enough informing and arousing support?

Which forms of support are used? (Circle)

detailed examples | background data | specific instances
analogies | | statistics
explanations of logic | | testimonies of authorities

Explain what is needed to improve this subargument.

____

____

____

____

____

(Write additional comments on student's paper)

Is subargument three

+ √ − clearly identified and explained?
+ √ − inherently related to the main argument?
+ √ − backed with enough convincing support?
+ √ − backed with enough informing and arousing support?

Which forms of support are used? (Circle)

detailed examples | background data | specific instances
analogies | | statistics
explanations of logic | | testimonies of authorities

Explain what is needed to improve this subargument.

(Write additional comments on student's paper)

+ √ − Is this section of the paper clearly summarized?
+ √ − Are the subarguments shown to clearly support the main argument?

II. *Proposed plan of how to change*:
+ √ − Is the plan easy to understand?
+ √ − Would the plan remove the problems described in subargument one?
+ √ − Would the plan remove the problems described in subargument two?
+ √ − Would the plan remove the problems described in subargument three?
+ √ − Does the plan sound practical and feasible?
Write your evaluation of this plan.

(Write additional comments on student's paper)

III. *Advantages of the new proposal*:
+ √ − Are each of the subarguments in this section clearly identified by a forecast summary, headings, or both?

Is advantage one
+ √ − clearly identified and explained?
+ √ − inherently related to this proposal rather than an advantage that could be obtained as easily in other ways?
+ √ − backed with enough convincing support?
+ √ − backed with enough arousing and informing support?
Write a short evaluation of this advantage.

(Write additional comments on student's paper)

Is advantage two
+ √ − clearly identified and explained?
+ √ − inherently related to this proposal rather than an advantage that could be obtained as easily in other ways?
+ √ − backed with enough convincing support?
+ √ − backed with enough arousing and informing support?
Write a short evaluation of this advantage.

(Write additional comments on student's paper)

Does the conclusion
+ √ − summarize the paper effectively?
+ √ − bring the original statement of the topic back to your attention?
+ √ − draw the conclusion for the reader that the proposal has been supported, that the plan of change is a good one, that there are clear advantages to adopting the proposal, and that we therefore should adopt it?

Do Not Put a Grade on This Form. Record the Author's Grade Only on the Exercise 7 Grade Computation Form (page 313) and Grading Form (page 315).

Your Name ____________________

No. ________ Group ________ Sec. ________

Exercise 7: Feedback Form to Author ____________________ **No.** ________

Yes No Is this paper of proper length and does it have proper margins?

Does the introduction do the following:

+ √ − introduce the topic and gain and focus attention on it?
+ √ − clearly define the terms?
+ √ − build rapport—did its appearance and style make you feel this paper would be worth reading?

Write what specific things are effective or need improving in the introduction.

(Write additional comments on student's paper)

I. *Arguments showing need for change*:

+ √ − Are each of the subarguments clearly identified by headings, a forecast summary, or both?

Is subargument one

+ √ − clearly identified and explained?
+ √ − inherently related to the main argument?
+ √ − backed with enough convincing support?
+ √ − backed with enough informing and arousing support?

Which forms of support are used? (Circle)

detailed examples background data specific instances
analogies statistics
explanations of logic testimonies of authorities

Explain what is needed to improve this subargument.

(Write additional comments on student's paper)

Is subargument two

+ √ − clearly identified and explained?
+ √ − inherently related to the main argument?
+ √ − backed with enough convincing support?
+ √ − backed with enough informing and arousing support?

Which forms of support are used? (Circle)

detailed examples background data specific instances
analogies statistics
explanations of logic testimonies of authorities

Explain what is needed to improve this subargument.

(Write additional comments on student's paper)

Is subargument three

+ √ − clearly identified and explained?
+ √ − inherently related to the main argument?
+ √ − backed with enough convincing support?
+ √ − backed with enough informing and arousing support?

Which forms of support are used? (Circle)

detailed examples background data specific instances
analogies statistics
explanations of logic testimonies of authorities

Explain what is needed to improve this subargument.

(Write additional comments on student's paper)

+ √ − Is this section of the paper clearly summarized?
+ √ − Are the subarguments shown to clearly support the main argument?

II. *Proposed plan of how to change*:
+ √ − Is the plan easy to understand?
+ √ − Would the plan remove the problems described in subargument one?
+ √ − Would the plan remove the problems described in subargument two?
+ √ − Would the plan remove the problems described in subargument three?
+ √ − Does the plan sound practical and feasible?

Write your evaluation of this plan.

(Write additional comments on student's paper)

III. *Advantages of the new proposal*:
+ √ − Are each of the subarguments in this section clearly identified by a forecast summary, headings, or both?

Is advantage one
+ √ − clearly identified and explained?
+ √ − inherently related to this proposal rather than an advantage that could be obtained as easily in other ways?
+ √ − backed with enough convincing support?
+ √ − backed with enough arousing and informing support?

Write a short evaluation of this advantage.

(Write additional comments on student's paper)

Is advantage two
+ √ − clearly identified and explained?
+ √ − inherently related to this proposal rather than an advantage that could be obtained as easily in other ways?
+ √ − backed with enough convincing support?
+ √ − backed with enough arousing and informing support?

Write a short evaluation of this advantage.

(Write additional comments on student's paper)

Does the conclusion
+ √ − summarize the paper effectively?
+ √ − bring the original statement of the topic back to your attention?
+ √ − draw the conclusion for the reader that the proposal has been supported, that the plan of change is a good one, that there are clear advantages to adopting the proposal, and that we therefore should adopt it?

Do Not Put a Grade on This Form. Record the Author's Grade Only on the Exercise 7 Grade Computation Form (page 313) and Grading Form (page 315).

Your Name ______________________

No. ________ Group ________ Sec. ______

Exercise 7: Feedback Form to Author ______________________ No. ________

Yes No Is this paper of proper length and does it have proper margins?

Does the introduction do the following:

+ √ − introduce the topic and gain and focus attention on it?
+ √ − clearly define the terms?
+ √ − build rapport—did its appearance and style make you feel this paper would be worth reading?

Write what specific things are effective or need improving in the introduction.

____

____

____

____

____

(Write additional comments on student's paper)

I. *Arguments showing need for change*:

+ √ − Are each of the subarguments clearly identified by headings, a forecast summary, or both?

Is subargument one

+ √ − clearly identified and explained?
+ √ − inherently related to the main argument?
+ √ − backed with enough convincing support?
+ √ − backed with enough informing and arousing support?

Which forms of support are used? (Circle)

detailed examples, background data, specific instances, analogies, statistics, explanations of logic, testimonies of authorities

Explain what is needed to improve this subargument.

____

____

____

____

____

(Write additional comments on student's paper)

Is subargument two

+ √ − clearly identified and explained?
+ √ − inherently related to the main argument?
+ √ − backed with enough convincing support?
+ √ − backed with enough informing and arousing support?

Which forms of support are used? (Circle)

detailed examples, background data, specific instances, analogies, statistics, explanations of logic, testimonies of authorities

Explain what is needed to improve this subargument.

____

____

____

____

____

(Write additional comments on student's paper)

Is subargument three

+ √ − clearly identified and explained?
+ √ − inherently related to the main argument?
+ √ − backed with enough convincing support?
+ √ − backed with enough informing and arousing support?

Which forms of support are used? (Circle)

detailed examples, background data, specific instances, analogies, statistics, explanations of logic, testimonies of authorities

Explain what is needed to improve this subargument.

(Write additional comments on student's paper)

+ √ − Is this section of the paper clearly summarized?
+ √ − Are the subarguments shown to clearly support the main argument?

II. *Proposed plan of how to change*:

+ √ − Is the plan easy to understand?
+ √ − Would the plan remove the problems described in subargument one?
+ √ − Would the plan remove the problems described in subargument two?
+ √ − Would the plan remove the problems described in subargument three?
+ √ − Does the plan sound practical and feasible?

Write your evaluation of this plan.

(Write additional comments on student's paper)

III. *Advantages of the new proposal*:

+ √ − Are each of the subarguments in this section clearly identified by a forecast summary, headings, or both?

Is advantage one

+ √ − clearly identified and explained?
+ √ − inherently related to this proposal rather than an advantage that could be obtained as easily in other ways?
+ √ − backed with enough convincing support?
+ √ − backed with enough arousing and informing support?

Write a short evaluation of this advantage.

(Write additional comments on student's paper)

Is advantage two

+ √ − clearly identified and explained?
+ √ − inherently related to this proposal rather than an advantage that could be obtained as easily in other ways?
+ √ − backed with enough convincing support?
+ √ − backed with enough arousing and informing support?

Write a short evaluation of this advantage.

(Write additional comments on student's paper)

Does the conclusion

+ √ − summarize the paper effectively?
+ √ − bring the original statement of the topic back to your attention?
+ √ − draw the conclusion for the reader that the proposal has been supported, that the plan of change is a good one, that there are clear advantages to adopting the proposal, and that we therefore should adopt it?

Do Not Put a Grade on This Form. Record the Author's Grade Only on the Exercise 7 Grade Computation Form (page 313) and Grading Form (page 315).

Your Name ______________________________

No. ________ Group __________ Sec. ______

Exercise 7: **Feedback Form to Author** _________________________ **No.** ________

Yes No Is this paper of proper length and does it have proper margins?

Does the introduction do the following:

+ √ − introduce the topic and gain and focus attention on it?

+ √ − clearly define the terms?

+ √ − build rapport—did its appearance and style make you feel this paper would be worth reading?

Write what specific things are effective or need improving in the introduction.

(Write additional comments on student's paper)

I. *Arguments showing need for change:*

+ √ − Are each of the subarguments clearly identified by headings, a forecast summary, or both?

Is subargument one

+ √ − clearly identified and explained?

+ √ − inherently related to the main argument?

+ √ − backed with enough convincing support?

+ √ − backed with enough informing and arousing support?

Which forms of support are used? (Circle)

detailed examples	background data	specific instances
analogies		statistics
explanations of logic		testimonies of authorities

Explain what is needed to improve this subargument.

(Write additional comments on student's paper)

Is subargument two

+ √ − clearly identified and explained?

+ √ − inherently related to the main argument?

+ √ − backed with enough convincing support?

+ √ − backed with enough informing and arousing support?

Which forms of support are used? (Circle)

detailed examples	background data	specific instances
analogies		statistics
explanations of logic		testimonies of authorities

Explain what is needed to improve this subargument.

(Write additional comments on student's paper)

Is subargument three

+ √ − clearly identified and explained?

+ √ − inherently related to the main argument?

+ √ − backed with enough convincing support?

+ √ − backed with enough informing and arousing support?

Which forms of support are used? (Circle)

detailed examples	background data	specific instances
analogies		statistics
explanations of logic		testimonies of authorities

Explain what is needed to improve this subargument.

(Write additional comments on student's paper)

+ √ − Is this section of the paper clearly summarized?
+ √ − Are the subarguments shown to clearly support the main argument?

II. *Proposed plan of how to change*:

+ √ − Is the plan easy to understand?
+ √ − Would the plan remove the problems described in subargument one?
+ √ − Would the plan remove the problems described in subargument two?
+ √ − Would the plan remove the problems described in subargument three?
+ √ − Does the plan sound practical and feasible?

Write your evaluation of this plan.

(Write additional comments on student's paper)

III. *Advantages of the new proposal*:

+ √ − Are each of the subarguments in this section clearly identified by a forecast summary, headings, or both?

Is advantage one

+ √ − clearly identified and explained?
+ √ − inherently related to this proposal rather than an advantage that could be obtained as easily in other ways?
+ √ − backed with enough convincing support?
+ √ − backed with enough arousing and informing support?

Write a short evaluation of this advantage.

(Write additional comments on student's paper)

Is advantage two

+ √ − clearly identified and explained?
+ √ − inherently related to this proposal rather than an advantage that could be obtained as easily in other ways?
+ √ − backed with enough convincing support?
+ √ − backed with enough arousing and informing support?

Write a short evaluation of this advantage.

(Write additional comments on student's paper)

Does the conclusion

+ √ − summarize the paper effectively?
+ √ − bring the original statement of the topic back to your attention?
+ √ − draw the conclusion for the reader that the proposal has been supported, that the plan of change is a good one, that there are clear advantages to adopting the proposal, and that we therefore should adopt it?

Do Not Put a Grade on This Form. Record the Author's Grade Only on the Exercise 7 Grade Computation Form (page 313) and Grading Form (page 315).

Your Name ____________________

No.________ Group________ Sec.______

Exercise 7: Feedback Form to Author ____________________ No. ________

Yes No Is this paper of proper length and does it have proper margins?

Does the introduction do the following:

+ √ − introduce the topic and gain and focus attention on it?

+ √ − clearly define the terms?

+ √ − build rapport–did its appearance and style make you feel this paper would be worth reading?

Write what specific things are effective or need improving in the introduction.

(Write additional comments on student's paper)

I. *Arguments showing need for change*:

+ √ − Are each of the subarguments clearly identified by headings, a forecast summary, or both?

Is subargument one

+ √ − clearly identified and explained?

+ √ − inherently related to the main argument?

+ √ − backed with enough convincing support?

+ √ − backed with enough informing and arousing support?

Which forms of support are used? (Circle)

detailed examples | background data | specific instances
analogies | | statistics
explanations of logic | | testimonies of authorities

Explain what is needed to improve this subargument.

(Write additional comments on student's paper)

Is subargument two

+ √ − clearly identified and explained?

+ √ − inherently related to the main argument?

+ √ − backed with enough convincing support?

+ √ − backed with enough informing and arousing support?

Which forms of support are used? (Circle)

detailed examples | background data | specific instances
analogies | | statistics
explanations of logic | | testimonies of authorities

Explain what is needed to improve this subargument.

(Write additional comments on student's paper)

Is subargument three

+ √ − clearly identified and explained?

+ √ − inherently related to the main argument?

+ √ − backed with enough convincing support?

+ √ − backed with enough informing and arousing support?

Which forms of support are used? (Circle)

detailed examples | background data | specific instances
analogies | | statistics
explanations of logic | | testimonies of authorities

Explain what is needed to improve this subargument.

(Write additional comments on student's paper)

+ √ − Is this section of the paper clearly summarized?
+ √ − Are the subarguments shown to clearly support the main argument?

II. *Proposed plan of how to change*:

+ √ − Is the plan easy to understand?
+ √ − Would the plan remove the problems described in subargument one?
+ √ − Would the plan remove the problems described in subargument two?
+ √ − Would the plan remove the problems described in subargument three?
+ √ − Does the plan sound practical and feasible?

Write your evaluation of this plan.

(Write additional comments on student's paper)

III. *Advantages of the new proposal*:

+ √ − Are each of the subarguments in this section clearly identified by a forecast summary, headings, or both?

Is advantage one

+ √ − clearly identified and explained?
+ √ − inherently related to this proposal rather than an advantage that could be obtained as easily in other ways?
+ √ − backed with enough convincing support?
+ √ − backed with enough arousing and informing support?

Write a short evaluation of this advantage.

(Write additional comments on student's paper)

Is advantage two

+ √ − clearly identified and explained?
+ √ − inherently related to this proposal rather than an advantage that could be obtained as easily in other ways?
+ √ − backed with enough convincing support?
+ √ − backed with enough arousing and informing support?

Write a short evaluation of this advantage.

(Write additional comments on student's paper)

Does the conclusion

+ √ − summarize the paper effectively?
+ √ − bring the original statement of the topic back to your attention?
+ √ − draw the conclusion for the reader that the proposal has been supported, that the plan of change is a good one, that there are clear advantages to adopting the proposal, and that we therefore should adopt it?

Do Not Put a Grade on This Form. Record the Author's Grade Only on the Exercise 7 Grade Computation Form (page 313) and Grading Form (page 315).

Your Name ______________________

No.________ Group ________ Sec. ______

Exercise 7: Feedback Form to Author ______________________ No. ________

Yes No Is this paper of proper length and does it have proper margins?

Does the introduction do the following:

+ √ − introduce the topic and gain and focus attention on it?

+ √ − clearly define the terms?

+ √ − build rapport—did its appearance and style make you feel this paper would be worth reading?

Write what specific things are effective or need improving in the introduction.

(Write additional comments on student's paper)

I. *Arguments showing need for change*:

+ √ − Are each of the subarguments clearly identified by headings, a forecast summary, or both?

Is subargument one

+ √ − clearly identified and explained?

+ √ − inherently related to the main argument?

+ √ − backed with enough convincing support?

+ √ − backed with enough informing and arousing support?

Which forms of support are used? (Circle)

detailed examples | background data | specific instances
analogies | | statistics
explanations of logic | | testimonies of authorities

Explain what is needed to improve this subargument.

(Write additional comments on student's paper)

Is subargument two

+ √ − clearly identified and explained?

+ √ − inherently related to the main argument?

+ √ − backed with enough convincing support?

+ √ − backed with enough informing and arousing support?

Which forms of support are used? (Circle)

detailed examples | background data | specific instances
analogies | | statistics
explanations of logic | | testimonies of authorities

Explain what is needed to improve this subargument.

(Write additional comments on student's paper)

Is subargument three

+ √ − clearly identified and explained?

+ √ − inherently related to the main argument?

+ √ − backed with enough convincing support?

+ √ − backed with enough informing and arousing support?

Which forms of support are used? (Circle)

detailed examples | background data | specific instances
analogies | | statistics
explanations of logic | | testimonies of authorities

Explain what is needed to improve this subargument.

(Write additional comments on student's paper)

+ √ − Is this section of the paper clearly summarized?
+ √ − Are the subarguments shown to clearly support the main argument?

II. *Proposed plan of how to change*:
+ √ − Is the plan easy to understand?
+ √ − Would the plan remove the problems described in subargument one?
+ √ − Would the plan remove the problems described in subargument two?
+ √ − Would the plan remove the problems described in subargument three?
+ √ − Does the plan sound practical and feasible?
Write your evaluation of this plan.

(Write additional comments on student's paper)

III. *Advantages of the new proposal*:
+ √ − Are each of the subarguments in this section clearly identified by a forecast summary, headings, or both?
Is advantage one
+ √ − clearly identified and explained?
+ √ − inherently related to this proposal rather than an advantage that could be obtained as easily in other ways?
+ √ − backed with enough convincing support?
+ √ − backed with enough arousing and informing support?
Write a short evaluation of this advantage.

(Write additional comments on student's paper)

Is advantage two
+ √ − clearly identified and explained?
+ √ − inherently related to this proposal rather than an advantage that could be obtained as easily in other ways?
+ √ − backed with enough convincing support?
+ √ − backed with enough arousing and informing support?
Write a short evaluation of this advantage.

(Write additional comments on student's paper)

Does the conclusion
+ √ − summarize the paper effectively?
+ √ − bring the original statement of the topic back to your attention?
+ √ − draw the conclusion for the reader that the proposal has been supported, that the plan of change is a good one, that there are clear advantages to adopting the proposal, and that we therefore should adopt it?

Do Not Put a Grade on This Form. Record the Author's Grade Only on the Exercise 7 Grade Computation Form (page 313) and Grading Form (page 315).

Your Name ____________________

No. ________ Group ________ Sec. ________

Exercise 7: Feedback Form to Author ____________________ **No.** ________

Yes No Is this paper of proper length and does it have proper margins?

Does the introduction do the following:

+ √ – introduce the topic and gain and focus attention on it?

+ √ – clearly define the terms?

+ √ – build rapport—did its appearance and style make you feel this paper would be worth reading?

Write what specific things are effective or need improving in the introduction.

(Write additional comments on student's paper)

I. *Arguments showing need for change*:

+ √ – Are each of the subarguments clearly identified by headings, a forecast summary, or both?

Is subargument one

+ √ – clearly identified and explained?

+ √ – inherently related to the main argument?

+ √ – backed with enough convincing support?

+ √ – backed with enough informing and arousing support?

Which forms of support are used? (Circle)

detailed examples | background data | specific instances
analogies | | statistics
explanations of logic | | testimonies of authorities

Explain what is needed to improve this subargument.

(Write additional comments on student's paper)

Is subargument two

+ √ – clearly identified and explained?

+ √ – inherently related to the main argument?

+ √ – backed with enough convincing support?

+ √ – backed with enough informing and arousing support?

Which forms of support are used? (Circle)

detailed examples | background data | specific instances
analogies | | statistics
explanations of logic | | testimonies of authorities

Explain what is needed to improve this subargument.

(Write additional comments on student's paper)

Is subargument three

+ √ – clearly identified and explained?

+ √ – inherently related to the main argument?

+ √ – backed with enough convincing support?

+ √ – backed with enough informing and arousing support?

Which forms of support are used? (Circle)

detailed examples | background data | specific instances
analogies | | statistics
explanations of logic | | testimonies of authorities

Explain what is needed to improve this subargument.

(Write additional comments on student's paper)

+ √ − Is this section of the paper clearly summarized?
+ √ − Are the subarguments shown to clearly support the main argument?

II. *Proposed plan of how to change*:
+ √ − Is the plan easy to understand?
+ √ − Would the plan remove the problems described in subargument one?
+ √ − Would the plan remove the problems described in subargument two?
+ √ − Would the plan remove the problems described in subargument three?
+ √ − Does the plan sound practical and feasible?
Write your evaluation of this plan.

(Write additional comments on student's paper)

III. *Advantages of the new proposal*:
+ √ − Are each of the subarguments in this section clearly identified by a forecast summary, headings, or both?
Is advantage one
+ √ − clearly identified and explained?
+ √ − inherently related to this proposal rather than an advantage that could be obtained as easily in other ways?
+ √ − backed with enough convincing support?
+ √ − backed with enough arousing and informing support?
Write a short evaluation of this advantage.

(Write additional comments on student's paper)

Is advantage two
+ √ − clearly identified and explained?
+ √ − inherently related to this proposal rather than an advantage that could be obtained as easily in other ways?
+ √ − backed with enough convincing support?
+ √ − backed with enough arousing and informing support?
Write a short evaluation of this advantage.

(Write additional comments on student's paper)

Does the conclusion
+ √ − summarize the paper effectively?
+ √ − bring the original statement of the topic back to your attention?
+ √ − draw the conclusion for the reader that the proposal has been supported, that the plan of change is a good one, that there are clear advantages to adopting the proposal, and that we therefore should adopt it?

Do Not Put a Grade on This Form. Record the Author's Grade Only on the Exercise 7 Grade Computation Form (page 313) and Grading Form (page 315).

Your Name ______________________

No. ________ Group ________ Sec. ________

Exercise 7: Feedback Form to Author ______________________ **No.** ________

Yes No Is this paper of proper length and does it have proper margins?

Does the introduction do the following:

+ √ − introduce the topic and gain and focus attention on it?
+ √ − clearly define the terms?
+ √ − build rapport—did its appearance and style make you feel this paper would be worth reading?

Write what specific things are effective or need improving in the introduction.

____

____

____

____

____

(Write additional comments on student's paper)

I. *Arguments showing need for change:*

+ √ − Are each of the subarguments clearly identified by headings, a forecast summary, or both?

Is subargument one

+ √ − clearly identified and explained?
+ √ − inherently related to the main argument?
+ √ − backed with enough convincing support?
+ √ − backed with enough informing and arousing support?

Which forms of support are used? (Circle)

detailed examples background data specific instances
analogies statistics
explanations of logic testimonies of authorities

Explain what is needed to improve this subargument.

____

____

____

____

____

(Write additional comments on student's paper)

Is subargument two

+ √ − clearly identified and explained?
+ √ − inherently related to the main argument?
+ √ − backed with enough convincing support?
+ √ − backed with enough informing and arousing support?

Which forms of support are used? (Circle)

detailed examples background data specific instances
analogies statistics
explanations of logic testimonies of authorities

Explain what is needed to improve this subargument.

____

____

____

____

____

(Write additional comments on student's paper)

Is subargument three

+ √ − clearly identified and explained?
+ √ − inherently related to the main argument?
+ √ − backed with enough convincing support?
+ √ − backed with enough informing and arousing support?

Which forms of support are used? (Circle)

detailed examples background data specific instances
analogies statistics
explanations of logic testimonies of authorities

Explain what is needed to improve this subargument.

(Write additional comments on student's paper)

+ √ − Is this section of the paper clearly summarized?
+ √ − Are the subarguments shown to clearly support the main argument?

II. *Proposed plan of how to change*:
+ √ − Is the plan easy to understand?
+ √ − Would the plan remove the problems described in subargument one?
+ √ − Would the plan remove the problems described in subargument two?
+ √ − Would the plan remove the problems described in subargument three?
+ √ − Does the plan sound practical and feasible?
Write your evaluation of this plan.

(Write additional comments on student's paper)

III. *Advantages of the new proposal*:
+ √ − Are each of the subarguments in this section clearly identified by a forecast summary, headings, or both?
Is advantage one
+ √ − clearly identified and explained?
+ √ − inherently related to this proposal rather than an advantage that could be obtained as easily in other ways?
+ √ − backed with enough convincing support?
+ √ − backed with enough arousing and informing support?
Write a short evaluation of this advantage.

(Write additional comments on student's paper)

Is advantage two
+ √ − clearly identified and explained?
+ √ − inherently related to this proposal rather than an advantage that could be obtained as easily in other ways?
+ √ − backed with enough convincing support?
+ √ − backed with enough arousing and informing support?
Write a short evaluation of this advantage.

(Write additional comments on student's paper)

Does the conclusion
+ √ − summarize the paper effectively?
+ √ − bring the original statement of the topic back to your attention?
+ √ − draw the conclusion for the reader that the proposal has been supported, that the plan of change is a good one, that there are clear advantages to adopting the proposal, and that we therefore should adopt it?

Do Not Put a Grade on This Form. Record the Author's Grade Only on the Exercise 7 Grade Computation Form (page 313) and Grading Form (page 315).

Your Name________________________

No.________ Group ________ Sec. ________

Exercise 7: Feedback Form to Author ____________________ **No.** ________

Yes No Is this paper of proper length and does it have proper margins?

Does the introduction do the following:

+ √ − introduce the topic and gain and focus attention on it?

+ √ − clearly define the terms?

+ √ − build rapport—did its appearance and style make you feel this paper would be worth reading?

Write what specific things are effective or need improving in the introduction.

____

____

____

____

____

(Write additional comments on student's paper)

I. *Arguments showing need for change*:

+ √ − Are each of the subarguments clearly identified by headings, a forecast summary, or both?

Is subargument one

+ √ − clearly identified and explained?

+ √ − inherently related to the main argument?

+ √ − backed with enough convincing support?

+ √ − backed with enough informing and arousing support?

Which forms of support are used? (Circle)

detailed examples	background data	specific instances
analogies		statistics
explanations of logic		testimonies of authorities

Explain what is needed to improve this subargument.

____

____

____

____

____

(Write additional comments on student's paper)

Is subargument two

+ √ − clearly identified and explained?

+ √ − inherently related to the main argument?

+ √ − backed with enough convincing support?

+ √ − backed with enough informing and arousing support?

Which forms of support are used? (Circle)

detailed examples	background data	specific instances
analogies		statistics
explanations of logic		testimonies of authorities

Explain what is needed to improve this subargument.

____

____

____

____

____

(Write additional comments on student's paper)

Is subargument three

+ √ − clearly identified and explained?

+ √ − inherently related to the main argument?

+ √ − backed with enough convincing support?

+ √ − backed with enough informing and arousing support?

Which forms of support are used? (Circle)

detailed examples	background data	specific instances
analogies		statistics
explanations of logic		testimonies of authorities

Explain what is needed to improve this subargument.

(Write additional comments on student's paper)

+ √ − Is this section of the paper clearly summarized?
+ √ − Are the subarguments shown to clearly support the main argument?

II. *Proposed plan of how to change*:

+ √ − Is the plan easy to understand?
+ √ − Would the plan remove the problems described in subargument one?
+ √ − Would the plan remove the problems described in subargument two?
+ √ − Would the plan remove the problems described in subargument three?
+ √ − Does the plan sound practical and feasible?

Write your evaluation of this plan.

(Write additional comments on student's paper)

III. *Advantages of the new proposal*:

+ √ − Are each of the subarguments in this section clearly identified by a forecast summary, headings, or both?

Is advantage one

+ √ − clearly identified and explained?
+ √ − inherently related to this proposal rather than an advantage that could be obtained as easily in other ways?
+ √ − backed with enough convincing support?
+ √ − backed with enough arousing and informing support?

Write a short evaluation of this advantage.

(Write additional comments on student's paper)

Is advantage two

+ √ − clearly identified and explained?
+ √ − inherently related to this proposal rather than an advantage that could be obtained as easily in other ways?
+ √ − backed with enough convincing support?
+ √ − backed with enough arousing and informing support?

Write a short evaluation of this advantage.

(Write additional comments on student's paper)

Does the conclusion

+ √ − summarize the paper effectively?
+ √ − bring the original statement of the topic back to your attention?
+ √ − draw the conclusion for the reader that the proposal has been supported, that the plan of change is a good one, that there are clear advantages to adopting the proposal, and that we therefore should adopt it?

Do Not Put a Grade on This Form. Record the Author's Grade Only on the Exercise 7 Grade Computation Form (page 313) and Grading Form (page 315).

Your Name ______________________

No. ________ Group ________ Sec. ________

Exercise 7: Feedback Form to Author ______________________ **No.** ________

Yes No Is this paper of proper length and does it have proper margins?

Does the introduction do the following:

+ √ − introduce the topic and gain and focus attention on it?

+ √ − clearly define the terms?

+ √ − build rapport–did its appearance and style make you feel this paper would be worth reading?

Write what specific things are effective or need improving in the introduction.

____

____

____

____

____

(Write additional comments on student's paper)

I. *Arguments showing need for change*:

+ √ − Are each of the subarguments clearly identified by headings, a forecast summary, or both?

Is subargument one

+ √ − clearly identified and explained?

+ √ − inherently related to the main argument?

+ √ − backed with enough convincing support?

+ √ − backed with enough informing and arousing support?

Which forms of support are used? (Circle)

detailed examples	background data	specific instances
analogies		statistics
explanations of logic		testimonies of authorities

Explain what is needed to improve this subargument.

____

____

____

____

____

(Write additional comments on student's paper)

Is subargument two

+ √ − clearly identified and explained?

+ √ − inherently related to the main argument?

+ √ − backed with enough convincing support?

+ √ − backed with enough informing and arousing support?

Which forms of support are used? (Circle)

detailed examples	background data	specific instances
analogies		statistics
explanations of logic		testimonies of authorities

Explain what is needed to improve this subargument.

____

____

____

____

____

(Write additional comments on student's paper)

Is subargument three

+ √ − clearly identified and explained?

+ √ − inherently related to the main argument?

+ √ − backed with enough convincing support?

+ √ − backed with enough informing and arousing support?

Which forms of support are used? (Circle)

detailed examples	background data	specific instances
analogies		statistics
explanations of logic		testimonies of authorities

Explain what is needed to improve this subargument.

(Write additional comments on student's paper)

+ √ — Is this section of the paper clearly summarized?
+ √ — Are the subarguments shown to clearly support the main argument?

II. *Proposed plan of how to change*:

+ √ — Is the plan easy to understand?
+ √ — Would the plan remove the problems described in subargument one?
+ √ — Would the plan remove the problems described in subargument two?
+ √ — Would the plan remove the problems described in subargument three?
+ √ — Does the plan sound practical and feasible?

Write your evaluation of this plan.

(Write additional comments on student's paper)

III. *Advantages of the new proposal*:

+ √ — Are each of the subarguments in this section clearly identified by a forecast summary, headings, or both?

Is advantage one

+ √ — clearly identified and explained?
+ √ — inherently related to this proposal rather than an advantage that could be obtained as easily in other ways?
+ √ — backed with enough convincing support?
+ √ — backed with enough arousing and informing support?

Write a short evaluation of this advantage.

(Write additional comments on student's paper)

Is advantage two

+ √ — clearly identified and explained?
+ √ — inherently related to this proposal rather than an advantage that could be obtained as easily in other ways?
+ √ — backed with enough convincing support?
+ √ — backed with enough arousing and informing support?

Write a short evaluation of this advantage.

(Write additional comments on student's paper)

Does the conclusion

+ √ — summarize the paper effectively?
+ √ — bring the original statement of the topic back to your attention?
+ √ — draw the conclusion for the reader that the proposal has been supported, that the plan of change is a good one, that there are clear advantages to adopting the proposal, and that we therefore should adopt it?

Do Not Put a Grade on This Form. Record the Author's Grade Only on the Exercise 7 Grade Computation Form (page 313) and Grading Form (page 315).

Your Name____________________________

No. ________ Group ________ Sec. ________

Exercise 7: Feedback Form to Author ________________________ **No.** ________

Yes No Is this paper of proper length and does it have proper margins?

Does the introduction do the following:

+ √ − introduce the topic and gain and focus attention on it?
+ √ − clearly define the terms?
+ √ − build rapport—did its appearance and style make you feel this paper would be worth reading?

Write what specific things are effective or need improving in the introduction.

____

____

____

____

(Write additional comments on student's paper)

I. *Arguments showing need for change*:

+ √ − Are each of the subarguments clearly identified by headings, a forecast summary, or both?

Is subargument one

+ √ − clearly identified and explained?
+ √ − inherently related to the main argument?
+ √ − backed with enough convincing support?
+ √ − backed with enough informing and arousing support?

Which forms of support are used? (Circle)

detailed examples | background data | specific instances
analogies | statistics
explanations of logic | testimonies of authorities

Explain what is needed to improve this subargument.

____

____

____

____

(Write additional comments on student's paper)

Is subargument two

+ √ − clearly identified and explained?
+ √ − inherently related to the main argument?
+ √ − backed with enough convincing support?
+ √ − backed with enough informing and arousing support?

Which forms of support are used? (Circle)

detailed examples | background data | specific instances
analogies | statistics
explanations of logic | testimonies of authorities

Explain what is needed to improve this subargument.

____

____

____

____

(Write additional comments on student's paper)

Is subargument three

+ √ − clearly identified and explained?
+ √ − inherently related to the main argument?
+ √ − backed with enough convincing support?
+ √ − backed with enough informing and arousing support?

Which forms of support are used? (Circle)

detailed examples | background data | specific instances
analogies | statistics
explanations of logic | testimonies of authorities

Explain what is needed to improve this subargument.

(Write additional comments on student's paper)

+ √ − Is this section of the paper clearly summarized?
+ √ − Are the subarguments shown to clearly support the main argument?

II. *Proposed plan of how to change*:
+ √ − Is the plan easy to understand?
+ √ − Would the plan remove the problems described in subargument one?
+ √ − Would the plan remove the problems described in subargument two?
+ √ − Would the plan remove the problems described in subargument three?
+ √ − Does the plan sound practical and feasible?
Write your evaluation of this plan.

(Write additional comments on student's paper)

III. *Advantages of the new proposal*:
+ √ − Are each of the subarguments in this section clearly identified by a forecast summary, headings, or both?
Is advantage one
+ √ − clearly identified and explained?
+ √ − inherently related to this proposal rather than an advantage that could be obtained as easily in other ways?
+ √ − backed with enough convincing support?
+ √ − backed with enough arousing and informing support?
Write a short evaluation of this advantage.

(Write additional comments on student's paper)

Is advantage two
+ √ − clearly identified and explained?
+ √ − inherently related to this proposal rather than an advantage that could be obtained as easily in other ways?
+ √ − backed with enough convincing support?
+ √ − backed with enough arousing and informing support?
Write a short evaluation of this advantage.

(Write additional comments on student's paper)

Does the conclusion
+ √ − summarize the paper effectively?
+ √ − bring the original statement of the topic back to your attention?
+ √ − draw the conclusion for the reader that the proposal has been supported, that the plan of change is a good one, that there are clear advantages to adopting the proposal, and that we therefore should adopt it?

Do Not Put a Grade on This Form. Record the Author's Grade Only on the Exercise 7 Grade Computation Form (page 313) and Grading Form (page 315).

Your Name ____________________
No.________ Group________ Sec.__________

Exercise 7: Feedback Form to Author ____________________ **No.** ________

Yes No Is this paper of proper length and does it have proper margins?

Does the introduction do the following:

+ √ − introduce the topic and gain and focus attention on it?
+ √ − clearly define the terms?
+ √ − build rapport–did its appearance and style make you feel this paper would be worth reading?

Write what specific things are effective or need improving in the introduction.

(Write additional comments on student's paper)

I. *Arguments showing need for change:*

+ √ − Are each of the subarguments clearly identified by headings, a forecast summary, or both?

Is subargument one

+ √ − clearly identified and explained?
+ √ − inherently related to the main argument?
+ √ − backed with enough convincing support?
+ √ − backed with enough informing and arousing support?

Which forms of support are used? (Circle)

detailed examples background data specific instances
analogies statistics
explanations of logic testimonies of authorities

Explain what is needed to improve this subargument.

(Write additional comments on student's paper)

Is subargument two

+ √ − clearly identified and explained?
+ √ − inherently related to the main argument?
+ √ − backed with enough convincing support?
+ √ − backed with enough informing and arousing support?

Which forms of support are used? (Circle)

detailed examples background data specific instances
analogies statistics
explanations of logic testimonies of authorities

Explain what is needed to improve this subargument.

(Write additional comments on student's paper)

Is subargument three

+ √ − clearly identified and explained?
+ √ − inherently related to the main argument?
+ √ − backed with enough convincing support?
+ √ − backed with enough informing and arousing support?

Which forms of support are used? (Circle)

detailed examples background data specific instances
analogies statistics
explanations of logic testimonies of authorities

Explain what is needed to improve this subargument.

(Write additional comments on student's paper)

+ √ − Is this section of the paper clearly summarized?
+ √ − Are the subarguments shown to clearly support the main argument?

II. *Proposed plan of how to change*:

+ √ − Is the plan easy to understand?
+ √ − Would the plan remove the problems described in subargument one?
+ √ − Would the plan remove the problems described in subargument two?
+ √ − Would the plan remove the problems described in subargument three?
+ √ − Does the plan sound practical and feasible?

Write your evaluation of this plan.

(Write additional comments on student's paper)

III. *Advantages of the new proposal*:

+ √ − Are each of the subarguments in this section clearly identified by a forecast summary, headings, or both?

Is advantage one

+ √ − clearly identified and explained?
+ √ − inherently related to this proposal rather than an advantage that could be obtained as easily in other ways?
+ √ − backed with enough convincing support?
+ √ − backed with enough arousing and informing support?

Write a short evaluation of this advantage.

(Write additional comments on student's paper)

Is advantage two

+ √ − clearly identified and explained?
+ √ − inherently related to this proposal rather than an advantage that could be obtained as easily in other ways?
+ √ − backed with enough convincing support?
+ √ − backed with enough arousing and informing support?

Write a short evaluation of this advantage.

(Write additional comments on student's paper)

Does the conclusion

+ √ − summarize the paper effectively?
+ √ − bring the original statement of the topic back to your attention?
+ √ − draw the conclusion for the reader that the proposal has been supported, that the plan of change is a good one, that there are clear advantages to adopting the proposal, and that we therefore should adopt it?

Do Not Put a Grade on This Form. Record the Author's Grade Only on the Exercise 7 Grade Computation Form (page 313) and Grading Form (page 315).

Your Name ______________________

No. ________ Group ________ Sec. ________

Exercise 7: Feedback Form to Author ______________________ No. ________

Yes No Is this paper of proper length and does it have proper margins?

Does the introduction do the following:

+ √ − introduce the topic and gain and focus attention on it?
+ √ − clearly define the terms?
+ √ − build rapport—did its appearance and style make you feel this paper would be worth reading?

Write what specific things are effective or need improving in the introduction.

____

____

____

____

____

(Write additional comments on student's paper)

I. *Arguments showing need for change*:

+ √ − Are each of the subarguments clearly identified by headings, a forecast summary, or both?

Is subargument one

+ √ − clearly identified and explained?
+ √ − inherently related to the main argument?
+ √ − backed with enough convincing support?
+ √ − backed with enough informing and arousing support?

Which forms of support are used? (Circle)

detailed examples background data specific instances
analogies statistics
explanations of logic testimonies of authorities

Explain what is needed to improve this subargument.

____

____

____

____

____

(Write additional comments on student's paper)

Is subargument two

+ √ − clearly identified and explained?
+ √ − inherently related to the main argument?
+ √ − backed with enough convincing support?
+ √ − backed with enough informing and arousing support?

Which forms of support are used? (Circle)

detailed examples background data specific instances
analogies statistics
explanations of logic testimonies of authorities

Explain what is needed to improve this subargument.

____

____

____

____

____

(Write additional comments on student's paper)

Is subargument three

+ √ − clearly identified and explained?
+ √ − inherently related to the main argument?
+ √ − backed with enough convincing support?
+ √ − backed with enough informing and arousing support?

Which forms of support are used? (Circle)

detailed examples background data specific instances
analogies statistics
explanations of logic testimonies of authorities

Explain what is needed to improve this subargument.

(Write additional comments on student's paper)

+ √ − Is this section of the paper clearly summarized?
+ √ − Are the subarguments shown to clearly support the main argument?

II. *Proposed plan of how to change*:
+ √ − Is the plan easy to understand?
+ √ − Would the plan remove the problems described in subargument one?
+ √ − Would the plan remove the problems described in subargument two?
+ √ − Would the plan remove the problems described in subargument three?
+ √ − Does the plan sound practical and feasible?

Write your evaluation of this plan.

(Write additional comments on student's paper)

III. *Advantages of the new proposal*:
+ √ − Are each of the subarguments in this section clearly identified by a forecast summary, headings, or both?

Is advantage one
+ √ − clearly identified and explained?
+ √ − inherently related to this proposal rather than an advantage that could be obtained as easily in other ways?
+ √ − backed with enough convincing support?
+ √ − backed with enough arousing and informing support?

Write a short evaluation of this advantage.

(Write additional comments on student's paper)

Is advantage two
+ √ − clearly identified and explained?
+ √ − inherently related to this proposal rather than an advantage that could be obtained as easily in other ways?
+ √ − backed with enough convincing support?
+ √ − backed with enough arousing and informing support?

Write a short evaluation of this advantage.

(Write additional comments on student's paper)

Does the conclusion
+ √ − summarize the paper effectively?
+ √ − bring the original statement of the topic back to your attention?
+ √ − draw the conclusion for the reader that the proposal has been supported, that the plan of change is a good one, that there are clear advantages to adopting the proposal, and that we therefore should adopt it?

Do Not Put a Grade on This Form. Record the Author's Grade Only on the Exercise 7 Grade Computation Form (page 313) and Grading Form (page 315).

Your Name ______________________

No. ________ Group ________ Sec. ________

Exercise 7: Feedback Form to Author ______________________ **No.** ________

Yes No Is this paper of proper length and does it have proper margins?

Does the introduction do the following:

+ √ − introduce the topic and gain and focus attention on it?

+ √ − clearly define the terms?

+ √ − build rapport—did its appearance and style make you feel this paper would be worth reading?

Write what specific things are effective or need improving in the introduction.

____

____

____

____

____

(Write additional comments on student's paper)

I. *Arguments showing need for change*:

+ √ − Are each of the subarguments clearly identified by headings, a forecast summary, or both?

Is subargument one

+ √ − clearly identified and explained?

+ √ − inherently related to the main argument?

+ √ − backed with enough convincing support?

+ √ − backed with enough informing and arousing support?

Which forms of support are used? (Circle)

detailed examples	background data	specific instances
analogies		statistics
explanations of logic		testimonies of authorities

Explain what is needed to improve this subargument.

____

____

____

____

____

(Write additional comments on student's paper)

Is subargument two

+ √ − clearly identified and explained?

+ √ − inherently related to the main argument?

+ √ − backed with enough convincing support?

+ √ − backed with enough informing and arousing support?

Which forms of support are used? (Circle)

detailed examples	background data	specific instances
analogies		statistics
explanations of logic		testimonies of authorities

Explain what is needed to improve this subargument.

____

____

____

____

____

(Write additional comments on student's paper)

Is subargument three

+ √ − clearly identified and explained?

+ √ − inherently related to the main argument?

+ √ − backed with enough convincing support?

+ √ − backed with enough informing and arousing support?

Which forms of support are used? (Circle)

detailed examples	background data	specific instances
analogies		statistics
explanations of logic		testimonies of authorities

Explain what is needed to improve this subargument.

(Write additional comments on student's paper)

+ √ − Is this section of the paper clearly summarized?
+ √ − Are the subarguments shown to clearly support the main argument?

II. *Proposed plan of how to change*:
+ √ − Is the plan easy to understand?
+ √ − Would the plan remove the problems described in subargument one?
+ √ − Would the plan remove the problems described in subargument two?
+ √ − Would the plan remove the problems described in subargument three?
+ √ − Does the plan sound practical and feasible?

Write your evaluation of this plan.

(Write additional comments on student's paper)

III. *Advantages of the new proposal*:
+ √ − Are each of the subarguments in this section clearly identified by a forecast summary, headings, or both?

Is advantage one
+ √ − clearly identified and explained?
+ √ − inherently related to this proposal rather than an advantage that could be obtained as easily in other ways?
+ √ − backed with enough convincing support?
+ √ − backed with enough arousing and informing support?

Write a short evaluation of this advantage.

(Write additional comments on student's paper)

Is advantage two
+ √ − clearly identified and explained?
+ √ − inherently related to this proposal rather than an advantage that could be obtained as easily in other ways?
+ √ − backed with enough convincing support?
+ √ − backed with enough arousing and informing support?

Write a short evaluation of this advantage.

(Write additional comments on student's paper)

Does the conclusion
+ √ − summarize the paper effectively?
+ √ − bring the original statement of the topic back to your attention?
+ √ − draw the conclusion for the reader that the proposal has been supported, that the plan of change is a good one, that there are clear advantages to adopting the proposal, and that we therefore should adopt it?

Do Not Put a Grade on This Form. Record the Author's Grade Only on the Exercise 7 Grade Computation Form (page 313) and Grading Form (page 315).

Your Name ____________________
No.________ Group__________ Sec.________

Exercise 7

GRADE COMPUTATION FORM

Rate each student from 1 to 10 on each of the three criteria described in the Grading Criteria section (pages 275 and 276). Then multiply each rating by the weight that follows it. Put the weighted grade on the double underlined blanks that follow. Transfer these grades to your Exercise 7 Grading Form.

Meaning of number grades

4%			55%				25%	15%	1%
	F	D	C–	C	C+		B	A	A+
1	2	3	4	5	6	7	8	9	10
	Poor			OK			Good	Excellent	Perfect

Copy No.	Author's No.	Criterion I Rating Weight	Criterion II Rating Weight	Criterion III Rating Weight
1	______	____ X 1 = ____,	____ X 3 = ____,	____ X 6 = ____
2	______	____ X 1 = ____,	____ X 3 = ____,	____ X 6 = ____
3	______	____ X 1 = ____,	____ X 3 = ____,	____ X 6 = ____
4	______	____ X 1 = ____,	____ X 3 = ____,	____ X 6 = ____
5	______	____ X 1 = ____,	____ X 3 = ____,	____ X 6 = ____
6	______	____ X 1 = ____,	____ X 3 = ____,	____ X 6 = ____
7	______	____ X 1 = ____,	____ X 3 = ____,	____ X 6 = ____
8	______	____ X 1 = ____,	____ X 3 = ____,	____ X 6 = ____
9	______	____ X 1 = ____,	____ X 3 = ____,	____ X 6 = ____
10	______	____ X 1 = ____,	____ X 3 = ____,	____ X 6 = ____
11	______	____ X 1 = ____,	____ X 3 = ____,	____ X 6 = ____
12	______	____ X 1 = ____,	____ X 3 = ____,	____ X 6 = ____
13	______	____ X 1 = ____,	____ X 3 = ____,	____ X 6 = ____
14	______	____ X 1 = ____,	____ X 3 = ____,	____ X 6 = ____
15	______	____ X 1 = ____,	____ X 3 = ____,	____ X 6 = ____
16	______	____ X 1 = ____,	____ X 3 = ____,	____ X 6 = ____

Do *not* turn in this sheet. It is only for your computation of grades.

Your Name ______________________
No. ________ Group ________ Sec. ______

Exercise 7

GRADING FORM

Record all weighted grades for Criteria I, II, and III on this form. Then sum those grades for each student to obtain his sum weighted grade.

Paper Copy No.	Author's No.	Weighted Grades on Criteria				Sum Weighted Grade
1	______	I ______	II ______	III ______	=	☐
2	______	I ______	II ______	III ______	=	☐
3	______	I ______	II ______	III ______	=	☐
4	______	I ______	II ______	III ______	=	☐
5	______	I ______	II ______	III ______	=	☐
6	______	I ______	II ______	III ______	=	☐
7	______	I ______	II ______	III ______	=	☐
8	______	I ______	II ______	III ______	=	☐
9	______	I ______	II ______	III ______	=	☐
10	______	I ______	II ______	III ______	=	☐
11	______	I ______	II ______	III ______	=	☐
12	______	I ______	II ______	III ______	=	☐
13	______	I ______	II ______	III ______	=	☐
14	______	I ______	II ______	III ______	=	☐
15	______	I ______	II ______	III ______	=	☐
16	______	I ______	II ______	III ______	=	☐

	I	II	III	
Sum of Grades:	I ______	II ______	III ______	______
÷ by number of grades in column =	______	______	______	______
the average grade you gave	I ______	II ______	III ______	______

When this sheet is completed, give it to the instructor. This form is due on the day the graded papers are returned.

Your Name ______________________
No. ________ Group ________ Sec. ________

Exercise 7

GRADER QUALITY REPORT

This form is to be used to grade the quality of the feedback your received on your Exercise 7 papers. For earlier assignments we gave the evaluators only feedback on how valuable their comments and suggestions were. Our evaluations were designed to help them improve their ability to write helpful feedback. On this form we are giving more than just feedback; in addition, we are giving a grade that will go on the student's permanent record. Be sure to give a fair and honest grade. If you grade too high, you are being unfair to those who have legitimately earned high grades. If you grade too low, you are cheating the person you are grading. There are many safeguards built into this grading system, which have already been explained, but remember the best safeguard is your own fairness. Rate students who evaluated paper copies 1-8 on Categories A, B, and C. Rate students who evaluated paper copies 9-16 on Category A only.

Rating Scale

Rating Category A	1 = not at all	3 = partially	6 = completely
Rate Categories B & C	1 = very poor 4 = good	2 = below average 5 = excellent	3 = acceptable 6 = outstanding

Copy No.	No. Grader	Category A Checklist was filled out		Category B How completely did written comments cover all aspects of your paper? Coverage was:		Category C The quality and value of the comments were:		Final Feedback Grade
1	____	____	+	____	+ 2 X	____	=	____
2	____	____	+	____	+ 2 X	____	=	____
3	____	____	+	____	+ 2 X	____	=	____
4	____	____	+	____	+ 2 X	____	=	____
5	____	____	+	____	+ 2 X	____	=	____
6	____	____	+	____	+ 2 X	____	=	____
7	____	____	+	____	+ 2 X	____	=	____
8	____	____	+	____	+ 2 X	____	=	____
9	____	____						
10	____	____						
11	____	____						
12	____	____						
13	____	____						
14	____	____						
15	____	____						
16	____	____						

These sheets are to be given to the instructor by the due date of ______________________

EXERCISE 8

The Business Presentation and Defense

PURPOSE OF ASSIGNMENT

This is the final exercise for this course. It is also the most complex and comprehensive exercise. It is structured as a panel discussion with introductory presentations pro and con. Because this type of presentation requires as much listening and reasoning skill as speaking skill, it was selected as the final assignment. This is a learning exercise; as well as one in which you display what you have learned. As with all of the previous exercises, this one has two parts, the presentation of material and the constructive evaluation of the presentations. The grade on your presentation and the grade on the quality of your constructive evaluation of others will account for a major part of your final course grade.

Introduction

This exercise is similar to what goes on in the type of business meeting in which new proposals are formally presented and in which those opposing the proposed change are given a chance to defend the current system and point out the possible ill effects of the proposed change. Proposals are usually presented in written form first, such as you did in Exercise 7. If this written document generates enough interest, the authors are asked to come in and formally present their proposals in person to the executive committee. The opening presentations are always made by those proposing the change. They are followed by presentations of those opposing the change, and then the meeting is opened for questions and discussion.

This type of discussion requires as much listening and reasoning skill as speaking skill. When opposing speakers counter your ideas, you must listen carefully, analyze their arguments, and prepare to resubstantiate your own. The glib speaker who is ill prepared is easily exposed in this type of situation. Those who have researched their material carefully and have thought through the arguments and counterarguments in advance are the ones who stand out.

ASSIGNMENT INSTRUCTIONS

Prepare for Pro and Con

Each team is to prepare a complete presentation supporting the class proposal. On the pro side of this topic, you are to show why there is a need to change from the present system, propose a plan of action by which that change can realistically be brought about, and show the advantages of the proposed change over the current system.

Each team is also to prepare a complete presentation opposing the class proposal. On the con side, you are to support the current system, using the positive approach as described in Exercise 5. You are to show that the problems with the current system are not serious enough to warrant a major change, and/or show that the proposed changes would not really correct the problems existing in the present system, and/or show that the proposed changes would not bring about any real advantage, and/or show what additional problems the change would likely create.

There will be at least two demonstration presentations of Exercise 8 given for the entire class to review. Each of you will also have a chance to participate in several practice rounds before giving your final presentations. Each team will have an opportunity to present the pro side and the con side in one of these practice rounds. Following the practice rounds, you will give the final presentations upon which a major part of your grade in this course will be based.

Prepare for First or Second Position

Each person must be prepared to speak in first or second position on his team, both supporting and opposing the topic. At the beginning of the final presentations, a coin will be flipped to determine which speaker on each team is first and which speaker is second. This forces each student to be equally prepared. No one has the advantage of preparing for a position which he thinks is easier.

Format Options

There will be two teams, or four persons, on each panel. These panels may be structured in a variety of ways, according to the preference of the class and the instructor. It is important that all panels be set up the same way for any given class so that grades are comparable among the various panels.

Panel Structure Sample I:

First Speaker Pro	6 min.	12 min.
Second Speaker Pro	6 min.	
Questions for clarification from audience		2 min.
First Speaker Con	6 min.	12 min.
Second Speaker Con	6 min.	
Questions for clarification from audience		2 min.
Break		2 min.
Discussion-debate of the pro and con arguments and counterarguments by the four panel members		18 min.
		Total time 48 min.

Panel Structure Sample II:

First Speaker Pro	8 min.	
First Speaker Con	8 min.	
Second Speaker Pro	8 min.	
Second Speaker Con	8 min.	32 min.
Discussion-debate of the pro and con arguments and counterarguments by the four panel members with questions permitted from the audience		15 min.
Summary of Positions		
First Speaker Con	3 min.	
First Speaker Pro	3 min.	
Second Speaker Con	3 min.	
Second Speaker Pro	3 min.	12 min.
		Total Time 59 min.

Importance of Discussion Period

There are numerous other possibilities for structuring these panels. One important consideration is whether the class meets for 50, 60, or 75 minutes. It is important no matter which option is chosen that the discussion-debate section be at least 15 minutes long. Many students who can perform well in the one-way communication speaking situation are not able to cope with the two-way interaction of the discussion-debate, which will follow almost any presentation of a proposal. This is the type of interaction that is required in virtually all business meetings and the type stressed throughout this course. Before going any further, members of the class should decide, with the instructor's advice, which format they are going to use.

SOME MORE BASICS

The Duties of Each Speaker

First Speaker Pro. The first pro speaker's job is similar to the presentations outlined in Exercises 4 and 6. In this presentation, you introduce the topic, define terms, and outline the presentation of your team, using a forecast summary. The forecast summary should outline both your own and your partner's presentations. Usually, in this first speech you should concentrate your efforts on showing why there is a need to change from the present system.[1] You may in this first speech present your team's proposal on how to change or you may leave that for your partner. The conclusion of the presentation should contain a summary of what you discussed and a forecast summary of what your partner will discuss in his speech. Of course, all of the presentations should contain running summaries, transitions, and adequate amounts of support to arouse, inform, and convince the audience.

First Speaker Con. The first speaker opposing the change should give an introduction, just as was done for the paper in Assignment 5. The introduction is intended not so much to gain attention as to break the prejudice or slant created by the first speaker or speakers. The audience will have been hearing only what is wrong with the present system. As the first opposing speaker, you might use the introduction to impress the audience with how good the present system is, or you might point out some real dangers that exist in the type of change proposed by the first speaker. It is important that the introduction refocus the listeners' attention and make them more receptive to counterarguments. Following the introductory material, the first speaker con should accept or reject the terms as defined by the previous speaker. The definitions should generally be accepted unless they distort the topic. Examples of distorted terms are presented later.

As the first speaker con, you should next outline the team's case in a forecast summary. The forecast should typically parallel the outline of the pro team. For example, you might state the following:

> First, we will deal with the objections the first speaker (or speakers) has made about our present system. Then we will go on to show how effectively the current system is actually working. In my partner's presentation, he will examine our opponent's proposal of how to change and will then compare the advantages of their proposal with those of the present system.

Following the forecast summary, you should begin developing arguments to counter the first argument of the previous speaker. Note that we can counter arguments by being positive as well as by being defensive. It is best to counter arguments by showing what is right with the present system. After countering each of the previous speaker's arguments, you might also present additional arguments supporting the present system. The presentation should end with a conclusion that summarizes what you have discussed and points out what your partner is going to cover in his presentation.

[1] As was mentioned in Exercise 3, there are certain types of proposals which require that the proposed plan of change be presented before the need arguments. This is usually done when the need for changing the present system is not critical but the advantages of a change seem great. The example given in Assignment 3 was as follows: If a business is doing well, a manager is not likely to change policies until he understands in detail exactly how the new policy would work and what advantages it would offer. However, a company facing bankruptcy is likely to accept almost any plan that will save it, once it is shown that under present policies bankruptcy is certain.

Second Speaker Pro. If no con speaker has given a presentation yet, you can pick up this presentation right where the first speaker pro left off. If the format option the class chose has a con speaker between the pro speakers, you cannot just pick up where your partner left off two presentations earlier. In the meantime, the audience has heard counter material.

For this presentation, you must design your introduction to focus the audience's attention once again on the problems with the present system. This is often done by including in the introduction a summary of what your partner covered in his earlier presentation and then adding a forecast summary of what you plan to present. Next, resupport any of your partner's arguments that were weakened by the opposing team. Once these arguments have been re-established, you are ready to present your team's plan of how to change. Outline and explain the proposed plan so the audience can see that the plan is practical and feasible. Next, you should show the advantages of adopting your plan as opposed to continuing with the present system. These advantages should be supported and documented in the same manner as the need arguments. If you plan to develop several advantages, you might need to introduce these with a forecast summary.

The one type of advantage that is the easiest to develop is that derived by removing or substantially reducing the problems pointed out in the need for change arguments. The plan should be designed to remove or substantially reduce these problems. Removing those problems thus becomes one of the primary advantages of the plan.

You should carefully point out to the audience that there is a definite and consistent relationship between your need for change arguments, your proposed plan of change, and the advantages of the change. Following is an example of how such a relationship can be developed. The example used is based on the no-fault insurance topic described in Exercise 3.

The need for change subargument one is as follows:

> "It would enable victims to receive compensation more rapidly."

The proposed plan to deal with this problem might have the following provision:

> "Victims would receive partial payment within 5 days. The amount would be set by the claims office at 50% of the expected damages. The insurance company would then have 30 days to complete its investigation and pay the claim in full."

The advantage argument would be as follows:

> "Victims would not have to suffer long-term financial burdens while waiting for payment under our no-fault plan. Under the present insurance system, victims often receive no compensation for years while their case is being fought in court."

Note the relationships among each of these subparts. The one basic theme—compensation—flows through all of the subparts and ties them together. It is primarily the second speaker's job to review the flow of these ideas through the entire presentation and to show the listeners how the team's case holds together. The conclusion to this presentation should contain a summary of the entire case, showing how each need for a change is corrected by the plan and also showing the advantages of adopting your proposed plan.

Second Speaker Con. If the panel you are on does not alternate pro and con speakers, for this presentation you can just continue where your partner left off. As the second speaker con in the alternating pro-con format, you are the first to have a chance to deal with the entire case of the pro team. At this point, all of the arguments, proposed plans for change, and advantages of the change have been presented. As the final speaker, your job is to go over the opponents' entire case and point out weaknesses and inconsistencies. Before you do that, it is often wise to resupport the arguments of your partner. Then you can compare the pro and con arguments to show any weaknesses on the pro side.

There are several additional things to do in this presentation. You must point out the problems that might arise in trying to implement the pro team's plan. For example, you might point out that it would be too cumbersome to work, too costly to implement, too slow to implement, unconstitutional, and so on.

You have all already heard and read dozens of plans in your earlier exercises. You have already analyzed these and prepared counterarguments against them. Since you have done this advanced preparation, it will be easy for you to adapt these counterarguments to the specifics of this pro team's proposed plan.

Next, you should bring out possible disadvantages that might be created by adopting the pro team's proposal. For example, it might cause higher taxes, loss of rights, or rebellion. General counterarguments should be prepared in advance and then adapted to the specifics of the opponent's case.

The conclusion of this final presentation should contain a summary and review of the flow of arguments through the four presentations. You should again point out where the pro team has failed to adequately support its arguments or has not considered possible harmful side effects which might be created by its plan.

Discussion Period. No completely new arguments or plans can be presented during the discussion periods; however, new evidence concerning existing arguments or plans should be presented. If new arguments were permitted, each team could shift positions instead of defending what has already been presented. There would not be enough time to have an effective discussion of what had already been proposed during the initial presentations. One of the main functions of the discussion period is to allow each team to add additional clarification and support to its arguments and plans. The discussion period allows the two teams to question each other. If you feel that one of the other team's points was not properly documented, you can point this out and then ask for documentation. If you have evidence that contradicts that given, you can present that new evidence. It is this discussion period that will reveal who has done the best preparation. This is where you have an opportunity to display your reasoning ability and your skill at two-way communication. You must be ready to ask pertinent questions that reveal possible weaknesses in the arguments of the opposition. You must also be able to answer similar questions regarding your own arguments. This is why you practiced giving counter and counter-counterarguments in Exercise 6.

Audience Participation. During the discussion-debate period, *those in the audience are permitted to ask short questions* of any of the four panel members. These questions should be used to seek information and should not be argumentative questions. It is the opposing team's duties to present the arguments. Those in the audience should ask questions only to seek clarification or when they feel one of the teams has failed to deal with an issue raised by the other team. The discussion periods are to last the full time allotted, regardless of whether or not anyone is speaking.

Rejoinders (optional). (In the longer class periods it is suggested that a format be used that allows time for rejoinders. For shorter class periods the material normally covered in a rejoinder can be included in the discussion-debate periods). The presentation following the discussion period allows the speakers to review all that has been said and to add any new evidence that will strengthen their case. It is also a last chance to point out the weaknesses of the opponent's case.

These speeches are to be used to tie together and summarize all that was said during the discussion period. The speakers should show how the comments in the discussion period either support or contradict the arguments, counterarguments, and proposals made earlier.

These speeches are a final opportunity to convince those in the audience that they should accept your position either pro or con on the topic. They are also your last chance to demonstrate to the audience that you have worked hard and deserve a favorable evaluation.

Listening

The team opposing the change must be extremely good listeners. You have already practiced listening in earlier assignments, although some students may not have realized that is what they were doing. The exercise feedback sessions forced everyone to actively listen, so everyone could give each other feedback. The Feedback Forms were teaching you how to organize your listening and what to listen for.

Notes for Multiple Presentations

There is a new phase to the listening in Exercise 8. You must in this exercise listen to and keep track of four intertwined presentations. In the discussion period, you must listen to and adapt your statements to deal with what the other participants are saying. This requires that you keep careful track of all that is presented during both the speaking and discussion-debate sections of Exercise 8.

The skill of taking clear notes is extremely vital to businessmen and is an important part of listening. Unless we have photographic memories, it is difficult to recall all that was proposed, how it was supported, and how countered during an hour meeting. It is even more difficult to recall such information a month or even a week later if the topic comes up again. Most people take some notes during meetings to help them with recall. Some even try to tape record entire meetings. Taping is good, but the tape must later be listened to and summarized into notes before the information is of much use. You have already practiced taking notes in Exercise 6. Taking notes will be even more important during this exercise.

Notes Are Required

You are required to use a Note Sheet to assist you when you are in the role of an evaluator for Exercise 8. As a speaker on a panel, the use of a Note Sheet is optional but highly recommended. The Note Sheets for Exercise 8 should look like those used in Exercise 6, page 278. However, no forms are provided; just use a plain sheet of paper. A sample sheet is shown on page 335.

There will be one or two demonstration presentations of Exercise 8 given before the entire class. This will enable you to learn by watching and evaluating others. During these review sessions, you will also practice filling out a Note Sheet by outlining the entire presentation. The note-taking will follow the same format as described in Exercise 6, except in Exercise 8 you will need to take notes on both the pro and con presentations. Re-read the note-taking steps 1-5 (on pages 236-238) of Exercise 6. Then come back to this page for step 6.

How to Take Notes

6. This step begins on the con (or counterargument) side of the Note Sheet. The opposing team may either accept or reject the definition of terms offered by the pro team. If they accept, simply write, "Definitions accepted." If they do not accept, as they well may not if the definition is as far askew as the sample one in Exercise 6, then write, "Definitions rejected." Then later (in the discussion period), the two sides must resolve their definition problem. The pro team would need to explain why an unarmed nuclear vessel is included as a weapon. Let's assume that the pro team corrects the definition and says they mean only nuclear-armed vessels. Then your Note Sheet would read as follows:

Pro	Con
All aboveground nuclear testing should be halted.	
Definition: Unarmed vessel weapon?	Definition ~~rejected.~~ accepted.
(Definition clarified to nuclear-armed vessel.)	

7. When you are on the con side, as you listen to the pro team, use your Note Sheet to outline how you are going to deal with the pro team's arguments and plan. Note in the following example that quoted cards or Xeroxed pages are referred to by numbers. You should index all of your reference material and quotes so you can find them fast and identify them easily on your Note Sheet.

Pro	Con
All aboveground nuclear testing should be halted.	
Definition: Unarmed vessel weapon?	Definition ~~rejected~~. accepted.
(Definition clarified to nuclear-armed vessel.)	
Need for change	
1. Fallout contaminates air.	1. Contamination exaggerated.
A. Linus Pauling: Caused birth defects in 1962.	A. Edward Teller (Card 53) Most tests underground.

3.	3. Cau
1. Spain situation (detailed example)	1.
2. Argentina	2. Not even seeking N arms (card 46).
B. Have started wars for frivolous reasons in past.	B. They are not likely to ever get weapons regardless of testing because of massive costs.
	4. Testing is needed to develop peaceful uses (project plowshare, Card 18).

Argument 4 is written after the point on the sheet where the pro speaker's material ended. This indicates that it is a new argument introduced by the con team. It is identified by a number 4 even though it may be the first argument the con speaker has presented. It is numbered 4 because it is the fourth argument presented, regardless of which speaker introduced it.

7A. When in the role of evaluators, you must wait until the con speakers present their material and then record it on the con side of the sheet. The instructions in 7 are applicable only for the con team members.

8. During the discussion period, add notes to your sheets as new evidence and explanations are made to explain arguments presented earlier. Remember, completely new arguments cannot be presented during the discussion period. The notes made during the first four speeches should be a complete record of the arguments with which either side wishes to deal.

Grading from Note Sheets

9. Summarize your notes on the Evaluation of Notes Form on the back of the Exercise 8 Grading Form. When you are an evaluator, weigh the arguments and points that you outlined on your note sheet. This form is to contain an evaluation of the material, not simply another record of it. Explain which arguments were or were not adequately supported. Also, report on this form which team had the better evidence and

which team did the more convincing job of presenting, supporting, and defending its case. At the bottom of the form, declare whether you believe the pro or the con team was more convincing in the panel discussion-debate.

PROCEDURE FOR PRESENTATIONS

All speakers are to give their initial presentations while *standing.* The room is to be set up so the four speakers are at the front, facing each other at an angle and facing the audience. (See diagram, Figure 8-1.) If the number of students in the class is too large, the class will divide into smaller groups to hear these presentations. The ideal size for a group is four speakers and twelve evaluators. No less than eight evaluators should be used or the peer evaluation technique may lose validity.

FIGURE 8-1 Room Arrangements for Exercise 8

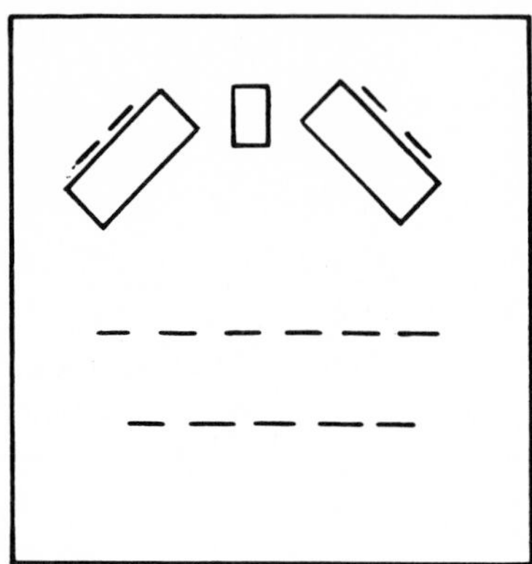

Group Coordinators and Assistants

The instructor will appoint group coordinators for each panel discussion. Their job is to collect the grading sheets and summarize them on the Panel Discussion Coordinator's Grade Summary Sheet. The two evaluators in the session who have the highest class numbers are to help the panel discussion coordinator compute the average grades and check these computations for accuracy. They and the coordinator must sign the Panel Discussion Coordinator's Grade Summary Sheet. If bonus points (see page 328) for winning are used by this class, the coordinator is to add on those points. The panel discussion coordinators will also act as the timers for all presentations and discussion periods. Since they will be busy timing, they will not have to fill out a Note Sheet or grade the speakers.

Timing

You should, if possible, use time cards during all presentations so that the speakers will continually know how much time they have remaining to speak. If a speaker takes more than 1½ minutes less than his allotted time, his presentation is not acceptable and is to be graded no higher than a 5 on content (Criterion III). If a speaker talks more than ½ minute over his allotted time, the timer is to stand and ask the speaker to stop. The time limits will depend on the format selected by your class.

Practice

For two people to jointly present a smooth, integrated, and internally consistent proposal requires much coordination and practice. Although some students might be able to fake their way through a one-way communication situation, it is much more difficult to do so under cross-examination by peers who have done their homework.

Do not merely practice the presentation part of the exercise. Remember, the discussion-debate period counts for half the grade. You should each practice countering your own arguments and then offering counter-counterarguments as was done in Exercise 6.

In-Class Review

We will spend two or three days in class reviewing this exercise. The first thing we will do in this review session is to have everyone fill out the Presentation Schedule (page 331). The information for the schedule will be provided by the instructor.

There will be at least two demonstrations of Exercise 8 given before the entire class. All of you who are not on the panels will act as evaluators during these sessions. You are to practice filling out a Note Sheet and evaluating the participants and their arguments during these demonstrations.

Workshop Practice Rounds

Since this is the final exercise and one on which you are graded, you will have a chance to participate in practice rounds. The practice rounds will be conducted the same as the final rounds except there will usually be no audience. In the practice rounds, you are to grade each other. In the final rounds, you will be graded by 10 to 14 of your peers. In the practice rounds, each team will speak on the pro side in one round and on the con side in the other. The pairings for the practice and final rounds will be assigned by the instructor. The time limits used will depend upon the format selected by this class.

Additional Practice

Following each practice round, it is suggested that the two teams get together and have an informal feedback session. Note that there is no feedback session as such scheduled for Exercise 8. That is because this is the final session. The final feedback comes in the form of grades. There is, however, time to improve between the practice rounds and the final rounds, so seeking feedback after the practice rounds will be helpful.

Grading

As with all of your earlier exercises, there are two parts to Exercise 8 which are graded separately. Part one consists of the presentation. You are to evaluate each participant in much the same way as you did for the presentation in Exercises 2, 4, and 6. Note that there is no set organizational format required for the Exercise 8 presentations. Students are free to use their own style. That does not mean they can omit any of the essential elements of a presentation. The introduction still must gain and focus attention. There still must be enough summaries and transitions in each presentation that it is clear for everyone to follow. The speakers must still create a proper atmosphere to show that they are enthusiastic, confident, and prepared. The delivery must still be free of distractions. And, most important, the arguments presented must be logical, internally consistent, adequately supported, properly documented, and *convincing*. You are to use the Grading Criteria Sheet (page 333) to assist you in grading the presentation part of this exercise.

Part two of the grading is similar to the type of grading you did in the workshop feedback sessions. You will grade the panel members' participation in and contribution to the discussion-debate period. This is a measure of each speaker's ability to listen, evaluate, and respond to counterarguments. The discussion-debate reveals the speaker's skill in handling a two-way communication situation. This is the type of interactive communication which takes up the majority of most administrators' time. It is the type of communication you have been working on in the feedback sessions where listening, reasoning, and speaking are all intertwined.

You are to rate each participant on listening ability, reasoning ability, and the content of the counter and counter-counterarguments. These three criteria are further explained in part two of the Grading Criteria Sheet (page 334). Parts one and two of the grading are weighted almost equally.

NOTE: The Exercise 8 Grading Criteria Sheet should be taken with you to all practice and final rounds to be used as a reference.

Bonus Points (optional)*

Bonus points, not to exceed five, are to be given to the team that is declared the winner in each round. If the decision of all the evaluators is unanimous regarding which team won, that team is to receive five bonus points. If from 80% to 99% of the evaluators give the victory to one team, that team gets four points. If from 65% to 79% of the evaluators give the victory to one team, that team gets 3 points. If no team received more than 64% of the votes, the round is declared a tie and neither team receives any bonus points.

Bonus points give the teams an incentive to evaluate and to counter opponents' arguments more carefully. Instructors may also give bonus points for exams or other assignments they include in the course.

How the Final Grades Are Computed (optional)**

The Exercise 7 and 8 presentations each count for roughly 50% of the total grade. Bonus points may throw off these percentages slightly. The Exercise 7 paper grade accounts for 40%, and the evaluation feedback grade accounts for 10% of the final course grade.

Part one of Exercise 8 accounts for 26%, and part two accounts for 24% of the total course grade. If two final rounds of Exercise 8 are used (one pro and one con), the two grades should be averaged.

To ease the computation of grades, the percentages have been multiplied by a constant of 2½. Note on the grading sheet that the maximum number of points you can receive for Exercise 7, part one, is 100, and part two, 25. For Exercise 8, the maximum number of points you can receive for part one is 65, and for part two, 60.

Exercise 7, Part 1	40% X 2½ = 100 points	
Exercise 7, Part 2	10% X 2½ = 25 points	125 points = 50%
Exercise 8, Part 1	26% X 2½ = 65 points	
Exercise 8, Part 2	24% X 2½ = 60 points	125 points = 50%
	100% = 250 points	250 points = 100%

The sum is 250 points. All grades will be computed in points, with 250 as the highest possible number of points (if bonus points are used, the total may be increased). If you wish to know the percentage value of these points, simply divide them by 2½. This system enables you (since the scores are already weighted) to simply add together the four final scores to compute your final score.

The instructor will make an array of the total points received by each student. The instructor's job will then be to compare this class with previous classes and with his own standards to set the cutoff scores between A's and B's, B's and C's, and so on. The instructor does not grade individual students; that is the class'

*Check with your instructor to see if bonus points are to be used.

**Check with your instructor to see exactly how grades are to be computed.

own responsibility.[1] It is the instructor's responsibility to grade the over-all quality of the class.

Your instructor may also wish to use other components in computing the grades. For example, the instructor may give quizzes on assignment instructions or readings. These may be assigned additional bonus points. See your course syllabus for this information.

EXERCISE 8 CHECKLISTS

Checklist of Things to Do (before coming to class)

1. With your teammate, prepare a complete case, both pro and con. Use the time limits specified for the session format selected by your class.
2. Prepare sets of speaking notes for each team member for all four speaking positions: first speaker pro, first speaker con, second speaker pro, second speaker con.
3. Practice your presentation, using the Exercise 5, 6, and 7 Feedback Forms as checklists. This will help you to make sure you have included all the necessary elements in your presentations.
4. Practice for the discussion-debate section of the Exercise 8 presentation by trying to use your arguments on the con side to refute your arguments on the pro side, and vice versa. Remember, the discussion-debate section of the presentation accounts for nearly 50% of the grade.

Checklist for Final Presentation

1. The panel-discussion coordinator will be appointed by the instructor. He or she is to do the following:
   a. Call the group together and take attendance.
   b. Flip a coin to determine which team is on which side of the question. This is done if there is only one final round per team. If there are two final rounds for each team, the side may be assigned in advance.
   c. Flip again to determine who is first and who is second speaker on each team.
   d. Time all presentations and the discussion periods.
   e. Coordinate all activities of the group to make sure all comply with the exercise instructions.
   f. At the end of the session, collect all Exercise 8 Grading Forms.
   g. The coordinator and the two evaluators in the group with the highest class numbers are jointly to fill out the Panel Discussion Coordinator's Grade Summary Sheet. All three must sign that sheet.
2. All grades and forms from the evaluators are to be given to the coordinator within 15 minutes after the round is completed.

[1] Those who have any questions regarding the value, validity, or reliability of peer grading are referred to page 4 in the Introduction where this is discussed.

Your Name ____________________
No.________ Sec. ____________

Exercise 8

PRESENTATION SCHEDULE

My Team No. is ________

(circle one)
Practice Round A: we are the pro/con team opposing team no. ____________

date ______________ time ________________ room no. ____________

(circle one)
Practice Round B: we are the pro/con team opposing team no. ____________

date ______________ time ________________ room no. ____________

(circle one)
Final Round I: we are the pro/con team opposing team no. ____________

date ______________ time ________________ room no. ____________

(circle one)
Final Round II: we are the pro/con team opposing team no. ____________

date ______________ time ________________ room no. ____________

My schedule as an evaluator for the final rounds is:

Teams on Panel:

________ vs ________ date _____________ time _____________ room _____________

________ vs ________ date _____________ time _____________ room _____________

________ vs ________ date _____________ time _____________ room _____________

________ vs ________ date _____________ time _____________ room _____________

________ vs ________ date _____________ time _____________ room _____________

Exercise 8

GRADING CRITERIA SHEET

Instructions: Fill out one Note Sheet on each panel discussion. Use those notes and this sheet as guides for grading. Record your grades on the Exercise 8 Grading Form.

There are three criteria to use in grading these presentations; there are three more criteria for grading performance in the panel discussion-debate period. They are listed on the reverse side of this sheet.

1. *Criteria for grading initial presentations.*

Criterion I. Presentation. Consider under Criterion I eye contact, vocal quality, stance, dress, volume, and any other factors which affect your response to the speaker apart from the organization or content of his message. Also note the confidence, preparedness, and enthusiasm of the speaker.

Criterion II. Organization of presentation. Consider under Criterion II how easy it was to follow the speaker. Did he have a good introduction that caught your interest. Did he use adequate forecast summaries, running summaries, and final summaries? Were his key points clearly identified? Did he use a proper balance of informative, arousing, and convincing forms of support?

Criterion III. Content of presentation. Consider under Criterion III the logic of the author's arguments and the adequacy of the material used to support them in the presentations. Check the inherency of each subargument and the appropriateness and adequacy of the forms of support used to substantiate each. Be careful to check the continuity among (1) the argument for change, (2) the proposed plan, and (3) the advantages attributed to the change. These arguments should all be internally consistent.

2. *Criteria for grading panel discussion-debate period.*

Criterion IV. Listening. Consider under Criterion IV how carefully the participant paid attention to the arguments of the opponents. Note whether or not he picked up and responded to the key points made by the opponents.

Criterion V. Reasoning Ability. It is not enough just to listen and respond; the response must show clear reasoning. Consider under Criterion V how sound the participant's reasoning was. Consider whether or not he could logically support his own arguments and at the same time identify logical weaknesses in the opponent's arguments. Consider also how well he refuted the opponent's logic.

Criterion VI. Content of counter and counter-counterarguments. In the discussion-debate period, no completely new topic areas are to be introduced, but new information, documentation, and reasoning should be present to further support previous arguments and to counter arguments of the opposition. On Criterion VI, grade the amount and the quality of the new support material used.

The following graph shows the meaning of the number grades by comparing them to letter grades and percentile ranks.

Meaning of Number Grades

4%	55%	25%	15%	1%
F D	C– C C+	B	A	A+

1 2 3 4 5 6 7 8 9 10

poor OK good excellent perfect

Note: The percentages for the grades on Exercises 7 and 8 are shifted upwards. This is because many of the poor students will already have dropped out.

These grading percentages should be followed rather closely. *Students who give disproportionately high or low grades may be asked to justify their grading standards.*

NOTE SHEET - SIDE 1

Note: Before this round begins, read the Grading Criteria Sheet (page 333).

Pro Team No. _______
Names ____________ No. _______
____________ No. _______

Arguments:

Plan

Advantages

Con Team No. _______
Names ____________ No. _______
____________ No. _______

Arguments:

Evaluator Name __________ No. ______________
Section ________ Round __________ Date _____

Exercise 8
GRADING FORM

Note: Before filling out this grading form, read the criteria description on the Grading Criteria Sheet and complete the Evaluation of Note Form on the reverse side of this sheet.

First Speaker Pro: Name ____________________ No. ________ Team No. ______

												Weighted Grade
Presentation	I	1	2	3	4	5	6	7	8	9	10 X 1 =	______
Criteria:	II	1	2	3	4	5	6	7	8	9	10 X 2 =	______
	III	1	2	3	4	5	6	7	8	9	10 X 3½ =	______
Panel												
Discussion-	IV	1	2	3	4	5	6	7	8	9	10 X 1½ =	______
Debate	V	1	2	3	4	5	6	7	8	9	10 X 1½ =	______
Criteria:	VI	1	2	3	4	5	6	7	8	9	10 X 3 =	______
							Total Weighted Grade					☐

Second Speaker Pro: Name ____________________ No. ________ Team No. ______

												Weighted Grade
Presentation	I	1	2	3	4	5	6	7	8	9	10 X 1 =	______
Criteria:	II	1	2	3	4	5	6	7	8	9	10 X 2 =	______
	III	1	2	3	4	5	6	7	8	9	10 X 3½ =	______
Panel												
Discussion-	IV	1	2	3	4	5	6	7	8	9	10 X 1½ =	______
Debate	V	1	2	3	4	5	6	7	8	9	10 X 1½ =	______
Criteria:	VI	1	2	3	4	5	6	7	8	9	10 X 3 =	______
							Total Weighted Grade					☐

First Speaker Con: Name ____________________ No. ________ Team No. ______

												Weighted Grade
Presentation	I	1	2	3	4	5	6	7	8	9	10 X 1 =	______
Criteria:	II	1	2	3	4	5	6	7	8	9	10 X 2 =	______
	III	1	2	3	4	5	6	7	8	9	10 X 3½ =	______
Panel												
Discussion-	IV	1	2	3	4	5	6	7	8	9	10 X 1½ =	______
Debate	V	1	2	3	4	5	6	7	8	9	10 X 1½ =	______
Criteria:	VI	1	2	3	4	5	6	7	8	9	10 X 3 =	______
							Total Weighted Grade					☐

Second Speaker Con: Name ____________________ No. ________ Team No. ______

												Weighted Grade
Presentation	I	1	2	3	4	5	6	7	8	9	10 X 1 =	______
Criteria:	II	1	2	3	4	5	6	7	8	9	10 X 2 =	______
	III	1	2	3	4	5	6	7	8	9	10 X 3½ =	______
Panel												
Discussion-	IV	1	2	3	4	5	6	7	8	9	10 X 1½ =	______
Debate	V	1	2	3	4	5	6	7	8	9	10 X 1½ =	______
Criteria:	VI	1	2	3	4	5	6	7	8	9	10 X 3 =	______
							Total Weighted Grade					☐

Give this form to the panel discussion coordinator. He will record these grades on the Exercise 8 Panel Discussion Coordinator's Grade Summary Sheet. This grading form will then be given to the instructor for his files.

Exercise 8
EVALUATION OF NOTES FORM

1. Review your notes to evaluate the arguments presented by both sides. Identify each argument by its number. State whether or not the argument was *logical* and adequately *supported*. Note whether or not the Con team countered each argument. Did the Con team offer any positive arguments?

____

____

____

2. The Plan: Evaluate whether or not the plan is workable and whether or not it will completely correct (or substantially reduce) the problems mentioned in the need arguments. Evaluate how well the Con team countered the plan.

____

____

____

3. Advantages: Evaluate the same as the need arguments.

____

____

____

After evaluating both teams' presentations for logic, documentation, consistency, and defense during the presentation and discussion-debate section of this exercise, write a 100-word explanation of which team did the better job and *why*. Be specific as to *why*.

____

____

____

____

____

____

____

____

____

____

____

____

____

____

____

____

In my opinion, the more convincing presentation was done by team No.______ which was Pro/Con (circle one).

Signature ______________________ No. ____________

Print Name ______________________________________

Last First Initial

Evaluator Name ________ No. ______________
Section ________ Round ________ Date _____

Exercise 8

GRADING FORM

Note: Before filling out this grading form, read the criteria description on the Grading Criteria Sheet.

First Speaker Pro: Name ______________________ No. ________ Team No. _______

												Weighted Grade
Presentation	I	1	2	3	4	5	6	7	8	9	10 X 1 =	_______
Criteria:	II	1	2	3	4	5	6	7	8	9	10 X 2 =	_______
	III	1	2	3	4	5	6	7	8	9	10 X 3½ =	_______
Panel												
Discussion-	IV	1	2	3	4	5	6	7	8	9	10 X 2½ =	_______
Debate	V	1	2	3	4	5	6	7	8	9	10 X 2½ =	_______
Criteria:	VI	1	2	3	4	5	6	7	8	9	10 X 3 =	_______
								Total Weighted Grade				☐

Second Speaker Pro: Name ______________________ No. ________ Team No. _______

												Weighted Grade
Presentation	I	1	2	3	4	5	6	7	8	9	10 X 1 =	_______
Criteria:	II	1	2	3	4	5	6	7	8	9	10 X 2 =	_______
	III	1	2	3	4	5	6	7	8	9	10 X 3½ =	_______
Panel												
Discussion-	IV	1	2	3	4	5	6	7	8	9	10 X 2½ =	_______
Debate	V	1	2	3	4	5	6	7	8	9	10 X 2½ =	_______
Criteria:	VI	1	2	3	4	5	6	7	8	9	10 X 3 =	_______
								Total Weighted Grade				☐

First Speaker Con: Name ______________________ No. ________ Team No. _______

												Weighted Grade
Presentation	I	1	2	3	4	5	6	7	8	9	10 X 1 =	_______
Criteria:	II	1	2	3	4	5	6	7	8	9	10 X 2 =	_______
	III	1	2	3	4	5	6	7	8	9	10 X 3½ =	_______
Panel												
Discussion-	IV	1	2	3	4	5	6	7	8	9	10 X 2½ =	_______
Debate	V	1	2	3	4	5	6	7	8	9	10 X 2½ =	_______
Criteria:	VI	1	2	3	4	5	6	7	8	9	10 X 3 =	_______
								Total Weighted Grade				☐

Second Speaker Con: Name ______________________ No. ______ Team No. _______

												Weighted Grade
Presentation	I	1	2	3	4	5	6	7	8	9	10 X 1 =	_______
Criteria:	II	1	2	3	4	5	6	7	8	9	10 X 2 =	_______
	III	1	2	3	4	5	6	7	8	9	10 X 3½ =	_______
Panel												
Discussion-	IV	1	2	3	4	5	6	7	8	9	10 X 2½ =	_______
Debate	V	1	2	3	4	5	6	7	8	9	10 X 2½ =	_______
Criteria:	VI	1	2	3	4	5	6	7	8	9	10 X 3 =	_______
								Total Weighted Grade				☐

Give this form to the panel discussion coordinator. He will record these grades on the Exercise 8 Panel Discussion Coordinator's Grade Summary Sheet. This grading form will then be given to the instructor for his files.

Exercise 8
EVALUATION OF NOTES FORM

1. Review your notes to evaluate the arguments presented by both sides. Identify each argument by its number. State whether or not the argument was *logical* and adequately *supported*. Note whether or not the Con team countered each argument. Did the Con team offer any positive arguments?

___

___

___

2. The Plan: Evaluate whether or not the plan is workable and whether or not it will completely correct (or substantially reduce) the problems mentioned in the need arguments. Evaluate how well the Con team countered the plan.

___

___

___

3. Advantages: Evaluate the same as the need arguments.

___

___

___

After evaluating both teams' presentations for logic, documentation, consistency, and defense during the presentation and discussion-debate section of this exercise, write a 100-word explanation of which team did the better job and *why*. Be specific as to *why*.

___

___

___

___

___

___

___

___

___

___

___

___

___

___

___

___

In my opinion, the more convincing presentation was done by team No.______ which was Pro/Con (circle one).

Signature ____________________ No. ____________

Print Name ______________________________
Last First Initial

Evaluator Name ________ No. ____________
Section ________ Round ________ Date______

Exercise 8
GRADING FORM

Note: Before filling out this grading form, read the criteria description on the Grading Criteria Sheet and complete the Evaluation of Note Form on the reverse side of this sheet.

First Speaker Pro: Name ______________________ No. ________ Team No. ______

												Weighted Grade
Presentation	I	1	2	3	4	5	6	7	8	9	10 X 1 =	______
Criteria:	II	1	2	3	4	5	6	7	8	9	10 X 2 =	______
	III	1	2	3	4	5	6	7	8	9	10 X 3½ =	______
Panel												
Discussion-	IV	1	2	3	4	5	6	7	8	9	10 X 1½ =	______
Debate	V	1	2	3	4	5	6	7	8	9	10 X 1½ =	______
Criteria:	VI	1	2	3	4	5	6	7	8	9	10 X 3 =	______
											Total Weighted Grade	☐

Second Speaker Pro: Name ______________________ No. ________ Team No. ______

												Weighted Grade
Presentation	I	1	2	3	4	5	6	7	8	9	10 X 1 =	______
Criteria:	II	1	2	3	4	5	6	7	8	9	10 X 2 =	______
	III	1	2	3	4	5	6	7	8	9	10 X 3½ =	______
Panel												
Discussion-	IV	1	2	3	4	5	6	7	8	9	10 X 1½ =	______
Debate	V	1	2	3	4	5	6	7	8	9	10 X 1½ =	______
Criteria:	VI	1	2	3	4	5	6	7	8	9	10 X 3 =	______
											Total Weighted Grade	☐

First Speaker Con: Name ______________________ No. ________ Team No. ______

												Weighted Grade
Presentation	I	1	2	3	4	5	6	7	8	9	10 X 1 =	______
Criteria:	II	1	2	3	4	5	6	7	8	9	10 X 2 =	______
	III	1	2	3	4	5	6	7	8	9	10 X 3½ =	______
Panel												
Discussion-	IV	1	2	3	4	5	6	7	8	9	10 X 1½ =	______
Debate	V	1	2	3	4	5	6	7	8	9	10 X 1½ =	______
Criteria:	VI	1	2	3	4	5	6	7	8	9	10 X 3 =	______
											Total Weighted Grade	☐

Second Speaker Con: Name ______________________ No. ______ Team No. ______

												Weighted Grade
Presentation	I	1	2	3	4	5	6	7	8	9	10 X 1 =	______
Criteria:	II	1	2	3	4	5	6	7	8	9	10 X 2 =	______
	III	1	2	3	4	5	6	7	8	9	10 X 3½ =	______
Panel												
Discussion-	IV	1	2	3	4	5	6	7	8	9	10 X 1½ =	______
Debate	V	1	2	3	4	5	6	7	8	9	10 X 1½ =	______
Criteria:	VI	1	2	3	4	5	6	7	8	9	10 X 3 =	______
											Total Weighted Grade	☐

Give this form to the panel discussion coordinator. He will record these grades on the Exercise 8 Panel Discussion Coordinator's Grade Summary Sheet. This grading form will then be given to the instructor for his files.

Exercise 8
EVALUATION OF NOTES FORM

1. Review your notes to evaluate the arguments presented by both sides. Identify each argument by its number. State whether or not the argument was *logical* and adequately *supported*. Note whether or not the Con team countered each argument. Did the Con team offer any positive arguments?

 ____

 ____

 ____

2. The Plan: Evaluate whether or not the plan is workable and whether or not it will completely correct (or substantially reduce) the problems mentioned in the need arguments. Evaluate how well the Con team countered the plan.

 ____

 ____

 ____

3. Advantages: Evaluate the same as the need arguments.

 ____

 ____

 ____

After evaluating both teams' presentations for logic, documentation, consistency, and defense during the presentation and discussion-debate section of this exercise, write a 100-word explanation of which team did the better job and *why*. Be specific as to *why*.

____

____

____

____

____

____

____

____

____

____

____

____

____

____

____

____

In my opinion, the more convincing presentation was done by team No.______ which was Pro/Con (circle one).

Signature ____________________ No. __________

Print Name ________________________________

Last First Initial

Evaluator Name ________ No. ______________
Section ________ Round ________ Date ______

Exercise 8
GRADING FORM

Note: Before filling out this grading form, read the criteria description on the Grading Criteria Sheet and complete the Evaluation of Note Form on the reverse side of this sheet.

First Speaker Pro: Name ____________________ No. ________ Team No. ______

												Weighted Grade
Presentation	I	1	2	3	4	5	6	7	8	9	10 X 1 =	______
Criteria:	II	1	2	3	4	5	6	7	8	9	10 X 2 =	______
	III	1	2	3	4	5	6	7	8	9	10 X 3½ =	______
Panel												
Discussion-	IV	1	2	3	4	5	6	7	8	9	10 X 1½ =	______
Debate	V	1	2	3	4	5	6	7	8	9	10 X 1½ =	______
Criteria:	VI	1	2	3	4	5	6	7	8	9	10 X 3 =	______
											Total Weighted Grade	☐

Second Speaker Pro: Name ____________________ No. ________ Team No. ______

												Weighted Grade
Presentation	I	1	2	3	4	5	6	7	8	9	10 X 1 =	______
Criteria:	II	1	2	3	4	5	6	7	8	9	10 X 2 =	______
	III	1	2	3	4	5	6	7	8	9	10 X 3½ =	______
Panel												
Discussion-	IV	1	2	3	4	5	6	7	8	9	10 X 1½ =	______
Debate	V	1	2	3	4	5	6	7	8	9	10 X 1½ =	______
Criteria:	VI	1	2	3	4	5	6	7	8	9	10 X 3 =	______
											Total Weighted Grade	☐

First Speaker Con: Name ____________________ No. ________ Team No. ______

												Weighted Grade
Presentation	I	1	2	3	4	5	6	7	8	9	10 X 1 =	______
Criteria:	II	1	2	3	4	5	6	7	8	9	10 X 2 =	______
	III	1	2	3	4	5	6	7	8	9	10 X 3½ =	______
Panel												
Discussion-	IV	1	2	3	4	5	6	7	8	9	10 X 1½ =	______
Debate	V	1	2	3	4	5	6	7	8	9	10 X 1½ =	______
Criteria:	VI	1	2	3	4	5	6	7	8	9	10 X 3 =	______
											Total Weighted Grade	☐

Second Speaker Con: Name ____________________ No. ________ Team No. ______

												Weighted Grade
Presentation	I	1	2	3	4	5	6	7	8	9	10 X 1 =	______
Criteria:	II	1	2	3	4	5	6	7	8	9	10 X 2 =	______
	III	1	2	3	4	5	6	7	8	9	10 X 3½ =	______
Panel												
Discussion-	IV	1	2	3	4	5	6	7	8	9	10 X 1½ =	______
Debate	V	1	2	3	4	5	6	7	8	9	10 X 1½ =	______
Criteria:	VI	1	2	3	4	5	6	7	8	9	10 X 3 =	______
											Total Weighted Grade	☐

Give this form to the panel discussion coordinator. He will record these grades on the Exercise 8 Panel Discussion Coordinator's Grade Summary Sheet. This grading form will then be given to the instructor for his files.

Exercise 8
EVALUATION OF NOTES FORM

1. Review your notes to evaluate the arguments presented by both sides. Identify each argument by its number. State whether or not the argument was *logical* and adequately *supported*. Note whether or not the Con team countered each argument. Did the Con team offer any positive arguments?

___

___

___

2. The Plan: Evaluate whether or not the plan is workable and whether or not it will completely correct (or substantially reduce) the problems mentioned in the need arguments. Evaluate how well the Con team countered the plan.

___

___

___

3. Advantages: Evaluate the same as the need arguments.

___

___

___

After evaluating both teams' presentations for logic, documentation, consistency, and defense during the presentation and discussion-debate section of this exercise, write a 100-word explanation of which team did the better job and *why*. Be specific as to *why*.

___

___

___

___

___

___

___

___

___

___

___

___

___

___

___

___

In my opinion, the more convincing presentation was done by team No.______ which was Pro/Con (circle one).

Signature ____________________ No. ____________

Print Name ______________________________
Last First Initial

Evaluator Name ________ No. ______________
Section ________ Round __________ Date ______

Exercise 8
GRADING FORM

Note: Before filling out this grading form, read the criteria description on the Grading Criteria Sheet and complete the Evaluation of Note Form on the reverse side of this sheet.

First Speaker Pro: Name ____________________________ No. ________ Team No. ______

												Weighted Grade
Presentation	I	1	2	3	4	5	6	7	8	9	10 X 1 =	______
Criteria:	II	1	2	3	4	5	6	7	8	9	10 X 2 =	______
	III	1	2	3	4	5	6	7	8	9	10 X 3½ =	______
Panel												
Discussion-	IV	1	2	3	4	5	6	7	8	9	10 X 1½ =	______
Debate	V	1	2	3	4	5	6	7	8	9	10 X 1½ =	______
Criteria:	VI	1	2	3	4	5	6	7	8	9	10 X 3 =	______
											Total Weighted Grade	☐

Second Speaker Pro: Name ____________________________ No. ________ Team No. ______

												Weighted Grade
Presentation	I	1	2	3	4	5	6	7	8	9	10 X 1 =	______
Criteria:	II	1	2	3	4	5	6	7	8	9	10 X 2 =	______
	III	1	2	3	4	5	6	7	8	9	10 X 3½ =	______
Panel												
Discussion-	IV	1	2	3	4	5	6	7	8	9	10 X 1½ =	______
Debate	V	1	2	3	4	5	6	7	8	9	10 X 1½ =	______
Criteria:	VI	1	2	3	4	5	6	7	8	9	10 X 3 =	______
											Total Weighted Grade	☐

First Speaker Con: Name ____________________________ No. ________ Team No. ______

												Weighted Grade
Presentation	I	1	2	3	4	5	6	7	8	9	10 X 1 =	______
Criteria:	II	1	2	3	4	5	6	7	8	9	10 X 2 =	______
	III	1	2	3	4	5	6	7	8	9	10 X 3½ =	______
Panel												
Discussion-	IV	1	2	3	4	5	6	7	8	9	10 X 1½ =	______
Debate	V	1	2	3	4	5	6	7	8	9	10 X 1½ =	______
Criteria:	VI	1	2	3	4	5	6	7	8	9	10 X 3 =	______
											Total Weighted Grade	☐

Second Speaker Con: Name ____________________________ No. ________ Team No. ______

												Weighted Grade
Presentation	I	1	2	3	4	5	6	7	8	9	10 X 1 =	______
Criteria:	II	1	2	3	4	5	6	7	8	9	10 X 2 =	______
	III	1	2	3	4	5	6	7	8	9	10 X 3½ =	______
Panel												
Discussion-	IV	1	2	3	4	5	6	7	8	9	10 X 1½ =	______
Debate	V	1	2	3	4	5	6	7	8	9	10 X 1½ =	______
Criteria:	VI	1	2	3	4	5	6	7	8	9	10 X 3 =	______
											Total Weighted Grade	☐

Give this form to the panel discussion coordinator. He will record these grades on the Exercise 8 Panel Discussion Coordinator's Grade Summary Sheet. This grading form will then be given to the instructor for his files.

Exercise 8
EVALUATION OF NOTES FORM

1. Review your notes to evaluate the arguments presented by both sides. Identify each argument by its number. State whether or not the argument was *logical* and adequately *supported*. Note whether or not the Con team countered each argument. Did the Con team offer any positive arguments?

___

___

___

2. The Plan: Evaluate whether or not the plan is workable and whether or not it will completely correct (or substantially reduce) the problems mentioned in the need arguments. Evaluate how well the Con team countered the plan.

___

___

___

3. Advantages: Evaluate the same as the need arguments.

___

___

___

After evaluating both teams' presentations for logic, documentation, consistency, and defense during the presentation and discussion-debate section of this exercise, write a 100-word explanation of which team did the better job and *why*. Be specific as to *why*.

___

___

___

___

___

___

___

___

___

___

___

___

___

___

___

___

In my opinion, the more convincing presentation was done by team No.______ which was Pro/Con (circle one).

Signature ____________________ No. __________

Print Name ______________________________
Last First Initial

Evaluator Name ________ No. ______________
Section ________ Round __________ Date ______

Exercise 8
GRADING FORM

Note: Before filling out this grading form, read the criteria description on the Grading Criteria Sheet and complete the Evaluation of Note Form on the reverse side of this sheet.

First Speaker Pro: Name ______________________ No. ________ Team No. ______

												Weighted Grade
Presentation	I	1	2	3	4	5	6	7	8	9	10 X 1 =	______
Criteria:	II	1	2	3	4	5	6	7	8	9	10 X 2 =	______
	III	1	2	3	4	5	6	7	8	9	10 X 3½ =	______
Panel												
Discussion-	IV	1	2	3	4	5	6	7	8	9	10 X 1½ =	______
Debate	V	1	2	3	4	5	6	7	8	9	10 X 1½ =	______
Criteria:	VI	1	2	3	4	5	6	7	8	9	10 X 3 =	______
								Total Weighted Grade				☐

Second Speaker Pro: Name ______________________ No. ________ Team No. ______

												Weighted Grade
Presentation	I	1	2	3	4	5	6	7	8	9	10 X 1 =	______
Criteria:	II	1	2	3	4	5	6	7	8	9	10 X 2 =	______
	III	1	2	3	4	5	6	7	8	9	10 X 3½ =	______
Panel												
Discussion-	IV	1	2	3	4	5	6	7	8	9	10 X 1½ =	______
Debate	V	1	2	3	4	5	6	7	8	9	10 X 1½ =	______
Criteria:	VI	1	2	3	4	5	6	7	8	9	10 X 3 =	______
								Total Weighted Grade				☐

First Speaker Con: Name ______________________ No. ________ Team No. ______

												Weighted Grade
Presentation	I	1	2	3	4	5	6	7	8	9	10 X 1 =	______
Criteria:	II	1	2	3	4	5	6	7	8	9	10 X 2 =	______
	III	1	2	3	4	5	6	7	8	9	10 X 3½ =	______
Panel												
Discussion-	IV	1	2	3	4	5	6	7	8	9	10 X 1½ =	______
Debate	V	1	2	3	4	5	6	7	8	9	10 X 1½ =	______
Criteria:	VI	1	2	3	4	5	6	7	8	9	10 X 3 =	______
								Total Weighted Grade				☐

Second Speaker Con: Name ______________________ No. ________ Team No. ______

												Weighted Grade
Presentation	I	1	2	3	4	5	6	7	8	9	10 X 1 =	______
Criteria:	II	1	2	3	4	5	6	7	8	9	10 X 2 =	______
	III	1	2	3	4	5	6	7	8	9	10 X 3½ =	______
Panel												
Discussion-	IV	1	2	3	4	5	6	7	8	9	10 X 1½ =	______
Debate	V	1	2	3	4	5	6	7	8	9	10 X 1½ =	______
Criteria:	VI	1	2	3	4	5	6	7	8	9	10 X 3 =	______
								Total Weighted Grade				☐

Give this form to the panel discussion coordinator. He will record these grades on the Exercise 8 Panel Discussion Coordinator's Grade Summary Sheet. This grading form will then be given to the instructor for his files.

Exercise 8
EVALUATION OF NOTES FORM

1. Review your notes to evaluate the arguments presented by both sides. Identify each argument by its number. State whether or not the argument was *logical* and adequately *supported*. Note whether or not the Con team countered each argument. Did the Con team offer any positive arguments?

   ____

   ____

   ____

2. The Plan: Evaluate whether or not the plan is workable and whether or not it will completely correct (or substantially reduce) the problems mentioned in the need arguments. Evaluate how well the Con team countered the plan.

   ____

   ____

   ____

3. Advantages: Evaluate the same as the need arguments.

   ____

   ____

   ____

After evaluating both teams' presentations for logic, documentation, consistency, and defense during the presentation and discussion-debate section of this exercise, write a 100-word explanation of which team did the better job and *why*. Be specific as to *why*.

____

____

____

____

____

____

____

____

____

____

____

____

____

____

____

____

In my opinion, the more convincing presentation was done by team No.______which was Pro/Con (circle one).

Signature ____________________ No. ____________

Print Name ______________________________
Last First Initial

Section ________ Round No. ________
Date ________ Room ____________

Exercise 8

PANEL DISCUSSION COORDINATOR'S GRADE SUMMARY SHEET

Pro Team No. _______ Con Team No. _______

	First Speaker Pro	Second Speaker Pro	First Speaker Con	Second Speaker Con
Speakers' Last Names	____________	____________	____________	____________
	No. ______	No. ______	No. ______	No. ______
Evaluator Number				
______	______	______	______	______
______	______	______	______	______
______	______	______	______	______
______	______	______	______	______
______	______	______	______	______
______	______	______	______	______
______	______	______	______	______
______	______	______	______	______
Sum	______	______	______	______
÷ by number of evaluators	______	______	______	______
= Average Grade	☐ + ___	☐ + ___	☐ + ___	☐ + ___

(write number of bonus points, if any, on line after box–see page 328.)

This form must be checked by the two evaluators in this session with the highest class numbers. The undersigned signify that they have checked the grading forms and that this form is an accurate grade record of the students listed.

Coordinator's Signature __________________ No.___
Checker 1 Signature __________________ No.___
Checker 2 Signature __________________ No.___

Give the completed form to the instructor for recording. Also give him all evaluator's Exercise 8 Grading Forms.

PART II

Supplemental Readings

CHAPTER ONE

Communication: The Nervous System of Organizations

Why Communication is Necessary

Communication is central to all organizational behavior because it is the activity that connects the diverse parts. Without communication, there could be no organization. A review of definitions of the word *organizations* clearly reveals why communication is so central to the very existence of such institutions. Koontz and O'Donnell define an organization as a communication decision-making network. (27) Drucker states, "The organization, whether an army or a business, is above all an information and decision-making system." (14, p. 92) Longnecker refers to the act of forming an organization as being ". . . concerned with the determination of relationships among functions, jobs, and personnel." (32, p. 37) Simon defines an organization as ". . . the complex pattern of communication and other relations between human beings." (42, p. XVI)

The two key elements in all of these definitions are that organizations consist of separate parts (1) bound together by communication (2) to achieve common goals. Coordinating and focusing of organizational activities toward a common goal is the responsibility of a manager.* A manager is one who gets work done by coordinating and directing the activities of others. (27, p. 35) Communication skills are the manager's only means of letting others know what is to be done, when, where, and how. The effectiveness of an organization is therefore dependent upon the effectiveness of the communication skills of its managers.

Many authors have expounded the essential role of communication in organizations. Bavelas and Barrett, in their classic article on organizational communication, state that

> communication is not a secondary or derived aspect of organization—a 'helper' of the other presumably more basic functions. It is rather the essence of organized activity and is a basic process out of which all other functions derive.
>
> It is entirely possible to view an organization as an elaborate system for gathering, evaluating, recombining, and disseminating information. It is not surprising, in these terms, that the effectiveness of an organization with respect to the achievement of its goals should be so closely related to its effectiveness in handling information. (2, p. 368)

Barnard pointed out in 1938 that there are three conditions necessary for an organization to come into existence. They are: (1) there are persons able to communicate with each other (2) who are willing to contribute action (3) to accomplish a common purpose. From this reasoning, Barnard concluded, "The first executive function is to develop and maintain a system of communication." (1, p. 82)

A decade ago, Redding, in an introductory chapter to a book of readings in the area of business and industrial communication, presented an excellent summary of statements by noted authors regarding the central role of communication in organizations: (35)

> The manager has a specific tool: information. He does not handle people; he motivates, guides, organizes people to do their own work. His tool—his only tool—to do all this is the spoken or written words or the language of numbers.
>
> Peter F. Drucker (13, p. 346)
>
> Communication plays the central role in all administration. Administration is communication.
>
> Lee O. Thayer (44, p. 76)

---

*This manager need not be human. It need only be capable of receiving information, analyzing it, making a decision on how to respond, and communicating that response to other machines or humans for implementation. A further discussion of this point may be found in Beckett. (3, Chapter 6)

> What is the distinctive job of every manager or supervisor? What is the most important thing he has to do? None of the obvious answers gets to the heart of the manager's job. Nor does the usual breakdown into such activities as planning and assigning work, instructing subordinates, reviewing and appraising progress, establishing and maintaining controls.
>
> No matter how varied the activities or how special some of the skills involved, in the final analysis the job of every executive or supervisor is *communication.* Essentially, he must get work done through other people and to accomplish this he must communicate effectively with them.
>
> *American Management Association Text* (11, p. 15)

Redding concluded in 1965 that the logic supporting the assertion that administration is communication is a difficult assertion to refute. This assertion is even more difficult to refute today, even though the rapid growth of man-machine and machine-machine communication in the past decade has shifted the emphasis more toward lateral communication and away from vertical. Hampton discusses why interpersonal communication skills are still as important today even with the growth of automation and computerization.

> effective interpersonal relations are central to political and organizational leadership. Even in highly automated plants where technology eliminates subordinates, the number of persons with whom managers must maintain relations does not necessarily decrease. Those workers who are no longer required are replaced by systems engineers, computer programmers, executive assistants, and staff specialists. Relations with the latter may be more subtle and stressful than relatively clear-cut, boss-subordinate confrontations. Accordingly, interpersonal relations remain central to managerial careers and to organizational effectiveness. (20, p. 66)

Sanders in his text, *Computers in Business*, states, ". . . information is the substance of all of man's intellectual activities; it is basic to education, government literature, [and] the conduct of business. . ." (38 p. 7) Sanders goes on to point out that communication was as critical to management in ancient times as it is in our computer age. He illustrates this with the story about the tower of Babylon. God confused the workers' language. Foremen could not communicate with workers or with each other. With communication blocked, the project came to a standstill. Major authors on organizational behavior seem to agree that from ancient times to the present communication has been and still is the key activity for keeping an organization organized. Communication is the central nervous system that links the parts together. Without some form of communication, no organized activity could exist.

Communication Is the "Doing" Part of Management

Communication is the means by which the manager of a complex organization receives virtually all of the information that he needs to know to make decisions. He cannot be at ten different locations at once observing operations. He must rely upon reports from colleagues and subordinates. He also relies upon extraorganization reports of economic and market conditions. Since these internal and external reports contain the basic information upon which the manager must base his decision, the accuracy and adequacy of the communication contained in these reports limits the appropriateness of the manager's decision. Thus, the decision-making function cannot be seen as independent from the information-gathering part of the communication function.

Once information is gathered and analyzed and a decision is made, the manager must almost always depend upon someone else to carry out his decided upon course of action. The manager must communicate what he wants done. Communication is thus what a manager does to actually *do* his job. It is the way he converts his decision-making activity into useful, productive action. It is therefore no surprise to find that communication is the activity that consumes the majority of a manager's time. Horne and Lupton reported that communication activities consume from 50% to 90% of managers' time. (24).

Carl Duerr, the successful European executive noted for his success in taking over ailing companies and putting them on the road to stable profitability, says, "Management is communication." He states that all of the management techniques ". . . which we can look up in textbooks as readily as an electronics engineer can look up standard circuits for amplifiers. . ." have very little to do with management. These techniques, although they aid the manager and his staff in decision making, have little to do with the manager's "essential task of managing people."

> The one single thing that each and every manager depends on, that sorts the successes from the failures, is the ability to communicate with other people and to organize their communications among themselves. Your true manager is a catalyst: in his presence, work is achieved that otherwise wouldn't be, even if he himself does not contribute directly to it. But he can only succeed in that catalytic role if he can inform, instruct, persuade, and motivate other people (and not only those subordinate to him). He can do none of these things unless he can effectively communicate not merely information, but also attitudes, moods, emotions.
>
> As well as being able to communicate himself, he needs equally to be receptive; he needs to be able to listen to others, to understand them, to pick up signals from them even if they are unconscious ones. This means being sensitive to all of the physical signs, the nervous habits, the gestures, and expressions with which people supplement their verbal communications. This is a skill that is indispensable to management; but it is one that no management development program that I know of attempts to teach. (15, p. XIII)

The communication process seems to be considered by all as one that is crucial to organizational existence. But the question must be raised, are we all talking about the same thing when we talk about communication? Is the communication system the same thing to the computer expert and the plant superintendent? Are management communication skills the same as those communication skills we practice in freshman English and basic speech courses? The answer to all of these questions is "no."

Seventy-five per cent of managers' communication time is spent in oral face-to-face communication involving only two or three people. (21) The type of communication that takes up managers' time should not be confused with data processing systems or with the basic reading and writing skills taught in beginning speech and English courses. Management communication is most often a complex, dynamic, ongoing communication where listening, reading, writing, and speaking are all intertwined with reasoning and logic. Problems and opportunities are constantly being brought to managers. They listen and read to gain knowledge, insight, and understanding. They raise questions, probe deeper, propose solutions, and then seek still more feedback. If they decide to take action, they must deal with objections and try to win support. This requires more reading, listening, and talking while they also try to keep abreast of new problems and opportunities which require more communication. This dynamic, give-and-take, two-way mix of written and oral and nonverbal communication is the activity that is at the very heart of the manager's job. To clarify what is meant by managerial communication and how it differs from other uses of the word *communication*, three different levels of communication are identified in the following section.

Three Levels of Communication in the Computer Age

From the previous discussion, it appears almost universally accepted that communication is the key activity which links the parts of an organization together and is the thing that managers do to manage. Most early authors in the field of management also seem to assume that communication is an activity that takes place only among people. For example, Simon refers to the organization as "the complex pattern of communication and other relations in a group of human beings." (41, p. XVI) In the age of computers, such definitions no longer seem appropriate. As Beckett points out, machines, such as in a modern refinery, are managed by instrumentalities other than people. "They operate under the guidance and control [management] of a carefully designed system." (3, p. 137) These systems and subsystems must communicate with each other and with any humans who are employees or managers of systems that interact with these machine-managed systems.

For a meaningful discussion of organization communication, a distinction must be made between machine-type communication and human-type communication. Though the word *communication* is used to describe all of these, the activities themselves are certainly not the same.

Thayer makes a distinction between data systems and information systems. He defines *data* as the events in our environment which reach our sensory system. He says that data which is selectively received and selectively translated with meaning, structure, and utility imposed upon it by a human being, becomes *information*. The hardware of communication—books, radios, computers—by Thayer's definition, can handle only data, not information. Thus, he distinguishes between machine communication and human communication and human communication with the words *data* and *information*. (44, p. 29)

Limiting the term *information*, as Thayer does, is not totally acceptable to those in data processing who like to refer to their profession as *information science*. Sanders, in his book, *Computers in Business*, also distinguishes between data and information, but in a different way. (38, p. 8) He defines *data* as "facts, unevaluated messages, or informational raw material." He defines *information* as designated data arranged in ordered and useful form. *Information* is defined as the output of processing operations designed to "1) achieve specific purposes or 2) enhance understanding." Sanders' definition would not likely be acceptable to the semanticists such as Johnson (25) and Hayakawa (23) or to contemporary writers in the field of organizational communication such as Redding (35), Thayer (44), or Redfield (36). Sanders' definition does not distinguish between data which is systematically arranged by a complex, yet predictable, machine and data which is consumed by a complex but not totally predictable machine or organism such as a human.

To resolve this apparent disagreement, there are three levels or types of communication within organizations that we will distinguish among in this chapter. The first is *data communication*. This is the transfer from one point to another of unevaluated messages. They might be electrical impulses, printed numbers, or letters. Data can be physically transferred from one point in an organization to another virtually free of distortion. The data fed into a computer can be transferred by wire or satellite to another computer thousands of miles away with virtually no distortion.

The second level of communication we will call *type M information*. This is basically what Sanders defines as information. This is data that have been decoded, analyzed, and arranged by a machine or organism which is capable only of decoding, analyzing, arranging, and responding to the data according to predetermined and, therefore, consistent and highly predictable procedures. Thus, if the same data were sent to five organizational points or machines, we could predict that all five would respond to the data identically, given that all other factors were constant. However, if all other factors were not constant, different machines could process the data differently. Thus type M information becomes so only after it has been received and processed according to the programming of the receiving machine. The content of the information depends upon a combination of what is sent and the internal processing of the receiver machine. With type M information, the message sender must not only be concerned with the message that he, she, or it prepares, but must also be aware of the way the receiver will interpret the message.

The third level of organizational communication is by far the most complex. This is the level with which we will deal almost exclusively in this book. We will call this *type H information.* This is data or type M information that has been selectively received and selectively translated with meaning, structure, and value added to it by a complex and constantly changing organism (or possibly a machine). Since such complex organisms change constantly to adapt as they receive each new input, their response to any particular input is not totally predictable. Since these organisms select what they are willing to receive and select how they will process it, any two such organisms receiving the same data at the same time may respond in completely different fashions. Any one organism receiving the same data, but at two different times, will likely respond somewhat differently each time.

All machine-to-human and human-to-human communication falls into the type H information exchange category. The type of information a communication act involves depends upon the type of receiver rather than upon the type of sender. Thus, it is obvious that type H information cannot be sent from one human to another human, because the material becomes type H information only after it has been received and processed by a receiver. The message sender, in the case of the type H information communication process, must be aware not only of the message he prepares, but he must also be aware of the many factors which might influence the receiver to interpret that particular message at that particular time in a variety of ways.

Type H information must be considered unstable. Data or type M information can be frozen on a printed or electronic record and stored unchanged. Type H information is dynamic, constantly changes over time, and differs among receivers.

This description of the three levels of organizational communication should make it apparent that in order for a manager to communicate with a human or even with a machine receiver involves much more than simply sending accurate and pertinent messages. There is a common complaint from managers who are not aware of the complexity of human-to-human communication: "But I told him." Communication is more than just the telling.

More will be presented on the complexities of the human communication process in Chapter Two. There are also many excellent books and articles available on this topic that any serious student of management would be well advised to study. A few of the classics in this area are Korzybski (28), Lee (29, 30), Cherry (7), Chase (6), Johnson (25), Berlo (4), Thayer (44), Redding and Sanborn (35), and Haney (21).

Communication Is Not a Cure-All

Although it is safe to say that effective communication is a vital skill of managers, it would indeed be narrow to conclude that if a manager becomes an effective communicator, he will be an effective manager. Drucker (14, p. 92), Dorsey (12, p. 309), Duerr (15, p. XII), and others have pointed out that an organization is a communication-*decision-making* network. If the manager's decision is wrong, effective communication of that poor decision does not improve the decision. Certainly, to have something worth communicating, the manager must understand how to plan, organize, and control. He must be able to effectively analyze the data he receives and be able to come to an appropriate decision. Conversely, for a manager to be merely an effective planner and decision-maker is also not enough. If a manager's decision is right, even brilliant, but he cannot communicate to others what he wishes, the decision has no utility.

Too many managers use the excuse, "Our problem is communication." The implication is that if the others—superiors, co-workers, or subordinates—only understood him, they would agree with and act in accordance. After all, the logic and motivation for the actions which the manager desires made perfect sense in terms of the manager's reality. Of course, since his reality is based on the input of type H information, his reality is based on selectively received and selectively processed information. Therefore, his reality is not necessarily going to fit the reality or needs of the other individuals. It is possible that if our manager achieved the better communication he was seeking—if people *really* understood him—they might really dislike him. He might get fired by his boss, have his employees strike, or be rejected by his co-workers.

Communication is not in and of itself *good*, nor does it necessarily bring about agreement. Research by Sherif, et al. (40) and by the author (17) have indicated that under certain conditions increased communication actually leads to increased organizational conflict. Communication is not a cure-all. It is rather a tool that is necessary to use to accomplish most organizational tasks. The organizational goal must not be to achieve good communication. Rather, communication should be considered as a tool which, when effectively used, facilitates the accomplishment of the organization's goals.

The Goal of Communication Is Influence

Communication is a means of *influencing behavior* or of being *influenced*. It is the way that administrators receive their information about the world so they can adapt to it, and it is the means by which they attempt to influence the world to adapt to them. It is the only tool we have to influence others (organisms or machines) to behave as we desire. Dale in his management text states, "In the sense that it (communication) is most often used, it is viewed as an essential way to motivate employees to accept management's goals and work wholeheartedly toward them." (8, p. 466) Hampton, Summer, and Webber suggest, "Understanding through communicating is usually only a means for the manager; the end is influence. . ." (20, p. 82)

The manager uses communication to influence or bring about behavior change. An analysis of all of the factors involved in behavior change would fill many books. Here we will attempt only to describe the key elements of messages identified in research studies as being essential for bringing about desired changes. (9, 10, 15, 17, 18, 33, 45)

There are three key elements that are essential to the success of any attempt to influence. They are trust, understanding, and motivation. They can be illustrated by the following example. A friend giving a lecture tried to induce some businessmen to stand on their chairs and dance by offering one hundred dollars to the first to do so. When he asked why no one would do such a simple act for one hundred dollars, they responded, "Well, you would not have really given us the money." They did not act because they lacked *trust*.

To gain trust, he produced a nickel, handed it to one of the group members, and publicly authorized him to give that nickel to anyone who would now stand on his chair and dance. Again, there was no response. Trust was present, but a nickel just did not provide adequate *motivation*. He then offered the one hundred dollars, the adequate motivation once again. He handed the money to a trusted member of the group to hold and publicly authorized him to give the one hundred dollars to anyone who would write a short paragraph on his favorite topic. Of course, he did not reveal his favorite topic. Motivation and trust were now present, but the businessmen could not act for they did not *understand* how to do the job. If any of these key elements—trust, motivation, or understanding—is missing in the communication environment, the message is not likely to influence behavior in the direction desired.

Another important consideration in communication is that the understanding, motivation, and trust must be designed in terms of the message receiver's reality not necessarily in terms of the message sender's reality. When managers use technical language beyond the understanding level of the workers, they are sending messages, but appropriate communication is not taking place and, thus, the message cannot change the workers' behavior in the direction desired.

Motivation must also be designed in terms of the receiver's reality. The message that says "just what we want to say" in "just the way we want to say it" is of little value if no one can (or will) read it. The message must not only contain motivational material, but the presentation of the material itself must be motivating. A two-hundred page book on the benefits of unions may convince all who read it to join a union, but the book will have little effect on those who become bored and stop after reading only two pages. It is possible, of course, that the worker may read the book, believe the arguments of the author, and still not be swayed to vote for a union. Motivation is not an absolute; it is personal. The motivation must be in terms of the needs of the worker, not the needs of the union or the company, or even in terms of the needs of the workers in another plant.

Trust is often the ignored ingredient in management communication. We often hear such statements as, "Well, that all sounds good, but I don't believe half of it." The reader is questioning the source. If the employee thinks the manager is biased, uninformed, or just plain dishonest, the material may be read and understood, but disregarded. The administrator must control these three elements—understanding, motivation, and trust—if he wishes to use communication effectively. The manager who can control those elements is well on his way to being an effective manager. As important as these skills are to managers, they receive very little attention in most academic training programs.

Employers' Call for Graduates with More Communication Training

College is a training ground in which we attempt to acquire the skills that will enable us to earn a living. During this training period, we should not just learn skills randomly; we should focus our efforts on learning those skills which are most essential to the profession we plan to enter. One of the best ways to determine which skills are most vital is to research what those in the field have found to be the most critical skills. A review of such research is presented here. First, we will examine what successful, experienced managers believe are the skills most needed by aspiring managers. The manager and author Carl Duerr has stated clearly his opinion of what type of skills are and are not needed:

What I have to say about management science techniques will not all be unfavorable, but for the moment I'd just like to point out that, as I see it, most of these techniques have very little to do with management. For every one like PERT or corporate planning, which actually do help to manage an enterprise, there are a bevy, like DCF analysis, queuing theory or value analysis, which just don't help the manager in his principle job of managing people. . .

If the secrets of management don't lie in the battery of techniques that the last few decades have brought forth, just what are the skills that the practicing manager needs? The one thing that each and every manager depends on, that sort the successes from the failures, is the ability to communicate with other people. . . This is the skill that is indispensable to management; but it is one that no management program I know of attempts to teach. (15, p. XIII)

Duerr's call for more communication *skills* development courses for managers is not an isolated one. In a keynote address to the Michigan section of the American Society for Engineering Education, H. R. Steding, executive engineer for the Chrysler Corporation, urged that engineering schools make effective communication skills training integral parts of their programs. He added, "More effective communication by engineers in industry will save man hours and money by making it possible to get more done right the first time." (43) Lower-level managers support the opinions of these executives. A survey of 3,800 engineering graduates asked those who had graduated between 1911 and 1956 to rank the items most important to their general education. They ranked highest: "To express one's thoughts effectively." (22)

In a survey of 13,386 college graduates working for General Electric, the question was asked, "What areas of college study have contributed most to your present position of responsibility with the General Electric Company?" The great majority of the non-engineering group reported the most helpful and valuable subject area was English communication. Both spoken and written English were cited as of extreme value in business success. Engineers, on the other hand, listed communication second only to mathematics in importance. (19)

A study of CPA's by Kiesey and Pavlock reported that traditionally the CPA's task-oriented environment has tended to produce managers who are unaware of or who ignore people-management skills. (26) They found that CPA firms have recently realized this shortcoming, and every major national CPA firm has initiated people-oriented management training programs for their managers. Management styles, communication, and motivation were the top three subjects on the list of training needs of CPA's.

In a survey of 252 personnel and marketing managers from two diverse cultures, Edge and Greenwood (16) asked the managers to rank in order of importance the skills that every business administration graduate should have. Communication skills were ranked most important by all of the managers, except for the New York marketing managers, who rated it second. The other items ranked in order of importance are as follows:

Skills	Personnel Managers		Marketing Managers	
	N.Y.	Hawaii	N.Y.	Hawaii
Communicate	1	1	2	1
Work with and use skills of others, motivate	2	3	3	2
Plan, develop, organize, and coordinate	3	2	1	3
Analyze data, propose solutions, and make decisions	4	4	4	4
Analyze financial data	5	6	5	5
Apply quantitative techniques	6	7	6	7
Analyze accounting data	7	5	7	6
Utilize a computer	8	8	8	8

Note that technical skills are consistently rated less vital than the human relations skills by all four groups. A concurrent study by Brickner (5) found basically the same results from managers in areas such as finance, accounting, computer systems, and operations management as well as personnel and marketing. Brickner's survey asked the managers to identify the major weaknesses of previous business school graduates. The six major shortcomings listed in order of importance are as follows:

1. Too theoretical, lack pragmatism
2. Lack verbal and written communication skills
3. Bypass hard work
4. Inadequate technical and quantitative knowledge
5. Poor human relations skills
6. Lack maturity

Brickner concludes of these findings:

> the perceived shortcomings of business school graduates could provide the most impetus for changing the current curricula. Viewed in its entirety, they [the findings] point out a lack of ability to execute an assignment in a clear, practical, thorough, and non-self-assertive manner. Perhaps more practicums, more cooperative job experience, and more organizational development labs would help students in making a less painful (to all) adjustment to their post-school careers. (5, p. 4)

Brickner's subjects stated the importance of the following nine major areas of knowledge or skill for a successful career in 1984. They are listed in order of importance:

1. Leadership and motivation
2. Computers and information systems
3. Communications
4. Human behavior understanding
5. Finance
6. Knowledge of technical fields
7. Awareness of outside environment
8. Planning
9. Quantitative techniques

Of significant interest is the surprisingly low rating by practicing managers of the value of skill in quantitative techniques. Note the disparity between the highly quantitative emphasis in business school curricula and the desires of managers for graduates with more human behavior and communication-type skills.

This same conclusion was drawn in another recent study. The emphasis on quantitative as opposed to human behavior training in management training programs was questioned in a study by Livingston, reported in an article entitled, "Myth of the Well-Educated Manager." (31) Livingston found that graduates of the Harvard MBA program were earning only median salaries after 15 years on the job. Those students who came to Harvard's Advanced Management Program after about 15 years of business experience, but with no formal education in management, were making a third more on the average than were business school graduates of the same age. Livingston, like Duerr, concluded that the men who get to the top have to develop skills that are not currently taught in formal management education programs. Livingston goes so far as to suggest that MBA programs with their stress on quantitative decision-making skills may actually contain much miseducation that actually blocks students' later ability to learn from experience.

Brickner looked at the problem of what skills are needed by managers later in their careers as opposed to now. He asked his managers to rate the knowledge area most important for managers in their first two years on the job and again after five years on the job. The practicing managers listed the following:

First Two Years	*After Five Years*
1. Communication theory	1. Decision making
2. Decision making	2. Communication theory
3. Individual creativity	3. Management economics
4. Planning skills	4. Individual creativity
5. Management economics	5. Planning skills
6. Financial analysis	6. Financial analysis

It is extremely interesting that communication theory was ranked so high, because few business colleges even offer courses that deal with this body of knowledge. The indication seems clear that if students are to become the type of person who can succeed in management at an above-mediocre level, some serious study of communication theory and skills is needed.

One final point must be made lest we fall in the trap of trying to learn basic communication skills for management by taking an English grammar, literature, or public speaking course. As Redding points out:

> the very fact of holding a position in an organization determines many of the ways in which a person speaks, listens, writes, and reads. If this view is a valid one, an important implication is that the person who excels in public speaking class, or the one who writes sparkling prose in letters and reports may not necessarily be an effective communicator in his role as a business manager." (35, p. 29)

Basic skills training in grammar, sentence structure, or speaking should never be confused with the complex communication skills needed for effective managing. The type of communication training outlined in the exercises in this book is designed to teach dynamic, ongoing communication skills in which reading, writing, speaking, and listening are all intertwined with logic, human relations, and decision making to meet the specific needs of managers in complex organizations. If communication is at the heart of management, perhaps it is time that it at least becomes part of the common body of knowledge required for all students aspiring to a management position.

One area listed to be of extreme importance for new managers was an understanding of communication theory. That is the topic of the next chapter.

REFERENCES

1. Barnard, Chester I. *The Functions of the Executive* (Cambridge: Harvard University Press, 1938).
2. Bavelas, Alex and Dermot Barret. "An Experimental Approach to Organizational Communication," *Personnel*, Vol. 27 (1951).
3. Beckett, John A. *Management Dynamics: A New Synthesis* (New York: McGraw-Hill Book Company, 1971).
4. Berlo, David K. *The Process of Communication* (New York: Holt, Rinehart and Winston Publishers, 1960).
5. Brickner, William H. "The Manager of Today Looks at Those of Tomorrow," Paper presented at the Academy of Management Covention, Seattle (1974).
6. Chase, Stuart. *Guides to Straight Thinking* (New York: Harper & Row, Publishers, 1956).
7. Cherry, Colin. *On Human Communication* (Cambridge: The Technology Press, Massachusetts Institute of Technology, 1957).
8. Dale, Ernest. *Management Theory and Practice* (New York: McGraw-Hill Book Company, 1965).
9. Deutsch, Morton. "Trust and Suspicion," *Journal of Conflict Resolution*, Vol. 2 (1958).
10. Deutsch, Morton and Robert M. Krauss. "Studies of Interpersonal Bargaining," *Journal of Conflict Resolution*, Vol. 6 (1962).
11. Dooher, M. Joseph and Vivienne Marquist, Eds. *Effective Communication on the Job* (New York: American Management Association, 1956).
12. Dorsey, John T. "A Communication Model for Administration," *Administrative Science Quarterly*, Vol. 2 (1957).
13. Drucker, Peter F. *The Practice of Management* (New York: Harper & Row, Publishers, 1954).
14. Drucker, Peter F. *Landmarks of Tomorrow* (New York: Harper & Row, Publishers, 1959).
15. Duerr, Carl. *Management Kinetics* (New York: McGraw-Hill Book Company, 1971).
16. Edge, Alfred G. and Ronald Greenwood. "How Managers Rank Knowledge, Skills and Attributes Possessed by Business Administration Graduates," *AACSB Bulletin*, Vol. II (1974).
17. Ellis, Dean S. *An Analysis of the Differential Effects of Various Types and Degrees of Communication Opportunity on Conflict Between Groups*, Unpublished dissertation (Purdue University, 1965).
18. Ellis, Dean S., Laurence Jacobs, and Carry Mills. "A Union Authorization Election: The Key to Winning, *Personnel*, Vol. 51 (1972).
19. Fine, Benjamin. "Most Valuable College Studies—Survey of G.E. College Graduates," *New York Times* (December 2, 1956).
20. Hampton, David R., Charles E. Summer, and Ross A. Webber. *Organizational Behavior and the Practice of Management*, Revised (Glenview, Ill.: Scott, Foresman and Company, 1973).
21. Haney, William V. *Communication and Organizational Behavior: Text and Cases*, 3rd ed. (Homewood, Ill.: Richard D. Irwin, Inc., 1973).
22. Hawkins, G. A. "A Report on the Purdue University Engineering Graduate," Mimeographed report, Department of Speech Communication (Purdue University, 1957).
23. Hayakawa, S. I. *Language in Thought and Action* (New York: Harcourt Brace Jovanovich, Inc. 1949).
24. Horne, J. H. and T. Lupton. "The Work Activities of Middle Managers," *Journal of Management Studies*, Vol. 1 (1965).
25. Johnson, Wendell. *People in Quandaries: The Semantics of Personnel Adjustment* (New York: Harper & Row, Publishers, 1946).

26. Kiesey, D. T. and E. J. Pavlock. "Trends in Management Education for CPA's," *Journal of Accountancy* (May 1975).

27. Koontz, Harold and Cyril O'Donnell. *Principles of Management: An Analysis of Managerial Function*, 5th ed. (New York: McGraw-Hill Book Company, 1972).

28. Korzybski, Alfred. *Science and Sanity: An Introduction to Non-Aristotelian Systems and General Semantics* (Lancaster, Pa.: Science Press Printing Company, 1933).

29. Lee, Irving J. *How to Talk with People* (New York: Harper & Row, Publishers, 1952).

30. Lee, Irving J. and Laura L. Lee. *Handling Barriers in Communication* (New York: Harper & Row, Publishers, 1957).

31. Livingston, Sterling J. "Myth of the Well-Educated Manager," *Harvard Business Review* (Jan. - Feb. 1971).

32. Longnecker, Justin G. *Principles of Management and Organizational Behavior*, 2nd ed. (Columbus, Ohio: Charles E. Merrill Publishing Company, 1969).

33. Pigors, Paul. *Effective Communication in Industry* (New York: National Association of Manufacturers, 1949).

34. Randall, Clarence. "Speak Up," *Think* (May 1962), publication of the International Business Maching Corp.

35. Redding, W. Charles. "The Organizational Communicator," in *Business and Industrial Communication: A source book*, W. Charles Redding and George A. Sanborn, Eds. (New York: Harper & Row, Publishers, 1964).

36. Redfield, Charles E. *Communication in Management*, Revised Edition (Chicago: University of Chicago Press, 1958).

37. Sanborn, George A. "Communication in Business: An Overview," in *Business and Industrial Communication: A source book*, W. Charles Redding and George A. Sanborn, Eds. (New York: Harper & Row, Publishers, 1964).

38. Sanders, Donald H. *Computers in Business* (New York: McGraw-Hill Book Company, 1974).

39. Sells, S. B. "Toward a Taxonomy of Organizations," in *New Perspectives in Organizational Research*, W. W. Cooper, et. al., Eds. (New York: John Wiley & Sons, Inc., 1964) p. 515.

40. Sherif, Muzafer. "Subordinate Goals and the Reduction of Intergroup Conflicts," *The American Journal of Sociology*, Vol. 43 (1958).

41. Sisk, Henry L. *Management and Organization*, 2nd ed. (Cincinnati, Ohio: South-Western Publishing Co., 1973).

42. Simon, Herbert A. *Administrative Behavior*, 2nd ed. (New York: Macmillan Publishing Co., Inc., 1958).

43. Steding, H. R. Keynote address given to the Michigan section of the American Society for Engineering Education (Michigan State University, 1961).

44. Thayer, Lee O. *Administrative Communication* (Homewood, Ill.: Richard D. Irwin, Inc., 1961).

45. Whyte, William H., Jr. and the Editors of *Fortune*. *Is Anybody Listening*? (New York: Simon & Schuster, Inc., 1952).

CHAPTER TWO

Communication Theory: A Quick Review

Communication is at the heart of all human understanding and all human relationships, for communication is the very process of human interaction. Eric Berne, the originator of *transactional analysis*, defines the *transaction* as the basic unit for studying human communication.

> If two or more people encounter each other. . . sooner or later one of them will speak or give some other indication of acknowledging the presence of the other. This is called the *transaction stimulus.* Another person will then say or do something which is in some way related to the stimulus, and that is called the *transaction response.* (3, p. 29)

A transaction response as well as a stimulus must exist before an action can be considered communication. A transaction need not involve a physical meeting. When an author writes, he is providing a transaction stimulus which may be responded to by thousands of others over a period of thousands of years. It should be noted that the communication occurs not when the message is written, but when it is "taken into account." (20 p. 26) Only when a stimulus is responded to is the communication process taking place. Therefore, to study communication, we must study much more than transaction stimuli skills, such as speaking and writing. We must be equally concerned with and aware of the transaction receiving, processing, and responding skills.

Human-to-human transactions are so common that we often take for granted that we understand the process involved; we lose our awareness of how dependent we are upon this process for our very survival. We forget that communication is the *only skill we possess for learning to adapt to our world and the major skill we use for affecting the world around us.* Communication is at the heart of the process by which we learn to adapt to the world and by which we try to change the world to adapt to us. (20, p. 33)

Carl R. Rogers and F. J. Roethlisberger point out in their classical article, "Barriers and Gateways to Communication," that this most vital of all human *skills* receives far too little attention in our universities. We attempt to teach students to write and to speak, but that is not enough. They must also learn to listen and to understand. Rogers points out that people in our complex society need more training in how to deal with simple face-to-face relationships "at the level of skill," because "In most human-to-human transactions, we are so busy thinking, judging, and evaluating, that we don't have time to listen to what the other person means." (17, p. 48) It is especially hard to realize why so little attention is paid to teaching communication transaction skills when we consider that the activity of communicating consumes nearly 70% of the average person's waking hours and up to 90% of a manager's on-the-job time. (2, p. 1)

It is helpful to understand how your own human communication equipment works if you wish to perfect your skill in using it. In the first part of this chapter, we will attempt to look at the human communication process with a microscope so that you may better understand the capabilities and the limitations of the human communication equipment. In the second half of this chapter and in Chapter Three, we will review some of the major implications for managers and students that can be drawn from the structure of the communication and learning process.

Communication Theory and Models

Most of the problems of communication stem from two assumptions. Assumption one: When you have told someone something, you have communicated with him or her. Assumption two: When you read something and understand what it "means." others who read the same message will (or should) understand it to mean the same thing as it means to you.

Such assumptions are consistent with what is sometimes referred to as the *conveyor theory* of communication. In this theory it is assumed that messages are somehow physically transferred from one mind to another. The name, coined by Berlo, comes from the analogy to a conveyor picking up a load in one location, transferring it intact, and setting it down in a new location. This theory is similar to the ancient Greek explanation of the communication process. They believed that the god Mercury plucked an idea out of one person's mind with the tip of his spear and thrust the idea into the mind of another.

There is the assumption in both of these theories that words contain meaning. When one person says a word such as *nine*, it is assumed in the conveyor theory that the meaning the sender intended has been transferred in the form of a word to the receiver. The fallacy of this assumption is easily exposed. If the receiver understands only Japanese or Turkish, the word *nine* will have no meaning. If the receiver understands only German, the word *nine* would likely elicit the meaning *no*. If he understands only English, the meaning of the numeral *9* would likely come to mind. Assuming the speaker was sending in German and the hearer was receiving in English, the meaning sent and the meaning received would not be the same.

Obviously, the meaning cannot be contained in the word. The meaning exists only in the mind of the receiver. In Chapter One it was pointed out that all human communication is limited to what we defined as type H information exchanges. Type H information is input which has been selectively received and selectively translated with meaning structure and value added to it by a complex and constantly changing organism. If meaning exists in the receiver and is not transferred from the sender to the receiver, then you must accept that when you have sent a message, you may not have communicated anything or you may have communicated something different than what you intended. You must also accept that when others have read the same material as you have, they may have understood it to mean something different than what you understood it to mean.

The purpose of the first part of this chapter is to explain why and how such differences occur. A detailed explanation is given in the hope that such understanding will help facilitate your efforts to correct for the shortcomings of the human communication process. We will start by briefly reviewing the history of communication theory and some of the basic communication models.

History of Communication Theory

The importance of communication was recognized by Aristotle. More than 2,000 years ago, he wrote that the prime purpose of all human communication is to *influence*. (2, p. 6) In more recent times, this assumption was temporarily challenged. In the late eighteenth century, the concept of *faculty psychology* and the mind-body dualism led rhetoricians to distinguish between communication designed to persuade, inform, and entertain. With the falling out in psychology of the mind-body dualism of faculty psychology and the appearance of behaviorism, this distinction between the various purposes of communication has been greatly de-emphasized. Modern communication theorists have returned to the classical Aristotelian position that the prime purpose of all communication is to influence. (2, p. 9)[1] However, much of the training in speech and English classes even today shows the influence of the long since rejected theories of faculty psychology. In such classes, the arbitrary distinction is still frequently made between presentations designed to persuade, inform, and entertain.

The approach of this text is consistent with behavioral psychology theories. The position taken is that although informing and entertaining are involved in most transactions, the primary purpose of human communication is to influence. As is pointed out in the Introduction, the exercises in this text all focus on helping us develop communication skills for the purpose of either influencing the behavior of others or learning how to be properly influenced by others' behavior. As is pointed out in Chapter One, such skills are of vital importance to students of management since influencing through communication is the primary func-

---

[1] A more thorough discussion of this point can be found in Berlo (2, pp. 7-14).

tion of management.

The major scientific work on communication theory began in the late nineteenth century. Samuel Morse was one of the first to apply mathematical analysis to the communication process. (6, p. 4) He developed the Morse Code for telegraphy by assigning the shortest combinations of dots and dashes to the most frequently used letters. This code was a forerunner of the binary codes used as the communication median in modern computers.

With the advent of telephones, radios, and television, research on the theory of communication received massive financial backing. Most of the early research focused on data transmission. Men were concerned with the technical problems involved in transferring various types of signals from a transmitter to a receiver.

FIGURE 2-1 Shannon and Weaver Model

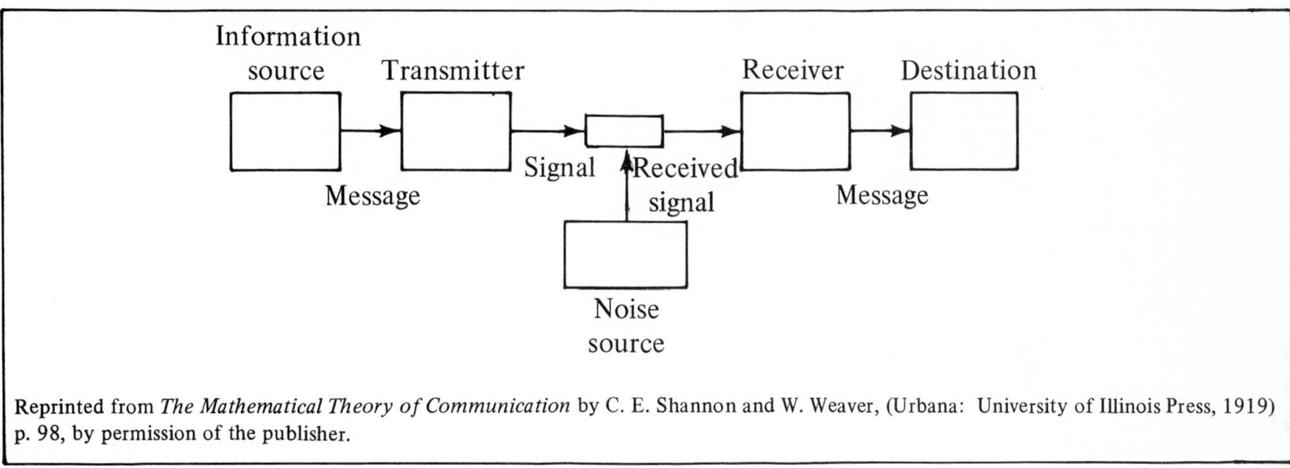

Reprinted from *The Mathematical Theory of Communication* by C. E. Shannon and W. Weaver, (Urbana: University of Illinois Press, 1919) p. 98, by permission of the publisher.

When Marconi first suggested that he could transfer such signals through the air, he was thought to be insane and was ordered to undergo a psychiatric examination.

Claud Shannon and Warren Weaver developed one of the first communication models, as shown in Figure 2-1. This model was designed primarily to represent telephone-to-telephone communication rather than human-to-human communication. This is why the information source and the transmitter are separated. Such a model does not accurately represent a human communicator in which the information source and transmitter are part of the same entity. Nevertheless, this first model greatly influenced the design of almost all of the human communication models that followed. Two of the most interesting and widely used are the Berlo Model (Figure 2-2) and the McCrosky Model (Figure 2-3). The focus of these models, as with

FIGURE 2-2 Berlo Model

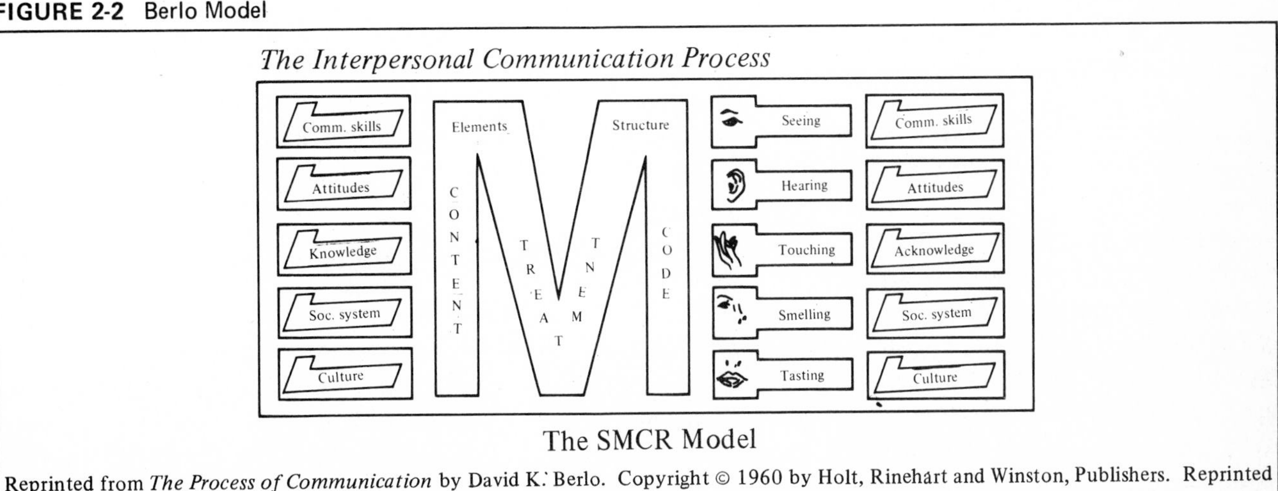

Reprinted from *The Process of Communication* by David K. Berlo. Copyright © 1960 by Holt, Rinehart and Winston, Publishers. Reprinted by permission of Holt, Rinehart and Winston, Publishers.

Shannon and Weaver's, tends to be on what happens to the message as it leaves the sender and travels to the receiver. This focuses attention on the sending and receiving of messages and tends to de-emphasize the functions of processing messages. Such a model is adequate for studying data transmission systems such as telephones. To study human-to-human communication, a model is needed that focuses attention on how we process the data we receive and how to convert the data into type H information. It is in this conversion process that most communication problems occur.

FIGURE 2-3 McCroskey Model

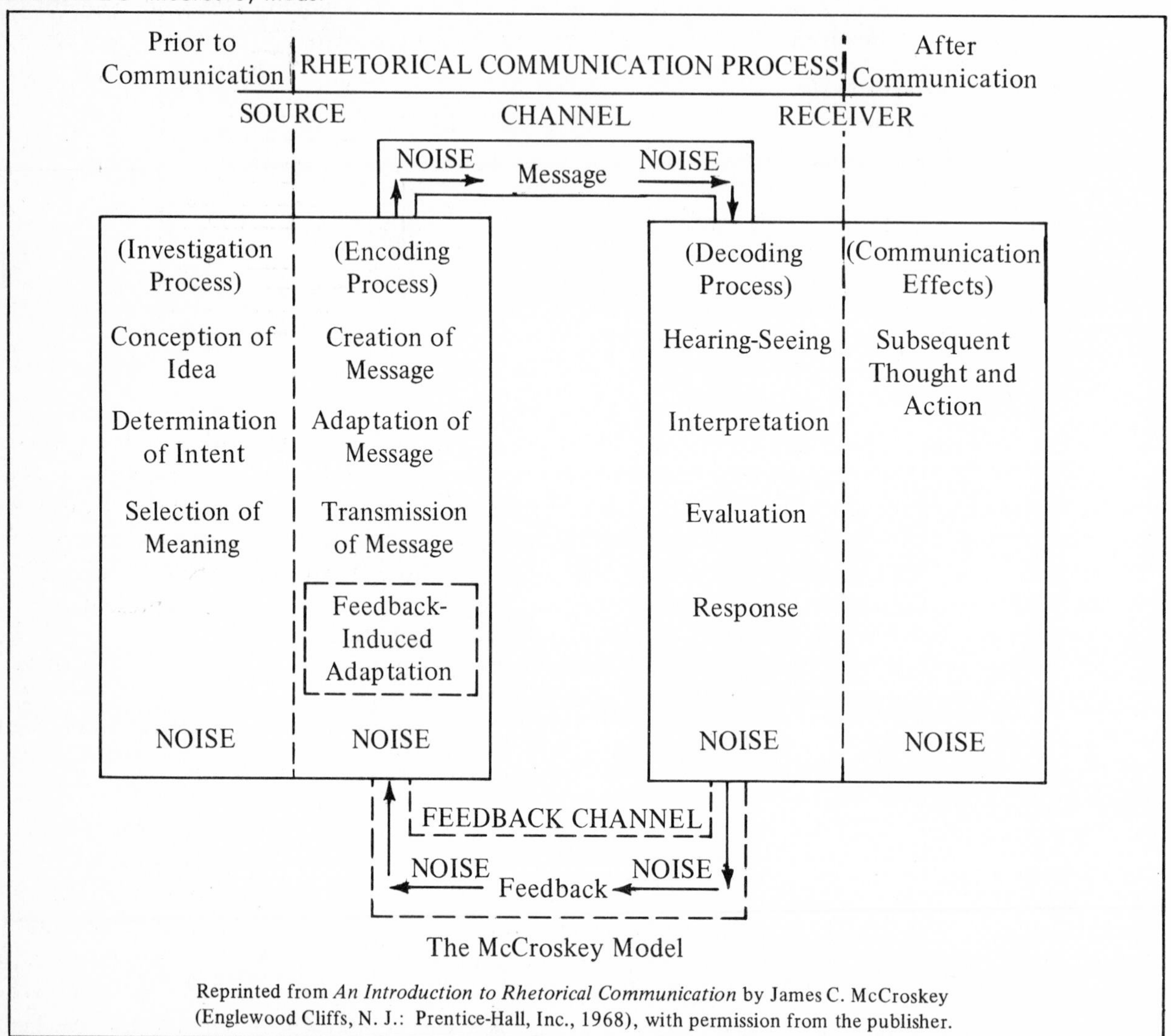

The McCroskey Model

Reprinted from *An Introduction to Rhetorical Communication* by James C. McCroskey (Englewood Cliffs, N. J.: Prentice-Hall, Inc., 1968), with permission from the publisher.

An early model developed by Johnson and a group of other semanticists deals entirely with human communication. It stresses the internal processing of messages as well as the interaction between the sender and the receiver (see Figure 2-4). (19) The Johnson Model is in some ways analogous to the way management systems are depicted. The basic components of the model are concerned with input, processes, and outputs. Note that the Shannon and Weaver model is more limited in that it depicts only the external communication activities, the output, transmission system, and receiver. As mentioned earlier, such a model can deal only with the communication of data. That type of communication is the problem of communication engineers rather than of managers. The manager is more concerned with the items depicted in the Johnson-type model. The manager is primarily concerned with how messages he sends will be received, processed into type H information, and responsed to.

FIGURE 2-4 Johnson's Model of Face-to-Face Communication

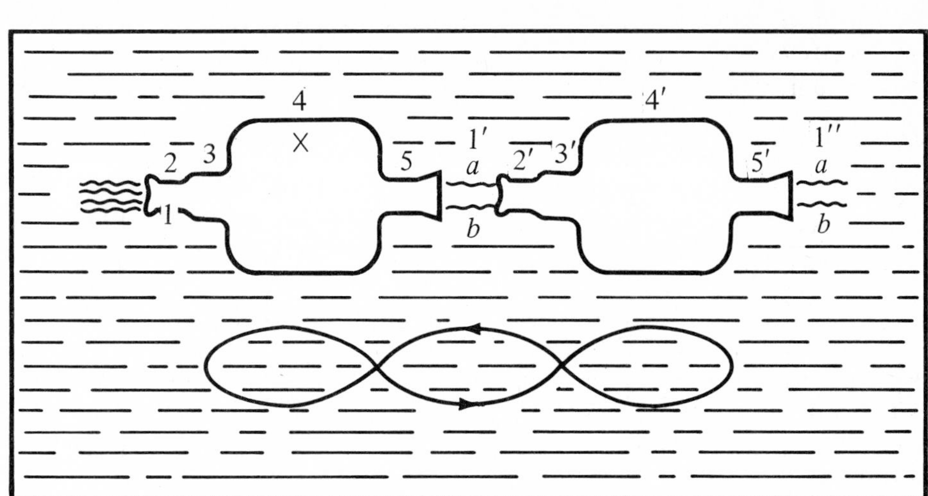

Key: Stage I, event, or source of stimulation, external to the sensory end organs of the speaker; State 2, sensory stimulation; State 3, preverbal neurophysiological state; State 4, transformation of preverbal into symbolic forms; State 5, verbal formations in final draft for overt expression; State 1′, transformation of verbal formations into (a) air waves and (b) light waves, which serve as sources of stimulation for the listener (who may be either the speaker himself or another person); States 2′ through 1″ correspond, in the listener, to States 2 through 1″. The arrowed loops represent the functional interrelationships of the stages in the process as a whole.

A New Model

A new model, called the *communication system model*, (Figure 2-5) is introduced here to help clarify the human communication process. This model (Figure 2-5) is greatly influenced by the Johnson model but is patterned after a basic production system model. This model like the Johnson model, focuses on what happens to stimuli after entering the human system. The three major parts of the model are inputs, processes and outputs. These parts are basic to all systems whether they be animal, plant, machine or human. The inputs are of two basic types. The first type is external and internal stimuli which activate sensors. The second type is internal feedback that the brain receives by monitoring its own processing and output activities. This second type of input includes attitudes, emotions, biases and all other types of thought processes. In the model this is represented by the arrow running from processes to outputs and back to inputs as feedback.

The primary skills used to improve input capability are reading, listening and observing. Of course you also receive other input such as smell or taste but rarely do persons consciously try to develop skills to improve their use of these senses. The reading and listening skills are those most critical to our ability to interact with other people. Of the input skills only reading receives much attention in basic schooling and reading is taught, for the most part, only at the level of the letter or word recognition. Few reading courses attempt to train students how to critically evaluate the writer's logic or the subtlety behind the words.

FIGURE 2-5 Communication System Model

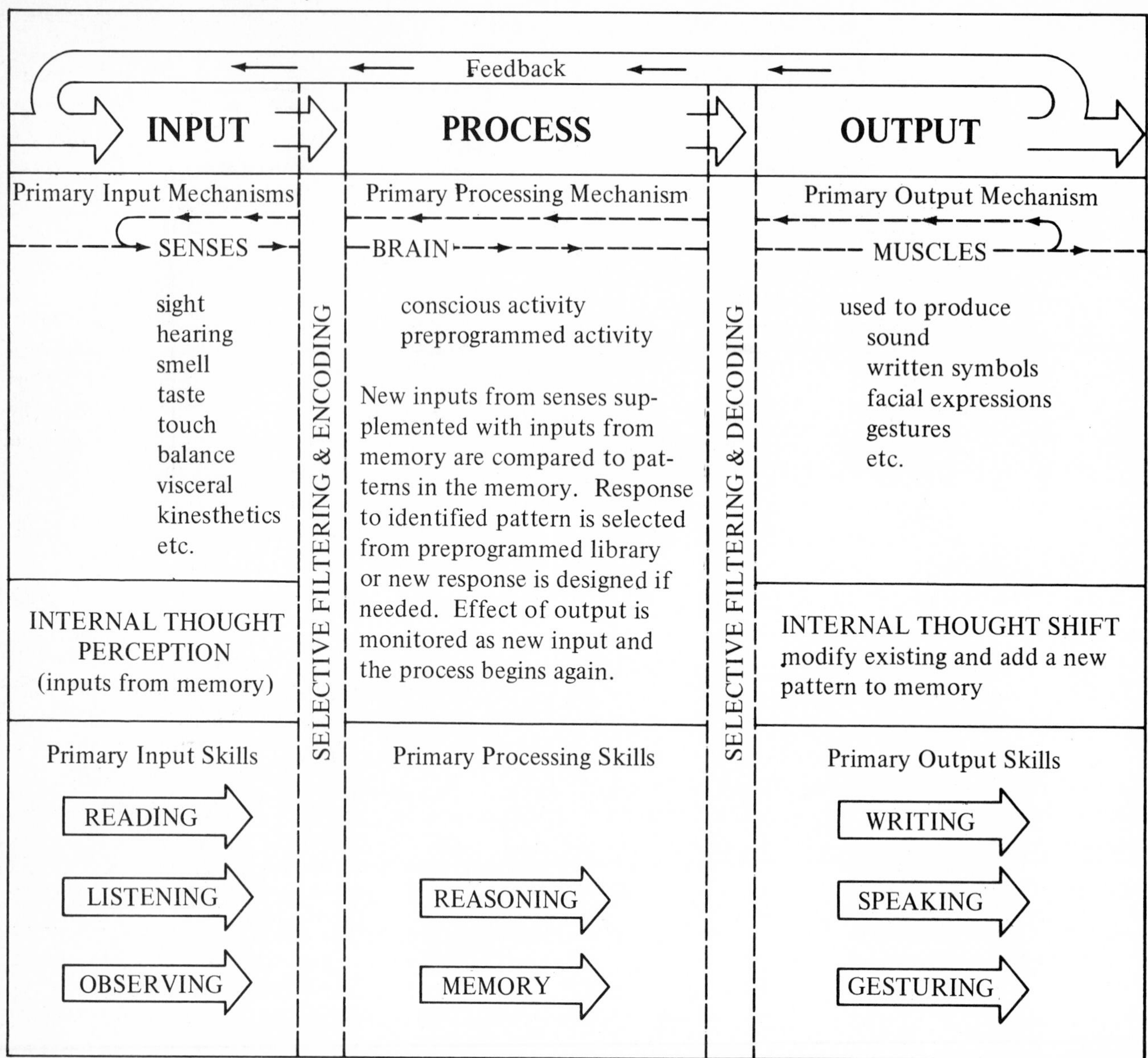

The second phase of the model depicts the data processing function of the brain. There are two major types of processing. The first is the conscious activity of searching for meaning. In this process we consciously probe our memories as well as outside sources of information in an effort to understand something. During this process people are often very aware of the limitations of their memories. The brain can recall a name one day and not the next. One also becomes aware that random memories from the past can suddenly pop into the consciousness for no apparent reason. This conscious part of processing is usually quite rational, within limitations. These limitations are the amounts of data the conscious mind can handle at any given moment. If the mind considered whether you should eat or go swimming, it might rationally decide what is the best activity at that time. The decision may have been made to go swimming even though a cut on the leg is likely to get infected. The cut on the leg at the moment of decision was not a variable the mind was consciously considering. At one time the mind can rationally deal with only a limited number of pieces of data.

It is difficult if not impossible to consider at one time all possible interactions of even ten variables. (There are thousands of possible combinations of ten variables) For this reason, the mind must filter out much data. It can select only a limited amount to deal with at a conscious level.

The majority of stimuli that the brain receives must be dealt with at a subconscious or preprogrammed automatic level. In this process the brain responds to stimuli according to learned patterns. These patterns automatically filter out unnecessary and unwanted data. Frequently you will have no conscious awareness of where your preprogrammed behaviors came from, the logic on which they were based, or the consequences of using them. You simply react that way because that is the way you react. This type of behavior, its origin and its consequences, are discussed in detail later in this chapter.

The primary skills involved in processing are reasoning and memory. In our school systems much effort is devoted to teaching students to memorize. Little time is devoted to the more important skills of logically supporting one's thoughts and of recognizing the difference between unsupported beliefs and supportable facts.

The third stage of the model depicts the output activities. Output is basically of two types. The first is muscle movement, which may form sound waves, written symbols or other types of body movement. The second type of output is related to internal thought shifts. These shifts modify memories and response patterns just as must as do outside stimuli. All outputs are monitored by the sender and are therefore also inputs. It is through the input and processing skills that you are able to control how you are effected by the world. It is through your output skills that you in turn are able to affect the world. The output skills are given great attention in our schools for these are the skills by which others observe and evaluate us. Speaking and writing are the most important of the output skills for they are the skills used in most dealings among people.

It is all too obvious that training students in these output skills alone has not been effective as a means of teaching them to communicate. You need only observe the typical communication skill level of high school and even college graduates with their 12 to 14 years of training in English and speech classes. As was reported in Chapter One, a major complaint of employers is that these graduates still cannot write reports that are understandable, documented, or convincing. These students still cannot stand before a group and give a simple, effective presentation. Teaching output skills alone is obviously not enough since the output can only reflect the quality of the input and processing skills on which it is based.

In the second part of the model we will refer to the first input-process-output system as Mr. A. The model shows his relationship to both himself and others in an ongoing communication situation. Note that Mr. A is not the same entity in time period two, T_2, that he was in T_1. This is because his own output was received by himself and processed. Every time you receive and process new data, you change slightly. That is because each new input is recorded in your memory and thus changes slightly the store of knowledge you have available to process every input which follows. In this fashion you are constantly changing. Note also that Mr. B at T_3 is not the same as Mr. B at T_2 when he first encountered Mr. A. He also was changed in some minute way by his transaction with Mr. A. In short, we are all dynamic living beings who are constantly receiving mental input as well as physical inputs such as food and air. With each input, mental or physical, you are changed slightly. Just as we use food and air to grow physically, we use sensory input to grow mentally.

Notice in the model in Figure 2-6 the line within the rectangle representing Mr. A that extends internally from his output end to his input end. This line represents internal thought. We are all constantly thinking of ways in which we might behave. Then we consider the possible consequences of such actions. This process of internal thought shift is one of the major ways in which one grows and changes. Instead of having to take an action and getting *feedback* from outside sources, you can think of the action and then provide yourselve with *internal feedback*. You can consult our memory for records of what happened to you in similar circumstances or what happened to others in similar circumstances that you saw or read about.

Once you take an action, you will get both *internal* and *external* feedback. When Mr. A thinks about asking Mr. B to stop tapping his pencil, he will probably first consider various ways to ask Mr. B and will

FIGURE 2-6 Communication System Model, Part II

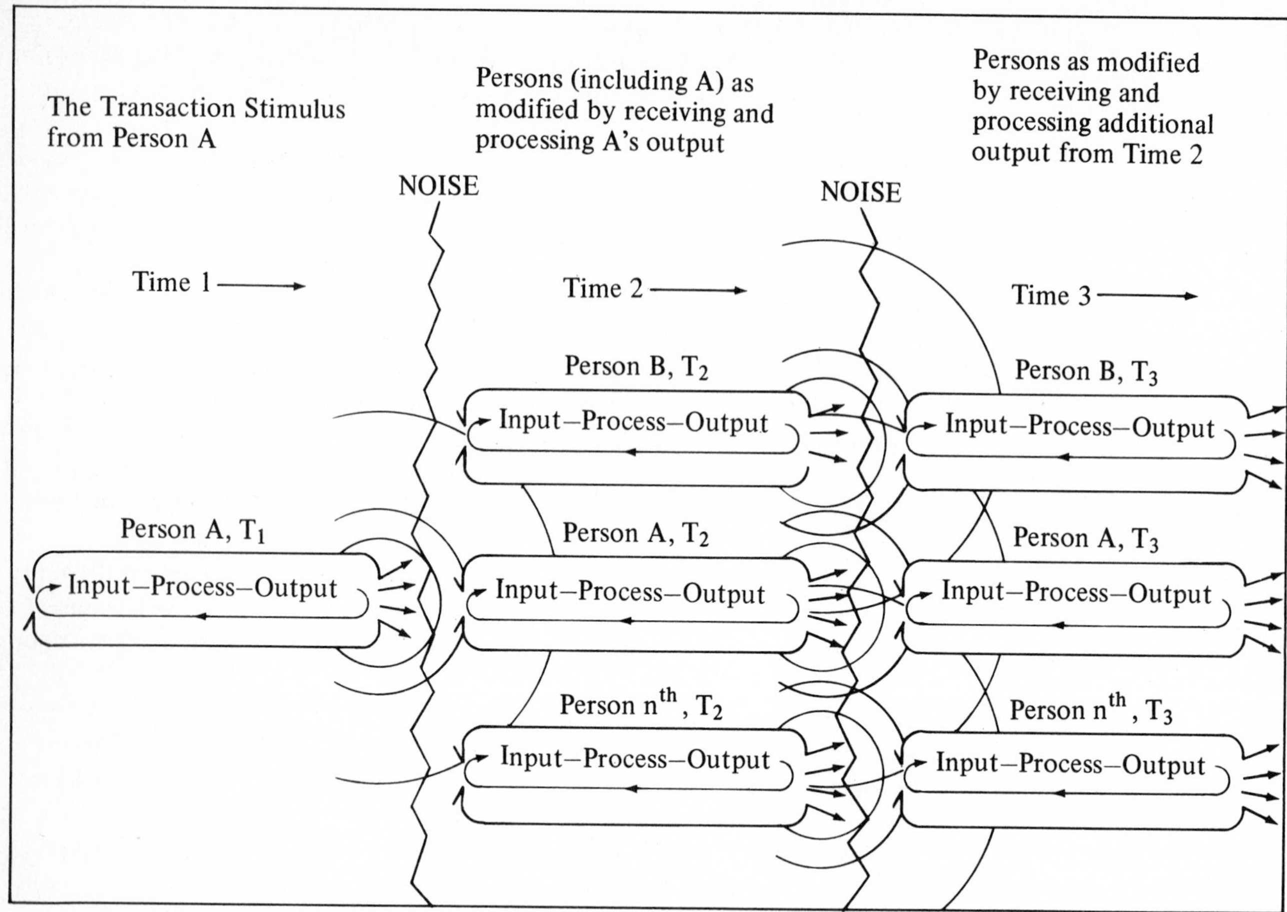

consider (internal feedback) how Mr. B will respond. If Mr. B is a close friend, Mr. A might just say, "Hey! Stop that." If Mr. B is Mr. A's boss, Mr. A might decide to use a more indirect message in hopes of distracting Mr. B from his nervous habit. He might say, "Is that a new watch you're wearing?"

Once Mr. A sends out the message, he will observe Mr. B's behavior. These observations provide *external feedback* to Mr. A on how successful his transaction stimulus was. The feedback becomes input and is processed. The desired *transaction response* is that Mr. B stops his tapping. If he does stop tapping, Mr. A's transaction stimulus was effective. When Mr. A processes the feedback (which is new input), he will then decide how to respond to that new input. One internal response will always be to record in his memory whether or not the method he used to stop Mr. B's tapping was a successful one that possibly could be used again.

If Mr. B did not stop tapping, Mr. A will have to consider that feedback and repeat the process of discovering a way to get Mr. B to stop tapping.

The lines in the model labeled *noise* are there to show that the message sent by Mr. A may be distorted by external forces before it reaches a receiver. The term *noise* is used because of the analogy to speech which a listener cannot understand because of nearby noise such as a jet taking off. Noise in the model is used in a much broader sense. Noise is all distractions or interference that distorts sensory perception.

The lines radiating out from Mr. A and Mr. B and Mr. n^{th} are to show that output goes in all directions, some of which they may not even be aware. The intersection of the radiating lines is to show that their output is mixed with that of many others. Thus, the input one receives is a conglomeration of many potential messages. Since one cannot respond to all of them, one must subjectively select those to which he or she wishes to respond. He will ignore the others.

Now that we have reviewed the major parts of the new communication model, we will take a microscopic look at why the human communication system works as it does. By examining the human communication system at a microscopic level, you should be able to gain a clearer understanding of the limitations of your own perceptual and communication systems.

It is important to distinguish between real limits and those limitations on your ability that are only creations of your own mind. That distinction is very important for managers to understand. If people believe that they are being asked to change reality—a thing that cannot be changed—they will see no purpose in even attempting to change. Managers are not likely to get people to try to change their physical height. Such changes are most likely not even seen as possible by employees. Others may see it equally impossible to change a racial bias if they truly believe that those whom they are biased against are in reality inferior. If you are to be open to change, you must learn that there always are differences between what is reality and what is only your limited *perception of reality*. On the basis of all of man's scientific knowledge, it is aerodynamically impossible for the bumblebee to fly. It is a good thing that the bumblebees do not share our reality on this point, for in their ignorance bumblebees fly happily from flower to flower. We only know reality based on our limited perception. To the extent that actual reality differs from your perceived reality, there is room for you to modify behaviors that you may now believe to be unchangeable.

A microscopic examination of the human communication system should make it apparent that man does not deal with reality, for we are incapable of perceiving it. We therefore create in our minds our own reality as best we can, based on our limited capacity to receive and process data. To clarify this assumption, we will take a closer look at the three main aspects of the communication system shown in the new model: inputs, processes and outputs.

Input: How You Know Something to Communicate

How do you know anything? That question is perhaps too broad. Let us narrow it to something more concrete. How do we know this book is here?

The obvious answer is you can see and feel it. In short, you sense it. You could also smell and taste the book, and, as you turn the pages, you can hear them. The five senses just mentioned are the primary sensory systems you use to receive data about things external to you and also the means by which you know about the internal status of your own body. The five best-known senses are by no means your only sensory systems. You have several sensory systems that tell you exclusively about the internal state of your body. The visceral senses tell you when your stomach is shrinking or cramping. Kinesthetic senses tell you about the movements and positions of various parts of your body. Your balance sensors tell you your body's position relative to the surface of the earth. It should be noted that all of these sensory systems are actually composed of several independent subsystems. For example, there are three different sensory systems involved in vision and eight separate systems involved in touch. (21, p. 414) All of these many systems are constantly monitoring our internal and external environment.

The interaction of our sensory and physical systems at a conscious and subconscious level is immense. For example, when Mr. A sees his boss watching him, it might make him tense, which makes his stomach stop digesting, which causes him to get a headache, which causes him to feel very uncomfortable with the young applicant whom he is interviewing for a job. At this point, Mr. A, at a conscious level, is probably completely unaware of why he is displeased with the young applicant. All Mr. A knows is that part of the over-all perception he has associated with the man is a feeling of being uncomfortable.

You do not perceive and remember individual events separately or separate from the emotions associated with them. You perceive and put in your memory an over-all interacting set of events. In the memory, the perceived event, emotional reaction, and feelings associated with the event are all recorded as one. The scientific evidence to back up this assumption is provided by experiments conducted by the noted brain surgeon Wilder Penfield. He stimulated patients' brains with tiny electrodes and found that touching points on a person's brain would cause him to remember clearly an event in his past. Not only did the patient remember the event, but he physically felt all of the emotion associated with the event. Penfield concluded, "An event and the feeling which was produced by the event are inextricably locked together in the brain so that one cannot be evoked without the other." (15)

The importance of understanding the working of the human sensory systems, if you are to understand behavior, cannot be overemphasized. Behavior is controlled by the mind, and there is nothing in your minds that did not enter through your sensory systems. To prove this, you need simply ask, "What would you now know if at birth all of your sensory nerves had been disconnected from your brain?" You might possibly be aware that you exist, but you would not know where you exist or what you look like or anything about the world around you. Even if all of your muscles were in working order and connected to your brain, you could not learn to walk or talk. You would not even know that you had legs or lips to move, and you would not know if they moved. You would know of no political, religious, or philosophical systems so you could have no beliefs or prejudices. It is obvious that you depend upon your sensory systems for the intake of the data upon which is based everything you learn, know, believe, hate, or fear.

If you accept the preceding assumption, then you must also conclude that *all of your knowledge and beliefs are limited by the limitations, distortions, and inaccuracies of your sensory systems.* An analogy can be made between your sensory systems and a production system. In both cases, the quality of the output is limited by the quality of the raw materials with which you start. Once you recognize that the limitations of your sensory systems do limit your ability to understand and perceive reality, then it is easy to understand how important it is to learn just how limited the sensors actually are. In the book, *The Symphony of Life,* Donald H. Andrews, a professor of chemistry at Johns Hopkins University, clearly describes the limitations of our sensory systems:

> In scientific laboratories all over the world thousands of experiments have been performed that establish the reality of these unperceived phenomena beyond any shadow of doubt, that prove that these waves of unseen light and sound are truly around us and within us at all times. What we see, the visible light, constitutes far less than a millionth part of all the radiation around us. What we hear, the audible sound, is far less than a millionth part of all the vibration constantly beating upon our bodies. And what is even more important, light waves and sound waves make up in their unseen and unheard totality only a small part of the truly complete sum of all the kinds of waves that are constantly churning in the ocean of space in which we exist. . . (1)

Through the use of special instruments, such as telescopes and X-rays, we can convert some phenomena beyond our sensory capacity into an observable form. Beyond that, we have instruments that can report the presence of such nonobservable things as magnetic fields. Even with these mechanical extensions of our sensory systems, our ability is extremely limited. This is especially so when we consider what a tiny part we actually see of that which we are capable of seeing. We are capable of seeing but do not have an opportunity to see all of those millions of events that happen in other countries or other cities. We even miss those events that are simply behind a closed door.

By both chance and by design, our sensory inputs are limited and selected. If by chance you were born into a Catholic family, you were likely exposed to many experiences describing Catholicism in a favorable light. If you grew up as a Catholic, you likely learned to select experiences that tend to support the belief you developed in Catholicism, experiences such as attending Mass and a Catholic school. In the case of birth, the pro-Catholic input was by chance; in the case of school, the pro-Catholic input was purposely selected.

Already the discussion is touching upon the processing phase of our communication system, for it is our processing that determines how we select inputs. We will avoid the temptation to delve further into processing at this point. First, it is important to understand exactly what it is that gets transferred from the sensory organs up to the brain to be processed.

The eyes and ears are man's primary sensors used in communication. Of all of our senses, sight seems to be the most used and most trusted, as is illustrated by the common expression, "I saw it with my own eyes." We will use this most trusted sense to illustrate how sensory impulses are transmitted to the brain.

Nerve Transmission

When light waves enter a human eye, they are focused on a roughly three-eighths-inch diameter area at the back of the eye, called the retina. The retina is composed of at least three different sets of nerve endings which are each sensitive to different types of light waves. Two of the sets have cone-shaped endings. There are about seven million of these cone endings. One set is believed to be sensitive to hues of light on the red-green spectrum and the other to hues on the blue-yellow spectrum. There is a third group of nerve endings which are shaped like rods. They respond only to shades of black and white light, and there are approximately 125 million of these sensors. (21, p. 419) The three sets of nerve endings work independently, much as the three color guns in a color TV set. If one gun in a color picture tube breaks, we can still use the set, but the color balance is off. If one of our three visual systems quits functioning, we can still see, but we are color blind.

When light waves strike these rod and cone-shaped sensory endings, a chemical reaction involving visual violet takes place. This reaction causes the nerve to "fire" sending an impulse to the brain. The impulses are often referred to as messages, implying that the impulses themselves possess some type of information. This is a major misconception about the input end of the human communication system. The impulses traveling along our nerves are all the same, regardless of what activated the nerve or of which sensory system the nerve is a part. Nerve impulses are simply electrochemical reactions. They are not electrical impulses traveling at the speed of light. They are electrochemical impulses traveling at about seven feet per second. When a nerve is stimulated, a sodium ion on the outer part of the nerve exchanges places with a potassium ion inside the nerve. This exchange stimulates the next set of sodium and potassium ions to do the same, causing a chain reaction along the nerve. Since the ions either exchange places or do not exchange places, the nerve is limited to either transmitting an impulse or not transmitting an impulse. (21, p. 396). There can be no different degrees of impulse and no different types of impulses.

The nervous system is a data transmission system. This system, which has only two types of signals, on and off, is referred to as a *binary* system. In new math, a binary system is also called a *base two* numerical system. Morse code is an example of a binary system for it has only two possible signals, dots and dashes. Most modern computers operate on binary systems. Like the human brain, the two signals for the computer binary system are the presence of a signal or the absence of a signal.

It is important to note that nerve impulses can carry no meaning. This is especially important to understand because as was pointed out earlier, your only connection with reality is through your sensors. Thus, your only connection with reality is also through your incoming nerve impulses. This is an almost frightening fact to realize. It should make you aware of how subject your perceptual system is to error.

Conversion of Nerve Impulses Into Type H Information

If the only things coming into the brain are identical nerve impulses, how is it that we can, in our mind, see images, hear sounds, and smell odors? We will use an analogy to illustrate how this happens. We will compare the human visual system to a simplified version of an early system that was used to transmit photographs of the moon to earth. The early photographs of the moon were transmitted to earth by a lightweight, simple radio, which could transmit only a beep. Since it could also not beep, it was a binary system.

The camera sent to the moon took and developed a photograph. The photo was a static reproduction of the ever-changing moon. A video tube was focused on a single spot in the upper left-hand corner of the photograph to measure the amount of light being reflected off of that spot. The computer connecting the video tube and radio converted that data into numbers, with 9 representing no reflection (black) and 0 representing maximum reflection (white). Once the computer received and coded the data from the video tube, it activated the radio to start sending beeps to earth. A simplified version of the code used is shown in Figure 2-7.

FIGURE 2-7 Computer Code and Rules

CONVERSION OF BINARY CODE TO ARABIC NUMBERS

0 = ----	5 = b-b-	b = a beep
1 = b---	6 = -bb-	- = no beep
2 = -b--	7 = bbb-	
3 = bb--	8 = ---b	
4 = --b-	9 = b--b	

RULES OF OPERATION
Turn on or off machine = bbbb
All signals are 1/10 second long.
All signals are sent in sets of four.
Each one thousand sets of signals comprise one line of the picture.

We are all familiar with newspaper pictures. They are simple rows of various size dots, as is shown in Figure 2-8. For the photographs from the moon, the computer converted the amount of light into a numerical value and activated the radio to transmit the pattern of beeps appropriate for that value. The video tube then moved to the right 1/1000 of the width of the photograph, focused on the next spot, and repeated the process. When one line was completed, the video tube focused back to the left side of the photograph and started on the next line.

FIGURE 2-8 Blow-up of a Picture from a Newspaper.

The radio receiver on the earth received the pattern of beeps and silence. The earth computer decoded this pattern and instructed a printer connected to it to begin making a row of appropriate size dots on a blank sheet of paper. The first dot would be made in the upper left-hand corner of the paper. The size of the first dot would correspond to the number transmitted for the first spot on the photograph. For a 9, the dot would be so large that it would completely cover a square 1/1000 of the width of the paper. The dot for a 5 would cover only slightly more than half that size, and for a 0, the square would be left blank. Thus, dot by dot, line by line, the photograph of the moon would be recreated on the earth by the receiver computer-printer system.

It is important to note that the photograph was never *transmitted* to earth. Only patterns of beeps were transmitted. So the printer could not possibly recreate an exact copy of the photograph that was still on the moon because that photograph was not composed of tiny dots. The recreated copy could not possibly show details finer than 1/1000 the width of the photo.

It is also important to our analogy to note that the recreation of the picture was controlled by the programming of the sending and receiving computers. If the computer on the moon controlling observation and transmission did not use the same code and rules of operation as the computer on earth, the recreated picture would most likely bear little resemblance to the original. For example, if 0 represented black and 9 white in the earth computer, we would get a negative image. If the earth computer was programmed to receive signals in sets of five instead of four, the recreated picture would probably become only a random sprinkling of dots, bearing no resemblance to the moon photograph.

When humans communicate, it is important that the sender and receiver operate with the same code and assumptions. If the human sender's code is based on liberal assumptions and the receiver's code is based on conservative ones, it is likely that the message sent and the message received will bear little resemblance.

If there is a discrepancy between a sending and a receiving computer, the problem is rather easy to correct; one or both of the computers are simply reprogrammed. With the human brain, reprogramming is not so simple. The brain is a self-programming device. It programs itself on the basis of past experience. Since no two people have identical bodies or brains, and since no two people can be in the same place at the same time, we must conclude that no two people have identical experiences. We must therefore also conclude that no two people are programmed exactly the same way. This means that no message between two humans will ever be received exactly as it was sent. It also means that no two people viewing a single event will perceive exactly the same thing. In Fabun's book, *Communication*, he points out, "Many of our problems in communication arise because we forget to remember that individual experiences are never identical." (4, p. 86)

Fortunately, groups of humans living in a single culture have many similar experiences. Certain behaviors consistently receive rewards or punishments. Through a process of trial and error, education, and experience, groups develop similar but not identical codes and assumptions. This greatly facilitates intragroup communication. Yet, even in the most tightly knit groups, there are still differences. Men have certain basic drives that are different from women's. The old have certain basic drives that are different from those of the young. Although communication may become effective enough among humans to get the work of the world done, you must always remember how subject your communication is to error. You must always remember you do not view reality; you recreate it in your own individual way in your own individual brain. Perception takes place only after you have selectively received and selectively processed incoming sensory data into your own pattern of type H information.

Processing

When you perceive a totally new pattern, your brain does not know exactly how to recognize it, for you have no classification system by which to organize it. The pattern and the background are likely to all be mixed. The ability to perceive a thing is a learned ability like all other abilities. For example, when most Americans see "へ" drawn on a page, they usually think of it as merely a curved line or maybe a picture of a mountain. To a Japanese student, it is the Hirigana symbol for the sound [hay]. The same symbol turned on its end "く" is the symbol for the sound [ku.] Japanese writing makes little sense to most Americans because we have not learned to recognize it. It is equally difficult for Japanese to recognize differences between such similar symbols as [aσ] or [λk]. It is also hard for them to understand that [A,A,a,ɑ,ɑ] are all the same symbol.

A more unusual example showing that recognition is a learned behavior was reported by anthropologists who found a tribe in New Guinea whose members could not recognize two-dimensional pictures. The tribe had no form of art and had never learned to convert three-dimensional reality into two-dimensional symbols or pictures. The ability to process sensory impulses into type H information is, indeed, a learned activity.

Brain Functions: Memory and Logic

The human brain is extremely complex and the way it functions is by no means completely understood. The brain, like a computer, is a data processing system. The system has two main components, one for *logic* and one for *memory*, or storage. We have already mentioned that the logical function of the human brain differs from a computer in that the brain is self-programming whereas a computer is limited to rigidly following programming imposed upon it by an outside entity.

Memory function of the brain. The memory unit of computers also differs greatly from the human memory. The memory unit in a computer can store uninterpreted data. The human memory can store only type H information. That is, human memories store only information that has been selectively received and selectively translated with structure, meaning, and values added to it. Thus, the human brain cannot record an event without simultaneously recording all of the emotions and feelings associated with the event. Penfield's research, quoted earlier, has shown that the human memory stores only ongoing events like a motion picture. He found that when he touched a patient's brain with an electrode, it would evoke emotion-laden memories of ongoing events as single recollections, rather than as mixtures of memories and generalizations. (15) The human memory, therefore, cannot be a cold, unbiased source of stored data. It is rather an active source of emotion-laden inputs that effect the way in which new data are received.

Logic function of the brain. The function of the logic section of the brain is to compare incoming data to stored information and to use this comparison as a basis for determining how to interpret and to respond to the new data. For example, you know that a girl is pretty only by comparing the selectively received and selectively processed image you have of the girl to other images you have in our mind of what pretty girls look like. The same is true when you hear abstract ideas such as political opinions. You can only evaluate new opinions by comparing them to the beliefs you already have. The more beliefs we become familiar with, the greater is our basis for comparison and, thus, for understanding even more. Literally, learning increases our ability to learn more. More on logic is presented later in this chapter.

As we have stated earlier, data sent by speaking, writing, facial expressions, and gestures and other means are only transaction stimuli and do not constitute communication. Communication takes place only when there is also a transaction response, that is, when someone "takes into account" the transaction stimuli. (20) Much data are sent out that are not selected by others for processing. Penfield, in his studies of memory, reported, "It appears that only those sensory elements to which the individual was paying attention are recorded, not all of the sensory impulses which are forever bombarding the central nervous system." (5, p. 30)

Input that is processed is responded to. The response is referred to as *output*. The output can be an internal thought shift, such as deciding you like a person you formerly disliked. The output can also be a physical action, such as to extend your hand or to say "welcome." The output might also be a decision not to change your attitude and not to take any physical action. All decisions, even the decision not to act, result in some internal or external output. All output is subsequently monitored and becomes input. This type of input is called feedback. It is by the process of getting feedback on your output that you learn. You modify your behavior, based on the responses of yourself and others to your output. This is the way one learns to correct behaviors that do not receive desired responses.

If your communication with yourself—your feedback—is not working properly, you will not be able to adapt properly to the world around you and you will become maladjusted. Carl Rogers states, "The emotional maladjusted person, 'the neurotic,' is in difficulty, first because communication within himself has broken down and, secondly, because as a result of this his communication with others has been damaged." (17, p. 46) Because communication is blocked, the person cannot get accurate feedback, and accurate feedback on behavior is the only way in which we learn to adapt our behavior to fit the world.

How Does Our Learning Get Started

If learning comes from feedback, and feedback is based on output being monitored as input, and input is evaluated by comparing it to memory, then how did we get the first bits of memory to start with? This is like the age-old problem, which came first, the chicken or the egg?

Harris suggests in *I'm OK, You're OK* that the newborn baby is like a tape recorder; it takes in events and commands with little or no evaluation. (5) He suggests that later in life the person will often still follow these commands without question and, will tend to judge other behaviors against these early unevaluated values, or as Harris calls them, "life scripts."

When the baby receives these first sensory inputs, it can make only limited responses. When the baby receives strong stimuli, it cries. About the only discrimination the infant makes is that for mildly strong stimuli it cries softer than for stronger stimuli. Loud noises, the prick of a pin, the sting of wet diapers all generate the same response. The baby cries.

When the baby cries, it becomes aware that a form usually appears. In the presence of this form, the loud noises stop, the stinging diapers and offending pins are removed, and the sore areas are softly caressed. This form becomes associated with pleasant stimuli. The physical appearance of the form is not important—it could be a mother, a dog, or a cat. The form, whatever it is, is recorded in the baby's memory as part of an event containing positive feelings.

The baby cannot record all aspects of the form separately. It cannot identify each hair separately because its nervous system is not fast enough to focus on and process that much information. The hair is probably perceived only as a mass of relatively uniform color. As the form turns and moves, the visual data entering the baby's brain constantly changes, yet maintains certain consistent relationships and patterns. The hair never leaves the head, and the nose stays above the mouth. Over a period of time, the baby forms in its memory a group of visual images and accompanying emotional responses that it relates to a single entity. This entity may eventually become associated with the written symbol "Mommy." The baby can now refer to its memory for a frame of reference against which to judge other persons. It can judge them against the ongoing set of events classified as "Mommy" persons.

Cues and Abstractions

Since the baby is not capable of responding to every hair on Mommy's head or every freckle on her body, the baby responds to cues. If at a given moment only certain parts of Mommy are visible, the baby may or may not receive enough cues to recognize what it is seeing as being Mommy. If the baby sees only half of the face and that contains enough cues for the comparison to the image in the memory to make recognition, then the memory will supply the rest of the needed input for the baby to form a complete mental image of Mommy.

The fact that babies use limited cues to recognize things can be illustrated. There is a common reaction of babies to cry in fright when picked up by a stranger, even when that stranger is the infant's own mother wearing a new hat. If the hair is part of the cue the baby uses to recognize its mother and the hat covers part of the hair (the cue), the baby will not be able to recognize that person as Mommy. As the baby ages and enlarges its memory, it will form more refined categories for Mommy, such as Mommy with a hat on,

Mommy with a mud pack, or Mommy in a swimsuit. The baby then uses logic to decide whether the input it is receiving is Mommy under any of several conditions.

The baby now has an abstract category called "Mommy." The baby will learn to respond to the word "Mommy" just as though it were Mommy. When it hears phrases like "Mommy is coming," the baby will respond with the emotion and joy just as though it had actually seen Mommy coming. It will learn through feedback ways to respond to Mommy to make her laugh or to get her attention. Eventually the baby's behavior toward its mother will become so common that the behavior will become habitual. The baby will no longer have to consciously think how to behave toward Mommy; it will just subconsciously behave in certain ways. In effect, the baby will have programmed its behavior toward its mother. *Programmed* behavior is behavior that is automatic in that it need not be controlled by the conscious mind.

How We Program Our Brain

There seem to be certain rules of logic that all of us as babies and even as adults use to organize into categories the events we perceive. The two main rules are as follows:

1. All events that are perceived at the same time are part of the same phenomenon.

1. When one event precedes another, the first event caused the second to happen.

The mind continues to make these assumptions until experience, or feedback shows they are not valid. For example, the Indians perceived de Soto's men on horseback as four-legged, two-headed gods. This was logical, for the Indians had never seen horses before. And de Soto was careful never to let the Indians see his men dismounted.

Just as the Indians assumed that the horse was part of a human body, we assume that the arms are part of a human body. If asked to draw a picture of a person whom we had not met, we would likely draw a person with arms. This is because we have collected data from observing many people and have formed a category called the human body. The category includes arms.

With experience, we learn to refine our categories and to expand beyond these two simple rules. As children, we divide the body into simple subcategories such as arms, legs, and so on. In school we learn to recognize more complex subcategories such as arteries, kidneys, and lungs. Later, we learn new ways of grouping the various parts together under terms such as respiratory system, circulatory system, and skeletal system. If one decides to become a doctor, he would have to learn even more refined subcategories such as the subparts in the sensory system of touch which include merkel discs, Meissner's corpuscles, and end-bulbs of Krause. We program ourselves by first grouping our sensory inputs into broad categories. Then we refine these categories into smaller and smaller subgroups. (21, Chap. 4) We also learn to expand and modify some categories to include things formerly not thought to be related. The process by which we do this is called logic.

Two Types of Logic. There are basically two types of logic we use, *inductive* and *deductive.* Inductive logic is used to form categories or general concepts by observing many events. For example, we might note that when mixed with baking soda, certain liquids begin to bubble. We notice that these liquids are vinegar, lime juice, and oil of vitrol. We conclude that these liquids have some common characteristic. Upon further checking, we find that these liquids are all acids. Through inductive logic, we hypothesize that all acids will bubble when mixed with baking soda.

Deductive logic is used after general rules are established by inductive logic. Deductive logic is the process of using general rules to see if a new concept or thing really fits into a given category. *Syllogisms* are the simplest form of this type of logic. They are arguments consisting of a *major premise*, a statement about all things in a category; a *minor premise*, a statement about the new concept or thing; and a *conclusion* based on a comparison of the two premises. For example:

Major Premise: All acid causes bubbling when mixed with bases.

Minor Premise: Lemon juice bubbles when mixed with bases.
Conclusion: Lemon juice contains acid.

The conclusion in this syllogism may appear logical, but it is not. The major premise does not state that *only* acids cause bubbling when mixed with bases. The premises on which we base our logic must be carefully examined. What at first appears to be obviously true is not always so. We must ask such questions as, "If all acids bubble when mixed with bases, do only acids bubble when mixed with bases? If so, what percentage of acid must a liquid contain before bubbling occurs? At what temperature must the liquid be to bubble? And, etc., etc."

Logic becomes even more complex and variable when human reactions are involved. Since no two humans think exactly alike, what is a fact for one person may not be a fact for another. When a manager decides upon a logical reason for taking some action, he may expect to find more often than not that someone else does not accept his logic, or the premises it is based upon, or both. In addition, rarely do managers ever have all of the facts necessary for making any final decision; therefore, most decisions must contain a degree of tentativeness or flexibility.

Rarely will any management decision, theory, or policy cover all people or all situations. This means that even more flexibility is necessary. Frederick Herzberg has developed a theory of how to motivate employees. One part of his theory states that money does not motivate people to work. Money is rather a hygienic factor. (7) Although there is much evidence to support Herzberg's theory, even he would not claim that *none* of the 80 million workers in the United States are motivated by money. His research shows only that the majority of workers tested in certain companies using one type of testing procedure were not usually motivated by money. General rules or theories such as Herzberg's are necessary; however, they must be considered only as general guides of how to motivate any specific individual. Each individual is different from every other individual. Each individual is different today than he was yesterday. The logic that applies to one person in one situation may not apply to another person in another situation.

The key to all human logic is that it must be flexible. As new feedback is received, the mind must be open to change. If all feedback is rejected, no learning is possible. If only feedback which you like is accepted, learning is not possible as a means of adapting but only as a means of reinforcing what may be a maladaptive behavior. You must constantly bring your beliefs before your *conscious* mind for reconsideration. You must ask yourself, "Do I hold that belief because it is supported by feedback?" If the answer is negative or if you are in doubt, it may help to ask yourself where this belief of yours came from. Possible sources are as follows:

1. A belief that you learned as a child and have never challenged.

2. A belief that you realize is not consistent with your other beliefs, but one which you have been taught is sinful or shameful to challenge. (Religion, politics, and sex are often in this category.)

3. A belief on which you have publicly taken a stand and on which you must accept only supportive feedback, for to do otherwise would mean to lose face and possibly to be rejected by our group. (This would be like a Palestine refugee leader or an Israeli leader questioning their own group's right to Palestine.)

These questions may help you to understand why you are rejecting needed feedback. They may also help you to understand why others reject your "logical feedback."

Preprogrammed Behavior and Cues

We have discussed how we program our behavior. Now we will examine why such programming is necessary. One reason that human response is so unpredictable is that humans have a slow data processing brain. We are not fast enough to process all of the millions of bits of feedback that are constantly bombarding our sensory systems, nor do we have the time or the ability to compare and evaluate each new input with the trillions of memories stored in the brain. To assist us, we deal primarily in abstracts and cues. We do not have to see every detail of a "mommy" or a "car" from every angle to recognize what it is. We do not have to see every aspect of a human to determine its race, sex, and age. A quick glimpse at the person's eyes might provide us with enough cues to determine that the person is an attractive, teenage girl who is happy, or a fat, elderly man who is tired. Although these determinations are based on previous conscious experiences, they are done automatically and without necessarily any conscious consideration. Along with the automatic recognition of the person, there is usually also an accompanying automatic way of responding. This automatic response is called *preprogrammed* behavior. As we begin to talk of responses, we are dealing with the output as well as the processing phase of the communication system.

We all build up in our memory a storehouse of behavior and judgment patterns. These judgments were originally made consciously, but as they became more and more common, they became habitual patterns of response and were relegated to the control of our subconscious mind. Once these behaviors are programmed, they save us time. We need no longer consciously consider how we will respond to someone; we simply respond. This phenomenon of preprogramming is also sometimes referred to as a *conditioned response*.

An analogy can again be drawn between the way the brain processes data and the way a computer does. When a programmer wants to determine the square root of a set of numbers, he does not have to write an elaborate program for computing square roots. It is more than likely that someone has already written such a program and has stored it in the computer's library of preprogrammed material. The programmer need know only the code to use to instruct the computer to process his data, using the existing program in the computer's memory banks or library.

A human driving a car goes through the same process. To illustrate this, sit up straight in your chair with both feet flat on the floor. Now completely relax your stomach muscles and without using them lift your foot off the floor. As you will quickly discover, it cannot be done. Yet, few people who drive a car are consciously aware that every time they put on the brake, they must tighten their stomach muscles. There are about 100,000 separate commands that your brain must issue to your muscles to complete the act of bringing a car moving at 60 miles per hour to a sudden stop.

There is no time to consciously think of each muscle to be tightened or loosened, let alone time to consider the degree of balance and smoothness required for the complex, coordinated activities of multiple muscle movement. We might tighten one side of our leg more than the other as we reach "off target" for the brake pedal, with possible disastrous results.

The existence of prerecorded programs in the human brain has been proven in numerous cases of brain damage in which the storage areas of the victims' brains were destroyed. Such victims have had to reprogram their brains. They have had to learn to crawl, walk, talk, and think all over again just as a child learns. This reprogramming process usually takes at least two years.

Not only are our physical behaviors such as walking and talking preprogrammed, but also our mental attitudes and interpersonal behaviors are preprogrammed. The ability to preprogram behavioral responses and to use only abstract cues to call up these responses is at the very center of the intellect. The ability to preprogram the way we process and respond to inputs and to act without being consciously aware of how or why we act or react the way we do is also a major cause of communication and behavioral problems.

Perhaps we can better understand why this ability is so central to our intellect if we consider the following example. We meet a man and show him a group of rocks. With little hesitation, he glances over the rocks and says, "That one contains some iron ore; this one is bauxite, and that one is rich in copper and gold. It looks like it came from the Bolivian mines." We look back at the rocks, and all we see is a bunch of rocks. We say, "Boy, is that guy smart! He must be a geologist or something." At one quick glance he knew exactly how to classify and respond to each rock.

We meet another man and we show him some insurance policies we have been trying to read. He glances over the policies and says, "You don't need this type of policy. This one offers better coverage for your children. That might cost you more later." He just glances at a phrase here and a clause there, and he knows exactly how to classify each policy, which is best, and why. Yet, we studied them for hours, and they meant nothing. We say, "Boy, is that guy smart. He must be an insurance underwriter." He just glanced at the policies and he could classify them.

The first man glanced at the rocks, and he knew how to classify them and respond to them; and we said, "Boy, is he intelligent!" The second man glanced over our insurance policies and with little conscious thought, he knew how to classify them. Again, we thought, "Boy, is he intelligent!" We now meet a third man who looks over a group of our employees and, by simply noting the color of their skin, he knows exactly how to classify them. He says, "This one is lazy, and that one is quiet and industrious." We say, "Boy, is that guy prejudiced!" But was not his behavior parallel to what we had just classified as being intelligence?

From this example, we could almost conclude that prejudice and intelligence are the same behavior. To a certain extent, that is true. Our ability to group things into abstract categories and then to respond in preprogrammed ways to all things that fit into those categories is certainly a part of both intelligence and prejudice. To make the distinction, we must quickly define *stupidity*. To do this, a quote from Wendell Johnson's book, *People in Quandaries*, is appropriate.

> To a mouse cheese is cheese [it does not matter whether the cheese is on the floor, in the fridge or on a trap; mice have only one category for all cheese.] That is why mouse traps are effective. To many human beings right is right, wrong is wrong, capital is capital and labor is labor. That is why propaganda is effective. In this connection it is interesting to consider what we call conditioned responses. A dog, as the Russian psychologist Pavlov demonstrated some fifty years ago, can be trained, or conditioned, to produce saliva at the sound of a bell. This is one example of the so-called conditioned response that has received so much attention from modern psychologists.
>
> Since farmers first began to call their hogs, essentially the same phenomenon has been demonstrated daily for centuries before Pavlov discovered it. What the farmers and Pavlov did was to train their animals in identification. They got them to the point where they behaved toward a bell or some other sound the same way they behaved toward food itself. (9, p. 192) (in brackets is author's addition.)

Up to this point, Johnson is describing intelligent behavior of the pigs. The pigs have learned a cue for a category and have learned a set of preprogrammed responses to that cue. That is intelligent, for if they could not learn to recognize the cue, they would probably starve. Now comes the kicker in his example.

> If you call the hogs and then give them corn, they will, after a few feedings, come even if you don't give them corn, provided you call them. The stupidity of a pig is to be measured in terms of the number of times he comes in response to your call after you have discontinued the corn—and in terms of the promptness, speed and lack of delay with which he continues to come.

The ability to form new categories and preprogram responses to these categories is a measure of one's *intelligence*. The resistence to changing these categories and responses, once formed, is a measure of one's *stupidity*.

Johnson makes a crucial distinction between Pavlov's animals and humans. He points out that although both can be trained to behave in a preprogrammed way, the human with higher intellect can learn to keep his responses conditional. He can realize that his preprogrammed response is not the only possible response to members of a category. Of course, humans must *learn* to behave conditionally and without rigid stereotypes, just as they learned these stereotypes and prejudices in the first place. We must learn to examine our preprogrammed stereotypes of people, things, and beliefs. As Johnson states:

> After all, the way we classify or label an individual or a thing determines very largely how we will react toward it. When our classification or labeling of an individual determines, entirely and without exception, our attitude and reaction toward that individual, our behavior is scarcely distinguishable from that of Pavlov's dogs. (9, p. 193)

Language Affects Our Thinking

The famous semanticist Korzybski blamed the structure of our language for part of our stereotype thinking. He said that we have words for classes of things which all too often cause us to assume that things classed under the same name are the same—for example, "all insurance salesmen," "all apples," "all Europeans," and so on. Of course, if we consciously think about it, we know that all apples are not the same. Some rotten apples—Delicious apples, for example—will not spoil the whole barrel. Only some kinds of rotten apples spoil a whole barrel. We must remember that words are only symbols representing abstract concepts. To understand the problems associated with the use of abstract words, we need to understand our own abstracting process.

Abstracting. The discussion of abstractions in this section is greatly influenced by the writing of semanticists, primarily Korzybski, Hayakawa, and Johnson. (12,6, 9) The semanticists have pointed out that men think in a language of abstract terms. The first question that raises is why do we abstract? We have already mentioned why we respond primarily to cues and how we form abstract categories. Now we will look more closely at what an abstract is and how it affects the understandability of our communication output.

All words are abstracts of reality. Words are merely static symbols to represent dynamic reality. The words Mississippi River can certainly not completely describe the thousands of miles of shoreline, or the billions of gallons of rushing, changing water that make up our largest river. The abstract words Mississippi River are used to represent the event Mississippi River because the reality of the river cannot be communicated whereas a word can be.

We can go a step further and ask what in fact the Mississippi River is. To answer this question, we must identify what a fact is. Facts are things that agree with our reality. Since reality is personal, facts are also personal. Johnson says that all facts are:

1. Incomplete (our perceptual system is too limited to perceive all)
2. Constantly changing (the world is dynamic, not static)
3. Personal observations (no fact is exactly the same for two people since each perceives and interprets data differently)
4. Useful only to the extent that they are held in common with other people (If you are the only one who perceives something and you insist to others that it exists, you are likely to be locked up) (9)

There are several different levels at which we acquire facts. *First-level facts* are things we personally sense (observe or experience). If you are standing on the banks of the Mississippi, the first-level facts that are the river are what you can at that moment see, hear, feel, and so on. *Second-level facts* are things we infer from the following:

a. reading, e.g. "The Mississippi River exists although I have never been there."
b. experimentation, e.g. "Atoms exist although one has never been seen."
c. rumors, e.g. "Jane said she thinks Harry is having an affair."
d. past experience, e.g. "I met a bad Turk; all Turks are bad."

Since first-order facts cannot be communicated, they must be abstracted into words to be communicated. Following is an explanation of what is involved in the human process of abstracting.

a. Abstracting involves leaving out details because many details cannot be converted into words.
b. Abstracting is personal; each person leaves out different details.
c. Each abstract can be abstracted further; thus, how the first abstract is made controls the material from which subsequent abstracts can be drawn.
d. Each person tends to fill in gaps in an abstract with material which is already in mind.
e. Abstracting is projective in that we tend to assume that our abstract is reality and therefore that others perceive what we perceive (or that they are stupid if they do not).

f. Abstracts can be based on other abstracts to go in a circle with no reference in reality. For example, we can describe ghosts based on others' descriptions, but no one has even seen a ghost.

g. Abstracts can potentially be corrected if they vary from the original event. The original event can often be reobserved and the abstract can be compared to the event. This process we have already labeled as feedback.

If we carefully consider the abstracting process and then realize that most of our attitudes and beliefs are based upon abstract concepts or our personal facts, it is no wonder that honest, intelligent people can disagree.

When we refer to how Russians behave, we are referring to how more than 200 million different people behave. Some of these Russians are cute little three-year-old girls flirting with their daddies; some are young soldiers guarding a lonely outpost; some are old, illiterate Oriental peasant women living in Siberian tribal villages. When we consciously think about what a diverse group Russians are, it indeed seems difficult for one to have any opinion that would apply to all of them. Yet, it is important that we be able to make a distinction, when studying culture or language, between the broad grouping Russians and the broad grouping Americans.

The danger is that sometimes we tend to forget that these are broad groupings and that these are only names for abstract concepts. We sometimes even make statements such as "Russians are bad" and "Americans are good." Here we add even less definable value-laden adjectives to our overgeneralized nouns. We cannot describe the characteristics of all communists, capitalists, labor leaders, or even mothers, for these are all names for broad categories. Yet, we often hear and perhaps even make statements such as, "Mothers are good" or "Capitalists are stingy." We ignore the possibility that some mothers are child-beaters and some capitalists are philanthropists.

Adjective sets such as good-bad, big-little, and beautiful-ugly tend to mislead us into two-valued judgments such as, "What is not good is bad." President Kennedy chastised his advisors for this type of thinking during the Cuban missile crisis when he stated that he refused to accept that there were no alternatives between total surrender and all-out nuclear war.

We must remember that when we use these two-valued adjectives, we are telling our listeners little about what we are attempting to describe. Instead, we are actually revealing our attitude towards the object. This lesson was made vivid to the author when he was working as a consultant for IBM. A friend sitting across the table was watching the secretaries file into the cafeteria line. Suddenly his eyes bulged, and he gasped in ecstasy, "Did you see that? That is the most beautiful girl I have ever seen." The author quickly turned around to see this modern Venus, but she had gone behind a counter. As he waited with great anticipation to see this most "beautiful" girl, out strolled a very overweight woman. Exceptionally large mammary glands seemed (to the author) to be her only exceptional attributes. When the friend had described the girl as beautiful, he had given no information that would have helped identify this particular female. What he had given was information about himself. The author used his own two-valued judgment and classified his friend as a glutton rather than a connoisseur.

Semanticists say that the danger of thinking in words is that we might subconsciously become so conditioned that we mistake certain words for the things they represent. Korzybski referred to this as confusing the map with the territory it depicts. (12) We must always remember that a word, like a map, is only a static abstract of the dynamic reality it represents.

Teaching Process Skills

Semanticists, as the preceding discussion has shown, focused attention on the relation of language to behavior. Modern psychologists have broadened that study to include how humans process data other than words. It is encouraging to see the increased interest transactional analysis has generated in the processing phase of communication, for this is the most neglected of the communication skills.

Much effort is devoted to teach young children to read, and most students are forced to take years of training in writing. Less, but still considerable time is devoted to classes in speech which usually include a little listening. These are all input and output skills. Few core curricula require that students take a course in logical processes. It seems to be assumed that somewhere along the line students will learn how to learn. It seems to be assumed that you will learn to control and override the defense mechanisms that block out important but undesired feedback. If you are lucky, you may learn all of this, but the frequency of communication problems in organizational life as well as in family life suggests that much more training is needed regarding how to process information. For this reason, the exercises in this workbook place a heavy emphasis on learning how to both give and receive feedback. It is by learning to *receive* feedback that we are able to improve our ability to process inputs. As was pointed out earlier, when feedback is blocked, we can no longer learn to adapt to the world. And as Johnson pointed out, the measure of one's stupidity is his inability to adapt.

Output

The output phase of communication is our primary means of affecting the world around us. We process incoming data in order to determine what response, output, is appropriate. It is our output that we are trying to learn to adapt. For the manager, communication output is what he or she uses to actually get the job done. Communication output can take many forms. The raising of an eyebrow or the extension of a hand are outputs and potential *transaction stimuli.* If they are taken into account by someone, they become communication. Although in this section we may talk of communication output, we must remember that the output itself is not communication. Communication takes place only in the mind of the receiver since a transaction is the basic unit of communication and a transaction occurs only if output is received and responded to. Normally, communication is considered to involve two or more people, although we communicate with ourselves when we take our own thoughts and actions into account.

The primary skills of our output system are speaking and writing. Most communication training focuses almost exclusively on one or the other of these skills to the point of almost ignoring input and processing skills. Perhaps this is a reason why so many high school and even college graduates are deficient in their ability to communicate. They have had courses on communication output but have never had training in the communication process. In traditional courses the main emphasis is on training students to "say what they want to say." The emphasis should be on training them to deal with the interaction among people or training them to say that which will get the desired response. To teach communication as a one-way process is like teaching a person to play chess with only one set of men on the board. They can make moves and be told by an instructor whether the moves are good or bad, but they will never really get a feel for the game until they experience how a variety of players of various skill levels respond to their moves. This is true in communication training. To learn to effectively communicate, we need feedback on how others will respond to and counter our attempts to influence. Just having an instructor give us such feedback on whether or not he thinks our moves are good or bad is no better in the game of influencing than in the game of chess. We need live opponents and real interaction before we can get a feel for the game of influencing people—the game called management.

In this section we will not discuss the mechanics of our output system; neither will we review the grammatical or stylistic rules of our language. If students have not learned these after 12 to 16 years in school, more repetition is not likely to help. The assumption made here is that if these skills were not learned, it was probably for one of two reasons:

1. The student did not find the skills necessary or even beneficial for communicating with his peers. That is, he rejected feedback from parents and/or teachers who said he should learn these skills. Before he will learn these skills, he must be in a situation in which peer group feedback shows these skills to be valuable.

2. If he now desires to learn the skills of grammar, spelling, pronounciation, logic, and organization, he will learn them most easily by actively practicing the skills in a protected environment in which he receives massive amounts of feedback.

The exercises in this book are designed to provide students this atmosphere and type of feedback.

Several teachers have suggested that a course involving communication interaction such as is involved in this course should be reserved only for advanced students. I could not disagree more strongly. Another course on output skill is not likely to help after all of the high school and freshmen English courses have failed.

Many students learn primarily through experience and are weak in their ability to learn through abstract generalization. (11) To learn rules and then try to apply them is the wrong approach for these students. These students need to try to communicate. Based on their experience, they can learn what does and does not work. Once they have built this frame of reference toward writing and speaking, they are ready to learn the rules and to profit from the advice they gain in a standard classroom setting. The student who learns best by doing will especially benefit from taking this type of course before he tries another English, speech, or letter writing course. For additional information on learning styles and how to identify your own learning style, see Kolb. (11)

Output skills, speaking, and writing are no better than the content we have to communicate. Often what is mistaken for poor speaking or writing is actually poor thinking and/or inadequate preparation. Specific output skills are discussed elsewhere in this book. The exercises discuss very specifically how to use output techniques, but they integrate these activities with process skill activities to assure that the students have done adequate research and analysis in order to have something of value to "put out."

Why Such a Microscopic Review

Now that we have reviewed the communication process with a microscope, one might well ask why. After all, it is not possible for one to communicate with others for an entire lifetime without knowing the limitations of nerve impulse, binomial coding, or the process of abstracting. Don Fabun in his excellent book, *Three Roads to Awareness*, answers this question very effectively.

> Here at the end of the road, some readers may feel that discussing electro-magnetic waves, visible spectra, electro-chemical coding, symbology and loop circuitry has little, if anything, to do with the conversation, dictation, giving or receiving orders, writing notes and letters, studying reports and participating in conferences that make up their working days.
>
> We'll go along with that. There's no need to understand the combustion engine in order to drive a car, providing the car is working properly. And that's the point. If human communications in everyday home and business life ran perfectly smoothly, there would be no need to understand the mechanism. But—most of us would agree—our daily communications frequently are faulty.
>
> When communications do go awry, it is often useful to review the process to see what went wrong. And this we cannot do unless we know what we mean by process.
>
> Then, too, it may be that there are some who feel that communications is something that technicians do (like the man who fixes the telephone). Thus, they feel, communications is someone else's job; not theirs.
>
> We cannot pretend, in this brief format, to have said very much about communications; but we have tried to say several things we feel may be important:
>
> (1) The ability to communicate is not something we are born with; we have to learn it—often the hard way.
>
> (2) Whenever we talk or write about anything, what we are talking or writing about is something that happened inside us—not outside us.
>
> (3) If we have difficulty understanding—or being understood—it is likely we have ignored some part of the communication process. It is up to us, individually, to find that part and correct it. This is not an easy thing to do. (4)

REFERENCES

1. Andrews, Donald H. *The Symphony of Life* (Lee's Summit, Mo.: Unity Books, 1967).
2. Berlo, David K. *The Process of Communication* (New York: Holt, Rinehart and Winston, Publishers, 1960).
3. Berne, Eric. *Games People Play* (New York: Grove Press, 1964).
4. Fabun, Don. *Communication* in *Three Roads to Awareness*, Don Fabun, Ed. (Beverly Hills: Glencoe Press, 1970).
5. Harris, Thomas A. *I'm OK--You're OK* (New York: Harper & Row, Publishers, 1967).
6. Hayakawa, S. I. *Language in Thought and Action* (New York: Harcourt, Brace Jovanovich, Inc., 1949).
7. Herzberg, Frederick. "One More Time, How Do You Motivate Employees," *Harvard Business Review* (January-February 1968).
8. Himstreet, William C. and Wayne Murlin Baty. *Business Communications*, 4th ed. (Belmont, Calif.: Wadsworth Publishing Co., Inc., 1973).
9. Johnson, Wendell. *People in Quandaries* (New York: Harper & Row, Publishers, 1946).
10. Johnson, Wendell. "The Fateful Process of Mr. A Talking to Mr. B," *Harvard Business Review* (January-February 1953).
11. Kolb, David A. "On Management and the Learning Process" in *Organizational Psychology: A Book of Readings*, 2nd ed., David A. Kolb, Irwin M. Rubin, and James M. McIntyre, Eds. (Englewood Cliff, N.J.: Prentice-Hall, Inc., 1974).
12. Korzybski, Alfred. *Science and Sanity: An Introduction to Non-Aristotelian Systems of General Semantics* (Lancaster, Pa.: Science Press Printing Co., 1933).
13. McCroskey, James C., *An Introduction to Rhetorical Communication*, (Englewood Cliffs, N.J.: Prentice-Hall, Inc., 1968).
14. McCrosky, J.C., C.E. Larson, and M.L. Knapp. *An Introduction to Interpersonal Communication* (Englewood Cliffs, N.J.: Prentice-Hall, Inc., 1971).
15. Penfield, Wilder. "Memory Mechanisms," *AMA Archives of Neurology and Psychiatry*, Vol. 67 (1952), pp. 178-198.
16. Roberts W. Rhys. "Rhetorica" in *The Works of Aristotle*, W.D. Ross, Ed., Vol. XI (Oxford University Press, Inc., 1946).
17. Rogers, Carl R. and F.J. Roethlisberger. "Barriers and Gateways to Communication." *Harvard Business Review* (July-August 1952), pp. 46-52.
18. Shanon, C.E., and W. Weaver. *The Mathematical Theory of Communication*, (Urbana, Ill.: University of Illinois Press, 1949), p. 98.
19. Smith, Ronald L. "General Models of Communication," Special Report No. 5, Communication Research Center, Purdue University (1962).
20. Thayer, Lee. *Communication and Communication Systems in Organizations, Management and Interpersonal Relations* (Homewood, Ill.: Richard D. Irwin, Inc., 1968).
21. Villee, Claude A. *Biology*, 5th ed. (Philadelphia: W.B. Saunders Company, 1968).

CHAPTER THREE

Implications of Communication Theory for Managers and Students

What are the specific implications for managers of all of this discussion of communication theory? Why should managers be familiar with communication theory? Why? Because the manager is a professional communicator and, as such, he must constantly remind himself to avoid certain behaviors that are natural for the average person. We will review some of these behaviors under the headings, Stereotyping, First Impressions, Self-fulfilling Prophecy, and Projection.

Stereotyping

The term *stereotyping* was coined by Walter Lippman in 1922. He wrote that there are pictures in people's heads called stereotypes, which guide their perception of others. The term is commonly used to describe judgments made about people on the basis of their sex, race, color, or religion. (19) Stereotyping is the process of categorizing a person or thing on the basis of one primary trait or cue and then assuming that all members of that category possess many other identical traits. Statements such as "All women are bad drivers" is an example of a stereotype. You might note that a stereotype is simply one form of the preprogramming discussed in Chapter Two. In the earlier discussion, we pointed out that you need not be like Pavlov's dogs; you do not have to follow only one pattern of response. You can keep all of your response patterns open to modification. Managers must go even one step further; they must be careful not to form too many stereotypes.

Instead of responding to his foreman Mary as a middle-aged Black woman, the manager might respond to her as a middle-aged woman, or better, as a middle-aged foreman, or even better, just as a foreman. There is, on the job, usually no reason to classify workers by age, race, or sex.

Although the manager must try to control his own stereotyping, he must remember that such behavior is normal and common for others. A study by Luft supports this conclusion. Luft found that personality perception is affected by stereotypes. In his study, persons said to have high incomes were perceived as being better adjusted mentally than persons said to have low incomes. (12) Research conducted by the author while at Purdue University revealed that when observers, called "judges," heard short recordings of subjects' voices, the judges were able to accurately (significant at the .001 level) and reliably identify the speakers' social status. (5) Not only did they identify the speakers' social status, but when later asked to rate the speakers' honesty, likeableness, intelligence, and the type of job for which they would hire them, all of those ratings were found to have extremely high positive correlations with the speakers' perceived social status. The judges seemed to feel that persons with high social status were more desirable people in general.

This tendency to generalize goodness or badness is called the *halo effect.* Halo effect in many ways is similar to stereotyping. In stereotyping, it is assumed that all members of some group are the same. In halo effect, it is assumed that if a person is a member of a "good" group, all aspects of his behavior must be good. The halo effect is present when a manager identifies one good (or bad) trait about a worker, and then, while ignoring all other data, he stereotypes the worker into the category "good worker" and proceeds to rate the worker as being good on all other attributes. Managers who are aware of the danger of stereotyping and of the halo effect can correct for them by making a point to routinely look at objective data about people or things. (The feedback rating form used in the exercises in this text are designed to help students practice this skill.) Objective data include such things as production rate, absenteeism, reject rate, sales volume, test scores, and most other measures that do not involve personal judgments.

In preparing proposals, managers must look for the dangers of stereotypes and halo effect as they apply to things as well as to people. We often tend to subsconsciously ignore data that disagrees with what we already believe; we sometimes reject objective data because it does not fit our stereotype. One method that sometimes helps people to overcome this problem is to have them role play that they are supporting the opposite side. To support the opposite side, they must actively seek arguments and evidence to disprove their current beliefs. (This technique is the basis for Exercise 5.)

One group of stereotypes deserves special attention. These are stereotypes that come from our childhood. In transactional analysis, Berne refers to these unflexible beliefs from childhood as the *Parent.* (3) The capital P is used to distinguish the Parent state of mind from the actual condition of being a parent. The Parent is defined as the ". . . huge collection of recordings in the brain of unquestioned or imposed external events perceived by a person in his early years, a period which we have designated as roughly the first five years of life." (9, p. 40)

During these formative years, the child's logic and reasoning processes are not yet fully developed. Rather than evaluating pronouncements from the adult world, the child is in a position only to accept them. These are pronouncements such as, "Remember, Son, wherever you go in the world, you will always find that the best people are Methodists; never tell a lie; pay your bills; you are judged by the company you keep; you are a good boy if you can clean your plate; waste is the original sin; you can never trust a man; you can never trust a woman; you're damned if you do and damned if you don't; you can never trust a copy; busy hands are happy hands; don't walk under ladders; do unto others as you would have them do unto you; do others in that they don't do you in." (9, p. 42)

Whether or not these pronouncements are accurate does not matter. The point is they are recorded as *truth* from the source of all security, the people who are "six feet tall," at a time when it is important for the two-foot-tall child that he please and obey them. (9) These preprogrammed behaviors are recorded and are available for replay throughout life. The reason these preprogrammed stereotypes are of special concern is that they are often loaded with great emotion.

These edicts that are impressed on our brains when we are children are recorded with all of the extreme emotions that we possessed as children. The manager may have forgotten the source of the edicts that created the stereotyped preprogrammed behavior, and yet, if he is not careful, he is likely to find himself expounding and following these in his adult life with the same emotional power with which they were told to him as a child. In a famous case, a top executive emotionally chastised and refused to hire a top nuclear physicist because the physicist came to the interview with unshined shoes. Somewhere in that executive's Parent state was the decree, "You can always tell a man by the shine on his shoes."

Managers must constantly be on guard for these Parent-state stereotypes and resultant preprogrammed responses. Many of these beliefs may still be valid guides for living; others may need to be updated or discarded. Such beliefs are abstractions and, like all abstractions, their validity can be checked by comparing the abstraction against present reality. The important thing is that if the manager is aware of this mental process that causes stereotypes he can be on the alert and can take corrective action. The unaware person is destined to live as an "Archie Bunker" with his mind closed to the needed feedback.

First Impressions

Managers are constantly exposed to new employees, new supervisors, and new ideas. For that reason, managers must be acutely aware of the biasing and lasting impact of first impressions. In a research project, the author investigated the effects of first impressions on hiring decisions. (6) A series of employment interviews for the position of stockboy were presented to judges over videotape. The experimental group of judges saw only a 30-second introduction of each applicant. The control groups saw the same introduction plus a 10-minute interview in which the applicants explained their interest in and qualifications for the job and described their work experience, education, and job aspirations.

The judges ranked the applicants according to how acceptable they felt each applicant was. The ranking of the judges for the control group who saw the whole interview were surprisingly similar to the rankings of those judges who saw only the 30-second introductions, Follow-up questioning revealed that most judges had made up their minds within the first 10 to 15 seconds. Most of the judges made early decisions about the applicants and then tended to interpret all later inputs so as to make them agree with the first impression.

Additional evidence of the strong bias effect of first impressions was reported in a study by Asch. (1) He used the words *warm* or *cold* to describe individuals, followed by a list of other traits such as intelligent, practical, and cautious. When the word *warm* was replaced in the description by the word *cold*, it caused radical changes in the evaluator's perception. A similar study by Kelley used the same words. He found that when individuals were led to expect to meet a warm person, they perceived the person very differently than did other subjects meeting the same person but who were led to expect him to be cold. (11)

Managers in addition to controling how they respond to such subtle initial cues about others must also try to control the type of cues they give off about themselves. They must remember that the first impression they make will have a tremendous effect on the way they are later perceived. This point is expanded in the following section describing self-fulfilling prophecy. Students should also be aware of the impact of first impressions and of the halo effect which often follows. A poorly laid out or sloppily typed business report or student paper is likely to have a great and negative effect on the way the readers perceive the paper's content. The way managers (or students) dress, their facial expression, the way they sit, and many other subtle behaviors have been found to have profound effects on the way in which other people respond to them. Even the environment of the room in which two people meet has been found to affect the attidues of both the persons regarding the credibility, honesty, and intelligence of the others. (13) There is not room in this book to discuss all of the factors which may bias perception, but there are excellent books on this topic. Some of the more popular are *The Naked Ape* (14), *Silent Language* (8), and *Body Language* (7). There are also some good journal articles on this topic. Especially good is a two-part article by A. H. Maslow and N. L. Nimitz, entitled "Effects of Asthetic Surroundings." (13)

Self-fulfilling Prophecy

The most important reason for managers to be aware of the distorting effects of first impressions, stereotyping, and halo effect is that persons tend to behave in ways that make their own and others initial predictions come true. Rosenthal and Jacobson found that when teachers were led to expect certain students to be more intelligent, those students soon actually demonstrated greater intellectual capacity. (16) Teachers in a California school were told that on the basis of intelligence tests about 20% of their students were expected to show significant increases in ability during the coming year. Each teacher was given the names of the potential spurters in their class. In reality, the names were drawn at random, so the difference between the "special children" and the "ordinary children" existed only in the teachers' minds. Four months later, and again six months later, the students were readministered the same intelligence tests. The "special children" did significantly better than the control group on the repeat tests. Twenty-one per cent of the "special children" increased their IQ scores by more than 30 points, and more than 50% of the special group increased their scores by more than 20 points. Only 19% of the control group showed a similar gain. The authors also reported that boys who were from minority groups benefited the most from the teacher's self-fulfilling prophecies, probably because the teacher's pre-experimental attitude toward these boys' abilities was the lowest. The authors summarized, "We may say that, by what she said, by how and when she said it, by her facial expressions, posture and perhaps by her touch, the teacher may have communicated to the children of the experimental group that she expected improved intellectual performance. Such communications, together with changes in teaching techniques, may have helped the child learn by changing his self-concept, his expectations of his own behavior, and his motivation as well as his cognitive style and skills." (16)

This technique of self-fulfilling prophecy can be used by all of us to our advantage. When the author moved to Honolulu, his son started the first grade in a poor school. Three months later when he changed schools, he was far behind his classmates and his new teacher had taken this as a sign that he was a "slow learner." Because the teacher saw him as slow, he began to lose confidence in himself and his former love of reading. Familiar with Rosenthal and Jacobson's research, the author decided to change the teacher's initial impression of the boy to see if this would in some way cause a restoration of his confidence. The author told the teacher that his son had recently been tested at the university and had exceptionally high IQ scores, so high that he was likely to become bored with school and might even appear to be a "slow learner." One month after this statement was made to the boy's teacher, the boy was at the top of his class in both reading and math. There is no way to prove what caused this sudden spurt in his academic achievement, but the author will always attribute it to self-fulfilling prophecy.

A study by Strickland showed that managers are affected by self-fulfilling prophecy. In his study he found that, based on prior expectations of managers, some employees were trusted more than others and were seen to need less supervision even though the performance records of the employees showed no reason to warrant such discrimination. (18)

A study by Berlo and Hall reported additional evidence of the effects of self-fulfilling prophecy on managers. They found that employees who by chance were assigned to more demanding initial jobs, during a four-year period did actually perform better than employees whose initial jobs were less demanding. (2) These findings tend to show that new employees live up to the prophecies made of them, thus making expectations come true. One of the most important single determinants of a new employee's success was found to be how successful his manager expects him to be. (17)

The implication of self-fulfilling prophecy for management behavior is tremendous. The manager must constantly ask himself if he is observing a new employee's behavior or if he is *causing* that behavior. Managers, workers and students must constantly ask themselves how much of their own poor behavior (including their communication skill) is poor only because of their own poor self-image, that is, their self-fulfilling prophecy of themselves.

You must also ask yourself how much of the feedback you give others is just a put down, the type of feedback that will cause people to lower their self- images and, therefore, possibly their performances. The person whose feedback to others is positive and supportive not only shows people how to improve, but also helps them to raise their own self-image and expectations of themselves. The fact that our self-image is a major factor controlling our success is well documented in books such as *Think and Grow Rich* (10), *The Power of Positive Thinking* (15), and in hundreds of books on salesmanship.

By being aware of the impact of self-fulfilling prophecy, you can control its effect. You can do things to induce others to expect more of you and thus to possibly create conditions that will enable you to actually do more. You can also help your subordinates and friends by acting positively towards them and helping them to improve their self-image. Possibly, even probably, a result, they will improve their actual. performance. You must also look at your subordinates who are poor performers and ask yourself if you did not possibly in some way contribute to their poor performance by your own preconceived attitudes, first impressions, and resultant self-fulfilling prophecy.

Projection

Projection is another trait that managers must control. This is the tendency to assume that others perceive the world as you do. It is natural if you are unaware of human perceptual limitations to assume that others see and hear what you do. Because of this you might also tend to assume that others who see the same facts as you do should agree with you, or if not, they are stupid or stubborn.

The fallacy of such assumptions was made vividly clear by a teen-age friend who used to like to listen to loud music, which his father detested. The boy could understand his father not liking the modern rock and roll, but he could not understand his father's objection to such music as a Chopin piano concerto. His father described such music as sounding as if someone were pounding on a bunch of tin cans. The boy concluded that his father did not appreciate good music and had no cultural appreciation. Several years later, as a young man studying audiology at the university, the friend tested his father's hearing. He found that his father could hear almost no sounds above a frequency of 1,500 cycles per second. My friend then had an opportunity to use a high-pitch filter to eliminate from his own hearing the sounds his father could not hear. Through the filter, he played a beautiful concerto by Chopin. Much to his dismay, it sounded as his father had described, as if somebody were pounding on a bunch of tin cans. The father was, after all, not the uncultured music hater my friend had always thought him to be. The father simply perceived a different world.

Managers must be aware that others do not see the world as they do and they should not be expected to. It helps once in a while to review the limitations of our perception and communication system, for it will help remind you not to project your view of the world onto others. You must learn to try to see how others view the world if you are to truly understand how to communicate with them.

The review of the perceptual and communication process in the last two chapters has tried to point out that we all perceive different worlds and should. That is what makes life so interesting. If you are aware of these differences and expect them, then you can accept them and can compensate for them. As Irving J. Lee pointed out, "the problem with communication is not so much that people disagree, it's that they become disagreeable."

How Much Change Can You Expect

Since the goal of communication is to influence, it is necessary for a manager to be aware of how much he can expect employees to change and how rapidly and completely he can expect them to do so. The following paragraph expresses in condensed form the author's attitude about behavior change.

> To me I am what I think I am because I am only what I think and if I could not think, I would not even know that I am and so if I think I am what I am, that is why I am what I am. Therefore, if I am to change from what I am, I must realize that I am that which I want to change from only because that is the way I think I am. So, if I could think that I could be different, I could be the different way I would think I am. But if I think I cannot change, I cannot. If I am to think I could be different, first I must learn that there are different ways to be and how these different ways would be for me; and second, I must learn ways to make me remember to think I am, and thus to be able to be the new me. Only when I have learned to control what I think I am, can I become what I want to be.

You are your own greatest restraining force. To change your own or someone else's preprogrammed behavior is not easy.

The first step toward changing is to be aware that you can change. You are what you are only because that is the way you believe you are. Once you realize that you can change, the next step is to learn a new behavior to change to. The exercises in this text are designed to help you learn new behaviors relevant to basic communication skills. But just knowing that there are new ways to behave is not enough. That would be like saying that because one can read and understand the writings of Shakespeare, one should be able to write like Shakespeare. Obviously, the ability to read and understand great literature is not enough to make one a great writer.

You must also have a chance to try out his newly learned behavior to see if it works for you; most important, you must be constantly reminded to use your new behavior instead of your old preprogrammed behavior. Every time you let your conscious mind lose control, the subconscious will automatically take you back to your old preprogrammed behavior.

To show how difficult it is to change, let us once again compare changing our programming to changing the programs in a computer. If someone like Einstein should come along in the future and instead of showing that parallel lines cross and that matter and energy are the same thing, suppose he should show that 4 + 4 may in certain cases equal 9. This would mean that all of the existing computer programs which are now in use would have to be examined. The programmers would immediately have to change the programs that are used everyday. This would require consciously reviewing each step of every program and where necessary, rewriting many steps or complete programs. Such a change would be similar to a human having to bring his old preprogrammed behaviors up to his conscious mind and rethinking and changing them. We refer to this updating of programs as the activity that distinguishes automatic preprogrammed behavior that is stupid from that which is intelligent. Remember that intelligence is not only the ability to form abstract categories, but is also the ability to update and modify those preprogrammed categories when new and conflicting data are received.

Of course computer programmers cannot change all of the tens of thousands of computer programs at once. They first must determine which programs contain cases where 4 + 4 should equal 9 and which contain cases where 4 + 4 should still equal 8. Then they would have to make a list of every program in the computer library storage that needed to be changed and begin the job by first changing those with the highest priority. Because of the enormity of the job, many rarely used programs would likely never be changed.

Changing a basic belief for a human is an even more enormous task. For example, let's look at the case of a normal, intelligent sixty-year-old man, Mr. A. Mr. A. was raised in the West and for 40 years was programmed that blacks were inferior. He had little contact with blacks except for Amos and Andy, Beulah, Step 'n Fetchit and Rochester. However, while he was growing up, he knew that the official United States government position was that "Negroes" (the word "blacks" was not used then) were inferior. They could not serve in the United States Navy except as stewards. They were not permitted to fly in the Army Air Force, and they had to ride in the rear of the buses. His favorite "Negro" was Beulah, the star of the radio show of the same name in the 1940s and 1950s. Beulah was a big, fat, black maid. She was good, strong, and helpful. But who were the men in Beulah's life?. For the most part, they were portrayed as little, lazy, and cowardly, much like the portrayals of Step 'n Fetchit and Rochester. All of these impressions were recorded in Mr. A's mind under the category "Negro." On one trip through the South in 1940, Mr. A met many blacks, and they did indeed act inferior. Most tended to keep their heads down when talking to whites. Most of the blacks Mr. A met also seemed to have poor educations and used "poor" English ("poor" meant English different than Mr. A was used to). In the early fifties, new information began to reach Mr. A regarding the black race. He read from reliable sources that blacks had IQ's as high as whites. He read that blacks had been made inferior by discriminatory treatment (self-fulfilling prohecy). The final input to Mr. A that convinced him that he should change his negative attitude toward blacks was the Supreme Court decision on segregation in 1954. After hearing that, he decided that his previous attitudes were wrong regarding blacks and that as an intelligent person he would change. But, by this time, Mr. A was forty years old. His prejudices were deeply ingrained. Each of his millions of subtle little preprogrammed behaviors toward blacks would have to be brought out of his subconscious mind and consciously reprogrammed. Of course, Mr. A was not even consciously aware of how many preprogrammed behaviors he had regarding blacks.

On the surface, Mr. A changed, or at least appeared to and honestly tried to. One day he found himself in his favorite plush bar where formerly no blacks had been allowed. A young black man came in and sat down next to him. This unexpected event caught him off-guard. He automatically started to move away to avoid this black intruder. Then he caught himself. He realized that his behavior was "stupid" and needed updated programming. He brought to his conscious mind the behavior program "Black sits next to me in bar." He reprogrammed his response from "move away indignantly" to "treat like anyone else."

Mr. A started talking to the young black man. Upon finding they had many interests in common, he soon almost forgot the man's color. He found the man to be, like himself, an engineer. They went to the same university and rooted for the same baseball team. As they began their second drink, the young man mentioned that he had not just come into the bar by chance, but was there because he had been dating Mr. A's daughter, and they were contemplating marriage. Suddenly all of Mr. A's programs "lost their cool." Suddenly Mr. A, who thought he had overcome his prejudice, found that he had much more reprogramming to do. For the conclusion of this story, the author recommends the movie *Guess Who's Coming to Dinner.* There is also available an excellent film by Bill Cosby that documents how anti-black sentiments were created in the mass media. (4)

Lifelong belief and behavior patterns may take as long to change as they took to be formed originally. Fortunately, all of our behavior is not as hard to change as are deep-seated racial prejudices.

For most behavior change, especially in skills such as communication, the change involves much trial, error, and practice. If the first time you try a new way of communicating you receive a serious putdown, such as a failing grade or a lost job, the odds are that you will quickly retreat to your old behavior. Most new behaviors begin with very awkward performances. To practice new behaviors, you need.a protected environment, where the consequences of failure are minimal. You need massive amounts of feedback that are supportive. You need many examples with which to compare your behavior. You also need opportunities to practice your behavior over and over in many different forms until your new behavior becomes as automatic and natural as your old behavior was.

The exercises in this text are designed to provide such an opportunity for students to improve some of their basic communication transaction skills. The exercises are designed to enable men and women to learn the communication skills which will make them competent and confident managers. Use this opportunity to start to change your attitude of yourself. Self-fulfilling prohecy will likely do the rest.

REFERENCES

1. Asch, S. "Forming Impressions of Persons," *Journal of Abnormal and Social Psychology*, Vol. LX (1946), 258-270.
2. Berlew, David E. and Douglas T. Hall. "The Socialization of Managers: Effects of Expectation on Performance," *Administrative Science Quarterly*, Vol. XI, No. 2 (1966), 207-233.
3. Berne, Eric. *Games People Play* (New York: Grove Press, Inc., 1964).
4. Cosby, Bill. *Bill Cosby on Prejudice* (Pyramid Films, 1972).
5. Ellis, Dean S. "Speech and Social Status in America," *Social Forces*, Vol. XLV (April 1967), 431-437.
6. Ellis, Dean S. "Limiting Communication Between Interviewers and Interviewees," Paper presented at the Southeastern Psychological Association Convention, Atlanta (April 1967).
7. Fast, Julius. *Body Language* (New York: M. Evans & Co., Inc., 1970).
8. Hall, Edward T. *Silent Language* (Garden City, New York: Doubleday & Company, Inc., 1959).
9. Harris, Thomas A. *I'm OK–You're OK* (New York: Harper & Row, Publishers, 1967).
10. Hill, Napoleon. *Think and Grow Rich*, revised edition (Greenwich, Conn.: Fawcett Publications, Inc., 1960)
11. Kelley, H. H. "The Warm-Cold Variable in First Impressions of Persons," *Journal of Personality*, Vol. XVIII (1950), 431-439.
12. Luft, J. "Monetary Values and the Perception of Persons," *Journal of Social Psychology*, Vol. XLVI (1975), 245-251.
13. Maslow, A. H. and N. L. Nimitz. "Effects of Aesthetic Surroundings," *Journal of Psychology* (1956).
14. Morris, Desmond. *The Naked Ape* (New York: McGraw-Hill Book Company, 1967).
15. Peale, Norman V. *The Power of Positive Thinking* (Englewood Cliffs, N. J.: Prentice-Hall, Inc., 1952).
16. Rosenthal, Robert and Lenore Jacobson. "Pygmalion in the Class Room," (New York: Holt, Rinehart and Winston, Publishers, 1968).
17. Schein, Edgar H. "Management Development as a Process of Influence," *Industrial Management Review*, **1**: 55-97 (May 1961).
18. Strickland, L. H. "Surveillance and Trust," *Journal of Personality*, Vol. XXVI (1958), 200-215.
19. Zalkind, Sheldon S. and Timothy W. Costello. "Perception: Implications for Administration," *Administrative Science Quarterly*, Vol. 7, (September 1962).

APPENDIX I

Selected References of Business Materials

Adapted in part from a list prepared by Shiro Saito for the University of Hawaii Library.

Guides to Reference Books

Winchell, Constance M. *Guide to Reference Books.* 8th ed. (Chicago: American Library Association, 1967). Supplements: 1965-1966 (1968), 1967-1968 (1970), 1969-1970 (1972).

Guides to Business Literature

Bakewell, K. G. B. *How to Find Out: Management and Productivity.* 2nd ed. (Elmsford, N. Y.: Pergamon Press, Inc., 1970), 389 pages.

Coman, Edwin T. *Sources of Business Information.* Revised ed. (Berkeley, University of California Press, 1964), 330 pages.

Daniells, Lorna M. *Business Literature: An Annotated List For Students and Businessmen.* (Cambridge, Mass.: Baker Library, Graduate School of Business Administration, Harvard University, 1968), 139 pages.

Daniells, Lorna M. *Business Reference Sources: An Annotated Guide for Harvard Business School Students.* (Cambridge, Mass.: Baker Library, Graduate School of Business Administration, Harvard University, 1971), 108 pages.

Hollander, Staley C. and Stephen R. Flaster. *Business Consultants and Clients: A Literature Search on the Marketing Practices and Problems of the Management Research and Advisory Professors.* (East Lansing, Mich.: Michigan State University, 1972), 226 pages.

Special Libraries Association. *Guide to Special Issues and Indexes of Periodicals.* (New York: 1962).

Wasserman, Paul, et. al. *Encyclopedia of Business Information Sources.* (Detroit: Gale Research Co., 1970), 2 volumes.

Wasserman, Paul. *Information for Administrators: A Guide to Publications and Service for Management in Business and Government.* (Ithaca, N. Y.: Cornell University Press, 1956).

Bibliographies

American Management Association, Research and Information Services. *Ten-Year Index of A. M. A. Publications, 1954-1963.* (1964).

American Management Association, Research and Information Services. *Ten-Year Index of A. M. A. Publications, 1957-1966.* (1967).

Bennett, John B. and Ronald L. Weiher. "The Well-Read Manager," *Harvard Business Review.* (July-August 1972), 134-146.

Bibliography of Asian Cases on Business and Management. (Monitor, Asian Productivity Organization, 1970).

Hills, William G., et al. *Administration and Management: A Selected and Annotated Bibliography.* (Norman, Okla.: University of Oklahoma Press, 1975).

Index of Economic Journals. (American Economic Association), Vol. 1, 1886-1924+

International Bibliography of Economics. 1951+

Massarik, Fred and Bruce E. Krueger. "Through the Labyrinth: An Approach to Reading in Behavioral Science," *California Management Review*, Vol. 13, No. 2. (Winter 1970), 70-77.

Rand Corporation. *Decision Making*. (Santa Monica, Calif., 1972), 26 pages.

Rand Corporation. *System Analysis*. (Santa Monica, Calif., 1970), 103 pages.

Sandeau, Georges. *Selected Management Bibliography*. (Boston, Herman Publishing, 1975).

Indexes and Abstracts

Business Periodicals Index. (New York, The H. W. Wilson Company, 1958+).

Journal of Economic Literature. (American Economic Association, 1969+. Successor to the Journal of Economic Abstracts, 1963-1968).

Management Research. (The monthly comprehensive research journal. Vol. 1+, 1968+).

Management Review. (American Management Association, Vol. 1+, 1914+, monthly).

Public Affairs Information Services. (Bulletin, New York, 1915+, weekly).

Social Sciences and Humanities Index. (New York, 1907+). (Formerly International Index to Periodicals).

Selected Rand Abstracts. (Santa Monica, Calif., Rand Corporation, 1963+, quarterly).

Wall Street Journal. Indexes. (New York, 1957+).

Encyclopedia and Handbooks

Editor and Publisher. Market Guide. (New York, Vol. 1+, 1924+, annual).

Moody's Investors Service:
Moody's Bank and Finance Manual
Moody's Industrial Manual
Moody's Municipal and Government Manual
Moody's Public Utility Manual
Moody's Transportation Manual

Sills, D. E., Ed. *International Encyclopedia of the Social Sciences* (Macmillan & The Free Press, 1968), 17 vols.

Standard & Poor's Industry Surveys (1973), 2 vols.

Statistics

Guides

Andriot, John L. *Guide to U. S. Government Statistics*, 4th ed. (McLean, Va., Documents Index, 1973), 431 pages.

Andriot, John L. *Guide to U. S. Government Serials and Periodicals* (McLean, Va., Documents Index, 1972).

Wasserman, Paul and Joanne Paskar, Eds. *Statistics Sources: A Subject Guide to Data on Industrial, Business, Social, Educational, Financial and other Topics for the United States and Selected Foreign Countries*, 4th ed. (Detroit: Gale Research Co., 1974).

Compendiums

Survey of Current Business. (Washington, D. C.: U. S. Department of Commerce, Vol. 1+, 1921+, monthly).

U. S. Bureau of the Census. *Statistical Abstract of the U. S.* (Washington, D. C.: 1878+, annual).

Robert Morris Associates. *Annual Statement Studies*. (annual).

Troy, Leo. *Almanac of Business and Industrial Ratios*, 1972 ed. (Englewood Cliffs, N. J.: Prentice-Hall, Inc.).

Biographical Sources

Standard & Poor's Register of Corporations, Directors and Executives. (annual).

Who's Who in Finance and Industry, 20th ed. (Chicago: Marquis, 1976).

Directories

Bradford's Directory of Marketing Research Agencies and Management Consultants in the U. S. and the World. (13th Biennial, 1971-72).

Wasserman, Paul and Janice McLean, Eds. *Consultants and Consulting Organizations Directory*. 2nd ed. (Detroit: Gale Research Co., 1973). (Supplements are issued from time to time.)

APPENDIX II Sample of Class Grade Summary Sheet

Student No.	Ex. 1 Grade	Ex. 2 Presentation Grade	Ex. 2 Feedback Grade	Ex. 3 Research Reference Form Received (√) when received	Ex. 3 Article Abstracts Received (√) when received	Ex. 3 Paper Grade	Ex. 3 Grader Quality Report Received (√) when received	Ex. 4 Presentation Grade	Ex. 4 Feedback Grade	Ex. 5 Paper Grade	Ex. 5 Grader Quality Report Received (√) when received	Ex. 6 Presentation Grade	Ex. 6 Feedback Grade	Ex. 7 Paper Grade	Ex. 7 Grader Quality Report Grade	Ex. 8 Presentation Grade + Panel Discussion–Debate Session Grade	Sum of Bonus Points	Sum of Grades for Ex. 7, Ex. 8 and Bonus Points	Final Grade

All Grades for Ex. 7 and 8 will be posted only after all final grades are computed.